THE TEACHING OF ARITHMETIC
IN PRIMARY SCHOOLS

processes should be dealt with one at a time. This means that the work must be arranged, by the teacher, in carefully graded steps. Suggestions for such grading are given in detail throughout the book.

A book of this kind cannot be written without frequent reference to and help from others. Our thanks are especially due to the many teachers and students from all parts of the world who have helped to throw light on the many teaching problems common to us all. We ought, too, to thank those of our pupils whose lack of understanding has caused us to think more carefully about what and how we teach and how children learn.

The authors are very grateful to the general editor of the series for his unfailing help, advice, criticism and patience, and to Miss R. Furze for her valuable help in the preparation of the manuscript.

L. W. DOWNES

D. PALING

St. Luke's College
Exeter
June 1957

NOTE

In some parts of the world people have retained original systems of number for their everyday affairs. In this book all examples are in the tens system, since this is in universal use for international and scientific affairs.

Units of money and measurement, however, differ greatly, and are by no means so generally accepted, although the metric system is commonly adopted for scientific purposes. But many countries stick to their own units for ordinary usage. In this book the authors employ the British systems—as examples, neither because these are widely understood nor on grounds of nationality, but *because they are probably the most difficult* in common use. Thus it is comparatively easy for any teacher to apply the principles and recommended teaching methods to any simpler system of units.

PREFACE

THIS is a book on the teaching of arithmetic for teachers who are not necessarily mathematicians.

It has been written at a time when, all over the world, there is an increasing and continuous demand for more and better scientists and technicians. This in turn creates a need for greater and quicker development of scientific and technological education. Unfortunately, this development is being held up in many areas owing to the shortage of suitably qualified teachers, particularly of mathematics. Investigations have shown that this shortage is largely due to lack of enthusiasm and wrong attitudes towards mathematics, often among people who intend to become teachers. Further investigations have shown that these wrong attitudes have first been formed during primary-school education.

We believe that a change of attitude is not possible without some reconsideration of the arithmetic now taught in the primary schools.

Arithmetic can be satisfying and enjoyable to those who teach and those who learn. Without this enjoyment and satisfaction, progress is bound to be slow and horizons are bound to be limited.

Most teachers will agree that it is possible to teach a certain amount of arithmetic without very much understanding on the part of either teacher or child. But real progress comes only when *both* understand, at their respective levels, the fundamental bases of the work they are doing. This understanding is not only necessary, but perhaps most important, *at the beginning*, when children first deal with arithmetic.

The understanding of number depends most of all upon the understanding of the meaning of spoken and written words. This book places particular emphasis upon these needs and discusses ways by which such understanding may be gained.

Another prerequisite of success is that new ideas and

CONTENTS

PREFACE   V

LIST OF ILLUSTRATIONS AND CHARTS   XV

I   THE PURPOSE AND USE OF THIS BOOK   1

The aim of the book · The arrangement—*Children's experience—Teacher's understanding—Planning and grading* · The use of the book—Adapting the book for different systems

II   WHY DO WE TEACH ARITHMETIC?   5

Arithmetic is useful in everyday life · It helps our understanding of the world · It helps to develop a healthy attitude towards learning · It is necessary in a study of science

III   THE MODERN APPROACH TO ARITHMETIC—WHAT SHALL WE TEACH AND HOW SHALL WE TEACH IT?   8

How much Arithmetic? · The necessity for arithmetical rules · The need for practice · Making sure progress · Grading the work · Enjoyment in Arithmetic

Something to think about—1 (Number names and symbols)   13

IV   THE CHILD'S FIRST IDEAS OF NUMBER   17

The need to study children and how they learn · The child's 'readiness' for learning · The child's pre-school experience—*Hearing—Seeing—Doing—Counting* · His first arithmetic in school—*Informal activities and games—Oral counting—Activities and games organized by the teacher—Recognition of groups* · Introducing the number-symbols—*Activities to help with their names, in giving them meaning, in writing*

*a**

V INTRODUCING CHILDREN TO ADDITION 38
The idea · The language—*Words and phrases—Signs—Recording the addition* · Giving further experience: totals up to 10—*Activities—Apparatus;* totals up to 9 plus 9 · Learning the primary facts —*What is a 'fact'?—The addition facts—Arranging them in sets—Activities to help memory: practice-cards, flash-cards, oral class-work* · 'Problems': the importance of words as well as figures

VI INTRODUCING CHILDREN TO SUBTRACTION 63
The idea · 'Comparing' and 'taking away' · Early experiences—*Activities—The language—Recording the results—Signs* · Examples set by the teacher · Learning the primary facts—*Practice-cards—Relation to addition facts—Flash-cards—Oral class-activities* · 'Problems': the importance of words as well as figures

VII INTRODUCING CHILDREN TO MULTIPLICATION 76
The idea · Early grouping activities · Counting in groups · Recording the activities—*The word 'times' —The sign—Working out the early facts* · Building tables of the early facts · Learning the early facts —*Practice-cards—Flash-cards—Oral class activities* · 'Problems': the importance of words as well as figures

VIII INTRODUCING CHILDREN TO DIVISION 91
The idea · Early school activities—*Sharing—Grouping* · Using everyday happenings · Recording the activities · Examples set by the teacher · Learning the early facts—*Practice-cards—Relation to multiplication facts—Remainders—Flash-cards—Oral class-activities* · 'Problems': the importance of words as well as figures

IX BEGINNING TO DEAL WITH MONEY 110
The child's first ideas · Early school experiences— *Practical approach—Using this approach (coin recognition, recording purchases, 'mixed' coins, 'getting change', simple multiplication and division, shopping-lists and practice-cards)*

X LEARNING TO MEASURE—LENGTH, WEIGHT,
CAPACITY, TIME   122
Pre-school experiences · Learning to measure
lengths—*Early activities—The need for standard
units—The foot, inch, yard* · Learning to measure
weight—*Handling weights—Using scales—Pounds
—Ounces* · Learning to measure capacity—*Early
activities—Pints, quarts, gallons* · Learning to
measure time—*Telling the time—Days, weeks,
months—Diaries*

Something to think about—2 (Addition)   143

XI LEARNING MORE ABOUT ADDITION   147
The idea of place-value—*Extending the ability to
count—Understanding our number-system* · Addition without carrying—*Tens and units—Hundreds,
tens and units* · 'Carrying'—*To the tens—To the
hundreds—Helping less able children* · Probable
causes and suggested remedies for common errors
· Points to remember
Analysis 1—Suggested stages and steps for teaching addition   158

Something to think about—3 (Subtraction)   167

XII LEARNING MORE ABOUT SUBTRACTION   169
The simple process—*'Upwards' and 'downwards'
subtraction* · The next stages—*Method of 'decomposition': the idea and how to teach it—Method of
'equal additions': the idea and how to teach it* ·
Probable causes and suggested remedies for common errors · Points to remember
Analysis 2—Suggested stages and steps for teaching subtraction   180

Something to think about—4 (Multiplication)   186

XIII LEARNING MORE ABOUT MULTIPLICATION   188
Introduction · Short multiplication—*Using the
early facts—Learning and using further facts* ·
Quick multiplication—*By ten—By twenty, etc.* ·
Long multiplication—*By two-figure numbers—By*

hundreds—By other three-figure numbers · Multiplication by factors · Probable causes and suggested remedies for common errors · Points to remember
Analysis 3—Suggested stages and steps for teaching multiplication 203

Something to think about—5 (Division) 212

XIV LEARNING MORE ABOUT DIVISION 215
Setting down the process: long or short form? · Learning and using the early facts · Using the facts to divide larger numbers—*Tens and units, with and without remainders—Hundreds, tens and units—Quick division by ten* · Dividing by easy two-figure numbers—*'Trying out'* · Dividing by other two-figure numbers · Dividing by larger numbers · Probable causes and suggested remedies for common errors · Points to remember
Analysis 4—Suggested stages and steps for teaching division 232

XV TABLES—HOW TO ENSURE THAT THE 'NUMBER FACTS' ARE KNOWN 240
The meaning of tables · Understanding comes first · Memorizing—*Through hearing and speaking—Through seeing: charts, patterns, flash-card games—Through touching and moving—Through class-activities—Through other games and activities* · The importance of using the facts—*Everyday examples—Written exercises* · The need for a school plan—*Time allocation*

Something to think about—6 (The 'history' of money) 261

XVI FURTHER STEPS IN MONEY 264
The changing of money—*Learning the facts—Practice-cards—Flash-cards—Tables of pence and shillings—Written calculations* · Addition of money — *Further activities — Written work — 'Carrying'* · Subtraction of money—*The method: 'decomposition' or 'equal additions'* · Multiplica-

tion—*Method of setting down—Short methods* ·
Division—*By sharing—By grouping* · Points to
remember
Analysis 5—Suggested stages and steps in the
    teaching of money 284

Something to think about—7 (Measurements) 292

XVII MORE ABOUT MEASURES 295
    'Natural' measurement · Standard units and their
    relationship · Making examples 'real' · The im-
    portance of estimation

Something to think about—8 ('Natural' and 'standard'
    lengths) 299

XVIII FURTHER WORK ON LENGTH 302
    Activities—*Measuring in fractions of an inch, in
    chains, furlongs, miles—Measuring wheel and pac-
    ing stick—Athletics—Keeping records—Drawing
    plans* · Changing units—*The facts—Written calcu-
    lations* · The arithmetical processes—*Use of work-
    cards—Addition—Subtraction—Multiplication—
    Division by sharing and grouping* · Points to
    remember
    Analysis 6—Suggested stages and steps in the
        teaching of length 315

Something to think about—9 (Weight) 322

XIX FURTHER WORK ON WEIGHT 325
    Activities—*Fractions of a pound, ounces—Stones,
    quarters, hundredweights—Spring balances—Col-
    lecting information* · Changing units—*The facts
    and the table—Written calculations* · The processes
    —*Use of work-cards—Addition—Subtraction—
    Multiplication—Division, by sharing and grouping* ·
    Points to remember
    Analysis 7—Suggested stages and steps in the
        teaching of weight 336

Something to think about—10 (Units of capacity) 346

XX   FURTHER STEPS IN CAPACITY   349
     Activities—*Making pots—Collecting information
     —Work-cards* · Changing units—*The facts—
     Written calculations* · The processes—*Use of
     work-cards—Addition—Subtraction—Multiplica-
     tion—Division, by sharing and grouping* · Points to
     remember
     Analysis 8—Suggested stages and steps in the
     teaching of capacity   354

Something to think about—11 (Time)   359

XXI MORE ABOUT TIME   362
     Activities—*Different ways of telling the time—
     Estimating time—Collecting information* · Chang-
     ing units—*Calendars* · Calculations—*Work-cards
     for the arithmetical processes, etc.* · Points to
     remember
     Analysis 9—Suggested stages and steps in the
     teaching of time   372

XXII INTRODUCING FRACTIONS   377
     The first approach · The idea—*Folding and cutting
     —In measurements of length—Fractions of shapes
     —Drawing   activities—Everyday   happenings* ·
     Changing fractions—*Apparatus, activities, state-
     ment of 'equivalence'; mixed numbers and improper
     fractions* · The early stages of addition, subtraction
     and multiplication

Something to think about—12 (Decimal fractions)   392

XXIII OTHER KINDS OF FRACTION   395
     Decimal fractions · Tenths—*Introductory activi-
     ties—Simple calculations* · Hundredths—*Activities*
     · Decimals as extension of H.T.U. notation ·
     Changing common fractions to decimals

     Percentages · Reason for teaching · The idea ·
     Explanation to children—*Introduction and develop-
     ment—Everyday examples—Changing fractions to
     percentages—Finding percentages of given quan-
     tities*

XXIV   LINES AND SHAPES   412
       Children's early experiences · Activities at school ·
       Suggested work—*Lines: straight, curved, parallel;
       drawing and measuring*—*Shapes: folding and cut-
       ting, patterns, circles, regular solids* · Direction and
       angles—*Compass points, right-angles* · Measure-
       ment—*Perimeters, areas, volumes* · Scale reading
       and drawing · Graphs—*Suitable examples*

XXV   FUN WITH FIGURES   432
       Attitude of teacher and children · Fun with
       numbers · Short methods · Lines and shapes ·
       'Problems'

Something to think about—13 (Fractions)   441

XXVI   MORE ABOUT FRACTIONS   444
       Further steps in addition · A further stage in sub-
       traction · Multiplication—*Of a fraction by a
       fraction; simplifying*—*Of mixed numbers* · Division
       —*By a whole number*—*Of a whole number by a
       fraction*—*By a fraction* · Points to remember
       Analysis 10—Suggested stages and steps in teach-
           ing fractions   454

Something to think about—14 (The metric system) 458

XXVII THE METRIC SYSTEM   459
       Introduction through activities · Length · Area ·
       Volume · Weight · Adoption of the system

XXVIII PROVIDING EQUIPMENT AND MAKING
           APPARATUS   466
       The need · Difficulties · Materials—*For general
       use*—*For special use* · Storage · Some further
       details of apparatus—*Number and place-value
       slides, flash-cards, a pair of scales, etc.*

XXIX   ORGANIZATION, TESTING AND MARKING   476
       Planning for the whole school · Class-room
       organization by the teacher · Testing—*Mental*

arithmetic, oral and written—Written tests · Marking and corrections · Keeping records

Something more to think about.   486

APPENDIXES

A USEFUL MATERIALS   487
B SOME DETAILS OF PAPER AND CARDBOARD 489
C SOME BOOKS FOR THE MATHEMATICS
   LIBRARY   490

INDEX   493

LIST OF ILLUSTRATIONS

FIGURES   *Page*

1   A number-tray, for sorting by size or colour   23
2   A peg-board, for arranging in order of length   23
3   A posting-box, for recognizing shapes   24
4   An inset-tray, for recognizing shapes   24
5   Playing skittles, for counting   27
6   The game of quoits, for counting   28
7   Pattern-cards, for recognizing groups   29
8   Bead-bars, for recognizing groups   29
9   Marked strips, for number recognition   30
10 The number-tray, used for matching groups and
        figures   32
11 The number-tray, used for matching picture-cards
        and figures   32
12 The number-tray, used for matching number-pattern
        cards and figures   32
13 Stringing beads and number-cards   33
14 'Flags and castles', for matching groups and number-
        cards   33
15 Number-symbol 'cut-outs', with holes for pegs   34
16 The '10' number-slide, for number estimation   34
17 A wall number-board, for matching groups and
        figures   35
18 Number-symbol stencils   36
19 Number-symbols on squared paper   37
20 Objects and number-cards, for addition   39
21 Picture-cards and number-cards, for addition   40
22 Strings of beads, with number-cards, for addition   43
23 Playing skittles, with number-cards, for addition   44
24 The '10' number-slide, with marked strips, for
        addition   44
25 A 'number-story' apparatus, for addition   45
26 'Number-tops', for addition   45
27 The 'fishing game', for addition   46
28 A specimen page from a teacher's record book   55
29 A practice-card, pictorial, for addition   56

30	A practice-card, of selected facts in addition	57
31	A practice-card, for addition	57
32	A practice-card, number-story type, for addition	58
33	A practice-card, 'changing-game' type, for addition	59
34	Self-corrective flash-cards, equation and process types, for addition	60
35	Blackboard 'problems' for young children	62
36	Practice-cards, for subtraction	70
37	A practice-card, for subtraction, with addition check	72
38	Self-corrective flash-cards, equation and process types, for subtraction	73
39	The number-tray, for equal groupings and number-cards	77
40	'Nests and eggs', for equal groupings	78
41	Stringing beads and number-cards, for equal groupings	78
42	A picture-card, for equal groupings	81
43	Practice-cards, for multiplication	86
44	Self-corrective flash-cards, equation and process types, for multiplication	88
45	Two meanings of '12 ÷ 3'	91
46	The number-tray, for sharing in division	94
47	Folded paper strips, for division	95
48	'Hoisting the flags', for grouping in division	96
49	The 'division train'	96
50	Practice-cards, for division	102
51	A practice-card, for division, with multiplication check	103
52	A practice-card, for division with 'remainders'	104
53	A practice-card, for division related to a multiplication table	104
54	A practice-card, for various groupings in division	105
55	A practice-card, for use with a number-slide in division	105
56	The '24' number-slide with runner, for division	106
57	Self-corrective flash-cards, equation and process types, for division	107
58	The 'open market', for 'shopping' activities	112
59	A 'table-shop'	112
60	A folding-frame 'shop'	113

61 A slotted-picture 'shop' 114
62 The number-tray, for coins with number and name cards 116
63 The child's record of shopping activities 116
64 The child's first record of addition of money 117
65 The child's record of 'getting change' 118
66 The number-tray, for equivalence of coins 118
67 A money-card, for making given totals with mixed coins 119
68 The child's first record of division of money 120
69 Shopping-list cards, for addition and subtraction of money 121
70 Practice-cards, for the four arithmetical processes with money 121
71 A child's 'measuring book' 126
72 Foot-sticks marked in inches 126
73 A work-card, for the measurement of lines 127
74 Cards, for the measurement of edges 128
75 A wall-scale, for children's heights 128
76 The child's record of measurements 129
77 Yard-sticks marked in feet and inches 130
78 A time-chart, for learning to 'tell the time' 137
79 A model clock-face with movable hands 138
80 A model clock-face with separate parts, for learning to 'tell the time' 139
81 The clock-face with Roman numerals 140
82 Diaries as time records 141
83 Making a simple time-graph: the height of a growing plant 141
84 An imaginary basis for a different number system 144
85 A number-chart based on a different system 145
86 Number-cards, for place-value 149
87 An addition-board and bead-bars, for 'carrying' in addition 154
88 'Decomposition' in the subtraction process 173
89 Screens, for showing 'twin facts' in multiplication 189
90 Screens, for showing the multiplication 'facts' with the product of twenty-four 190
91 The place-value slide 195
92 Number-pattern cards, for multiplication 'facts' 245

93 Number-square patterns, for multiplication tables 246
94 The 'spinning-arrow' game, for flash-card practice 249
95 A clock-face, for practice in the arithmetical 'facts' 250
96 The 'snakes-and-ladders' game, for flash-card practice 251
97 A four-way flash-card, for related 'facts' 252
98 An aid to memory: 'The elephant never forgets' 253
99 The tear-off calendar, for multiplication 'facts' 253
100 A revision practice-sheet 254
101 Practice-cards, for 'changing' money 266
102 Practice-cards, for subtraction and 'complementary addition' of money 266
103 Practice-cards, for addition, multiplication and division of money 266
104 Flash-cards, for 'changing' money 267
105 A simple shopping bill 272
106 A measuring-wheel 304
107 The pacing-stick 305
108 A work-sheet, for the measurement of lengths 308
109 Specimen work-cards, for the measurement and addition of lengths 309
110 Specimen work-cards, for subtraction of length 310
111 Specimen work-cards, for multiplication of length 312
112 A see-saw, for introducing the balance 326
113 A spring balance, with dial 327
114 A spring balance 327
115 A flash-card, for changing units of weight 330
116 Specimen work-cards, for addition of weights 331
117 Specimen work-cards, for subtraction of weight 332
118 Specimen work-cards, for multiplication of weight 333
119 A specimen work-card, for capacity 350
120 Flash-cards, for changing units of capacity 351
121 'Clock acting' 363
122 The twenty-four-hour clock-face 363
123 A day-by-day calendar 367
124 A month-by-month calendar 367
125 Specimen work-cards, for addition of time 368
126 Specimen work-cards, for subtraction of time 368
127 Specimen work-cards, for multiplication of time 369
128 Specimen work-cards, for division of time 370

129 Making fraction strips 380
130 Fractions of a circle 381
131 Fractions of a square 382
132 Fractional shapes on squared paper 383
133 A fraction board, for number and money 384
134 'Sewed circles', for equivalence of fractions 385
135 A measuring-card, for lengths in tenths and decimals 397
136 Decimal fractions on squared paper (tenths) 398
137 Measuring to hundredths: an enlargement for the
    blackboard 401
138 Decimal fractions on squared paper (hundredths) 403
139 Decimals as an extension of the H.T.U. notation 404
140 The place-value slide, for decimals 404
141 Fraction-boards, for decimals in number and money 405
142 The chalked-thread method of drawing a straight
    line on the blackboard 415
143 An ink-blot shape, for symmetry 416
144 Regular shapes, for patterns and 'pictures' 417
145 Folding circles, for various shapes 418
146 A cardboard strip for drawing circles 418
147 The points of the compass 420
148 Folding paper to form a right-angle 421
149 Building up a regular solid from cubic unit blocks 424
150 Surface-shapes of some common solids 425
151 Simple graphs of temperature readings 427-8
152 A column graph of daily attendance at school 429
153 A column graph of monthly rainfall 430
154 A 'circular graph' of population 431
155 The meanings of '$\frac{3}{4}$' 442
156 The cubic centimetre 462
157 A measuring cylinder 462
158 Construction of a number-slide 470
159 Making a runner for a number-slide 471
160 Making a 'number-top' 471
161 Making the 'fish' for the 'fishing game' 472
162 An easily-made pair of scales 473
163 The construction of a place-value slide 474
164 An exercise card, for use in individual work schemes 479
165 Wall-pockets, for storing exercise cards 480
166 Analysis of marks in a mental arithmetic test 483

LISTS

I	Simple addition 'facts' (totals not greater than ten)	42
II	Further addition 'facts' (totals from eleven to eighteen)	48
III	The hundred 'primary addition facts'	51
	A The 'primary addition facts' arranged in selected sets	54
IV	Simple subtraction 'facts' (from ten or less)	67
V	The other 'primary subtraction facts'	68
	B The 'primary subtraction facts' arranged in selected sets	71
VI	Early multiplication 'facts' (product not greater than twenty-four)	83
	C The 'facts' of List VI arranged in selected sets	87
VII	Early division 'facts' (dividend not greater than twenty-four)	100
	D The 'facts' of List VII arranged in selected sets	101
VIII	Multiplication 'facts' (up to twelve times twelve)	192
IX	Division 'facts' (up to one hundred and forty-four divided by twelve)	217
	E Early multiplication 'facts' (from Chart IV) arranged in selected sets	259

CHARTS

I	Early multiplication 'facts' (List VI) arranged as tables	85
II	The tables of thirteens to nineteens (to 'times nine')	228
III	Trial answers for division by thirteen to nineteen	228
IV	Building up tables: Chart I with twenty-eight more 'facts'	257
V	The pence table	268
VI	Building up a 'Ready reckoner'	281
VII	A table of lengths (British system)	306
VIII	A table of weights (British system)	329
IX	A table of liquid measure (British system)	351
X	A table of 'dry' measure (British system)	351
XI	A table of the units of time	366

CHAPTER I

THE PURPOSE AND USE OF THIS BOOK

(1) The aim of the book

This book has a practical aim. It is intended to show the many ways in which teachers may help children to learn arithmetic. It is hoped that it may also help teachers to get a better understanding of the subject, so that, in turn, children may understand better what they are taught. Any book on teaching method should ultimately benefit *children*, otherwise it has little value for the teacher.

A child's success in arithmetic depends largely upon three things. First, it depends upon whether the child, in school and out of school, has experiences which help him to understand what he is doing when he deals with number. That is, if the work is to have meaning for him, it must be related to previous experiences. Second, a child's success depends upon the teacher's own understanding of what he is teaching. Without real understanding, teaching cannot be effective. Third, a child's success depends upon careful planning and grading of the work: the child must proceed gradually, not meeting too many difficulties at the same time, and must be given adequate practice at every stage.

The material in this book is built up on the basis of these three points.

(2) The arrangement of the book

Each of the three points may be considered briefly.

(a) *Children's experience*—In order to satisfy the first of the conditions for a child's success, we have to consider how the child gets his first ideas of number and how we may develop these at school. We have to give him experiences which help him to understand and, later, to increase the speed and accuracy of his work. The early chapters of this book attempt to show how we may best deal with these early stages.

(b) *The teacher's understanding*—It is difficult for us as teachers to put ourselves in the position of a child who is trying to learn. We have forgotten the days when we began to learn arithmetic. Moreover, we know so much more than the children that it is not easy for us to see their difficulties. Several chapters in this book are each preceded by a piece of work, often similar to that to be done by the child, which the teacher may like to try. It is hoped that these sections will help the teacher's understanding of his topic; also that they will help him to imagine the child's position, and to appreciate and treat sympathetically the child's probable difficulties.

(c) *Planning and grading the work*—With regard to the third point, this book considers the steps by which most children develop their ability to do arithmetic. We must be aware of these steps in all their details if we are to help children to climb them. Further, it is not enough for us to know the steps in the particular process we are teaching: we should know what comes before and after. If we do not know the full range of the subject, we are unlikely to be able to help the child who is having trouble or plan ahead for the one who is doing well. The analysis of teaching steps, given at the end of various chapters, should help the teacher to keep this wider view in mind. It should also help him to find the source of certain difficulties, and to plan his lessons so that each stage leads naturally and easily to the next.

(3) *The use of the book*

It is hoped that the book will prove helpful in various ways.

(a) *To teachers* in their everyday class-room work. The book as a whole gives a broad background for the teaching of a primary course in arithmetic. But it is also arranged for day-to-day reference and planning. For example, a teacher with a class of children aged about seven or eight, may have to teach the subtraction process as part of the first term's work. It is suggested that he may read or re-read Chapter VI ('Introducing children to subtraction'), which covers the previous work. He may then try 'Something to think about—3', which precedes Chapter XII and may help him to see some probable difficulties. Next, the teacher may read Chapter XII ('More about subtraction') and take careful note of the method he intends to use. Lastly, he may go through the steps in teaching (Analysis 2) at the end of Chapter XII, in order to have a guide for future work.

The book suggests ways of preparing suitable examples for children. For instance, the lists and 'sets' of number 'facts' in various chapters provide the material for practice-cards and tests. Illustrations and descriptions offer help in the construction of apparatus needed for effective teaching. Varied lines of approach are suggested, so that learning may be and remain enjoyable.

(b) *To head-teachers* in planning the details of the arithmetic syllabus. The work of each class should fit neatly into that of the last and the next, so that every child works at the proper level according to his stage of development. The Analyses should help a head-teacher to check the progress of each class from time to time.

(c) *To teachers-in-training* by giving the beginner a wide and sure foundation for his future teaching. The student is recommended to read the early chapters of this book (I to X) as part of his general study of child development. Introductions to various chapters ('Something to think about') may be studied before the relevant lecture on Arithmetical method. This may give more emphasis to the particular chapter and help the student to see the child's probable point of view. (This approach is often used successfully in the mathematics departments of training colleges.)

(d) *To tutors, lecturers and inspectors* who may not be specialists in the teaching of arithmetic, yet may have to give advice or even supervise lessons. It is hoped, at least, to encourage standardization within a school, and within an area (particularly where some children go on from several primary schools to a central secondary school). Such standardization is essential for a child's rapid progress, and it helps to avoid many of a teacher's problems.

(4) Adapting the book for different systems

In a book of this kind it is impossible to discuss in detail the arithmetic of different number and money systems* and how it may be affected by different languages and environments. Nevertheless, this book is designed for use in many different parts of the world, because the underlying principles may be applied equally well to the teaching of arithmetic anywhere.

No two schools, no two teachers, no two children are quite alike: variation is inevitable. Each teacher has to adapt ideas to his own particular circumstances. For example, in an area where the units of money are different from those used here, a resourceful teacher may copy the relevant parts of the book, in note form, using the currency system of his own district. Similarly, he should take his illustrations and examples from the local surroundings and daily lives of the people. But, all the time, he should use the same general principles and a very careful grading of the work similar to that suggested.

* The British system of money is taken as an example in this book, partly because the authors are British, but chiefly because the system is probably *the most difficult* in common use. It is easy, therefore, for teachers to apply the principles and teaching methods to simpler systems.

CHAPTER II

WHY DO WE TEACH ARITHMETIC?

A well-known educationist once said that teachers never ask this question. They know that, in any case, they have to teach arithmetic, and are content to leave it at that.

Surely we should not be content. When we spend much time (usually one period per day, at least) on arithmetic, we ought to know why we think the subject is so important. If it is not important, we should not waste our own and the children's time and energy on it. Moreover we must be able to give a satisfactory reply to the question 'Why teach arithmetic?' because upon our answer depends not only the arithmetic we teach but our methods of teaching it.

(1) Arithmetic is useful in everyday life

In his early days, when Man lived in trees and caves, he did not need arithmetic. He had no ambition for the future, only immediate concern for the welfare of his children. His needs, apart from food and shelter, were very few. But when Man began to live in communities, he wanted better things for himself and his family. With developing civilization his needs grew and he found it necessary to calculate. He wanted to count his possessions, to compare and assess their value. He began to need the language of number and the ability to understand it when it was used by his fellows.

It may be said, in fact, that the urge for arithmetical knowledge arose in trading. A man had to be able to compare and estimate the value and prices of goods, in order to get food and clothes for his family, to buy tools for his work, and so on. To a certain extent such knowledge may be passed on from parents to children in a simple society. But the life and commerce of any community constantly increases in complexity. The new generation needs more knowledge of number than the old. Thus we come to teach arithmetic in schools.

(2) *Arithmetic helps our understanding of the world*

A knowledge of number is necessary for the understanding of many activities. To take just one example, 'time' is important in a child's school-day. It is also connected with the seasons, with farming and industrial activities, and with marketing. The question of time becomes even more important as new machinery and techniques are introduced into a community. A true appreciation of history depends upon a time-sense, which includes arithmetical ideas like those of time-charts, date-lines, etc.

Arithmetic is also important for the understanding and study of many natural phenomena: wind, rainfall, tides, heights and depths, temperatures, etc.

Moreover, aeroplanes, newspapers, radio and television bring ever closer contacts between people all over the world. News travels further and faster every day. Arithmetic helps people to understand the news, which often contains references to graphs, percentages, averages, index numbers and so on. It may also help them to be more critical of what they see and hear.

(3) *Arithmetic helps to develop a healthy attitude towards learning*

As teachers one of our tasks, perhaps the most important one, is to encourage in children a desire for the truth. We want our children to be obedient and respectful to their elders and to have high regard for good traditions. But we do not want them to grow up submissive, ready to believe anything they hear or read. If they merely absorb knowledge, as a sponge absorbs water, they are likely to grow up at the mercy of any trickster, ready to accept untruths and false propaganda without question.

To be able to pass examinations is not enough. We want children to learn to think for themsleves. They should be able to decide what knowledge is worth having. They should know how to apply and use their knowledge. We hope that they can see what is wrong or inaccurate and how it may be put right. In other words, their education should help them to become searchers after truth.

Arithmetic, properly taught, helps to develop this attitude.

Children begin to realize that a result may be right or wrong, that its accuracy may be tested, and that it is necessary to work in a logical order. They gradually build up a systematic approach to problem-solving, and learn that they must always deal with the facts as they are and not as they would like them to be.

(4) Arithmetic is necessary in a study of science

This book is one of a series on the teaching of science. It is included because a sound arithmetical knowledge is essential for a study of science. This requires the ability to make detailed observations, careful measurements and accurate calculations. Skill of this kind cannot be taught or acquired just when it is needed for science. It has to grow gradually with the developing mind of the child. For example, in a science lesson the teacher may be dealing with quantities of seed, fertilizer or produce in connexion with a certain area of land. He has no time to spend at that stage on multiplication, division, area, weight, percentage, etc. He expects the children to have learned these in the arithmetic lessons of earlier years. In fact a good arithmetic teacher may have used simple illustrations and examples based on agricultural matters. Thus arithmetic provides a necessary foundation of knowledge, and may also give increased meaning to subsequent science lessons.

Again, arithmetic may well give children their first ideas of scientific methods: for example, through the collection of material and data, the statement of a problem, the approach to new work, the use of apparatus, ways of solving problems, always proceeding from the known to the unknown. The good arithmetic teacher often uses a scientific approach in his work and thus encourages children, at a very simple level, to do the same.

CHAPTER III

THE MODERN APPROACH TO ARITHMETIC —WHAT SHALL WE TEACH AND HOW SHALL WE TEACH IT?

(1) How much arithmetic shall we teach?

One of the main reasons for teaching arithmetic is that it is useful in everyday life. In this case we must make sure that we teach, first of all, the topics which children and adults are most likely to need for their ordinary affairs. We should also use everyday things and events to give meaning to this arithmetic and its written symbols.

What, then, is this desirable minimum of arithmetic which we want *all* our children to know? Perhaps we may put it very briefly like this:—

(*i*) The ability to count quickly.

(*ii*) The ability to add, subtract, multiply and divide small numbers, mentally and on paper. (Everyday numbers seldom reach and very rarely go beyond thousands.)

(*iii*) A knowledge of coins.

(*iv*) The ability to buy (and sell) goods without making mistakes. This includes the ability to assess the value of goods in terms of money. In general, we are concerned with small amounts of money. (It is very rare indeed to find an occasion in everyday life for an example such as: £569. 17*s*. 10¾*d*. × 347.)

(*v*) The ability to tell the time and to use various kinds of time-table.

(*vi*) The ability to estimate and measure lengths or distances.

(*vii*) A knowledge of the common weights and measures of capacity.

In the past there has been a tendency to teach, to *all* children, much more than this, including parts of arithmetic which have little value. At the same time the important parts were not taught well enough. Processes and problems which had little meaning for children often took up much of the time. Consequently many children failed in the early stages of learning, lost enthusiasm and interest, and developed an unhealthy attitude to arithmetical work. Now it is only natural that we want to pass on to *all* our children *all* the arithmetic we ourselves learned at school. But it is wrong to assume that, because we did particular parts of arithmetic by a particular method, those are the most suitable parts and that the best method. They may not be suitable or best, particularly for the less able children. We have to remember that teachers are usually a selected group, most of whom, as children, found little difficulty in arithmetic. We cannot assume that *all* children find it easy. On the other hand, we should not go, as some present-day teachers do, to the opposite extreme. We must not make the mistake of assuming that all traditional subject-matter and methods are wrong and so we must scrap the lot. Change is not necessarily for the better. We have to find out where material is unsuitable and where methods fail, and then try to make improvements.

Thus, although we realize that the arithmetic needed by most people in everyday life is not very extensive, we should not forget that this is a *minimum*. There are many children who should progress further, particularly those who are able to go on to study mathematics and science. Such children need every opportunity we can find for stimulation and independent thought.

It appears, therefore, that what we teach must depend upon the individual abilities, needs and differences, of the children in our care. It is now acknowledged by teachers all over the world that we can no longer teach 'the class': we must not only know how children learn but study their individual development.

(2) The necessity for arithmetical rules

For quick and accurate calculation it is necessary to obey rules. A child who does not follow the rules makes many and frequent mistakes, whereas the habits formed by practising good rules lead to efficiency.

There are good and bad rules. Any rule which tends to stop

B

a child thinking is bad; it tends to prevent his learning something new. For example:—

Some teachers say: 'A quick way of multiplying by ten is "add on a nought".' This is a bad rule for three reasons:

(*i*) As stated, it is wrong. (If we 'add a nought' to 15, the answer is 15, *not* 150.)

(*ii*) It does not help a child to understand that he should make use of his knowledge of place-value.

(*iii*) When applied to decimals, it may lead to mistakes.

In general, rules should be explained, with many examples, and a good rule is one which is fully understood. (There are, of course, times when explanation or proof of a rule should not be attempted. For example, older children may have to use the formula, πr^2, for the area of a circle. The mathematical proof of the formula is too difficult for them and would merely confuse them. But even in a case of this kind we should show, by practical means, that the rule is reasonable and gives us a method of finding the right answer quickly.)

(3) *The need for practice*

Good habits come through practice. As children progress in their arithmetical work, the facts and processes they already know should become a matter of habit, leaving them free to devote their minds to fresh ideas. For example, by the time children begin to do 'long division' they should know all the simple number facts without having to stop and think about them.

Habits are acquired mainly through repetition. But we must remember that this repetition should be interesting and varied, and that it should be based on understanding. For example, tables should not merely be 'said', but should be studied and learned in a variety of ways. Moreover, the children should first understand each fact in the tables, and should know what tables are and how they are built up.

Some teachers may think that this is a slow and laborious way of 'getting results'. They may feel that it is better to leave out explanations and just 'hammer in the facts'. But, in the long run, children who understand prove superior to those who blindly follow rules. When they forget (and there are many reasons why children do forget) their understanding helps memory. They are also able to practise and study by themselves and so make greater progress.

(4) Making sure progress

'Proceed from the known to the unknown' is a well-worn phrase, but nevertheless an instruction to be followed. When children first come to us in a new class we must find out what they know. This gives us the foundation on which we may build firmly, and helps us to ensure that the children make good progress.

In arithmetic it is not easy to check the children's knowledge, because it is almost impossible to devise tests to cover the whole of a child's previous work. But it cannot be too strongly emphasized that we must never assume, without testing, that children know the previous steps in some part of the course. For example, it is waste of time to start teaching the later stages of the multiplication process if the children are not confident about the early number facts, and if some of them still count on their fingers. With these children we have to go right back to the beginning. In other words, we must make sure of the position before starting new work. *The good teacher takes nothing for granted.*

(5) Grading the work

Similarly, we should grade the work so that each child goes into the new 'unknown' step with sure knowledge of the steps behind him. Many detailed suggestions for the grading of the work in arithmetic are given in this book. But they should not be accepted uncritically. Each teacher should decide upon his own methods, choosing those which best suit him and his children in the particular circumstances of their own surroundings.

(6) Enjoyment in arithmetic

In this and the two preceding chapters it is implied that the child's attitude to learning is of the utmost importance in his education. When children dislike a subject they do not want to go on learning it at school, and so their progress, if any, is slow. They certainly want no more to do with it when their schooldays are ended. And in many ways their attitude will influence the education of future generations.

In some schools arithmetic has been a dull uninteresting subject. Many children gave it up as soon as they could, and would have no more to do with it. This need not have happened. Arithmetic, properly taught, can be fun: that is, enjoyable hard work. Not only should the children get the satisfaction of achievement and success, but they should also enjoy doing the work itself. For most children this is the secret of progress.

Arithmetic demands close concentration, at least for short periods. But anyone who watches their leisure-time activities knows that even young children show intense concentration. They concentrate because they enjoy what they are doing. We fail in our duty if children do not enjoy our lessons and show the absorbed interest of which they are capable.

SOMETHING TO THINK ABOUT—1
(*Number-names and -symbols*)

Like similar sections in later pages, this is intended to help teachers to get a better understanding of:—

(*a*) How children learn.
(*b*) How much children can be expected to learn at various stages.
(*c*) Why many children may not find the learning easy.
(*d*) Why good teaching methods are necessary.
(*e*) The reasons for teaching by methods such as those recommended in this book.

We grown-ups tend to forget our childhood very easily. Can we remember how we learned to read, or how we learned arithmetic? We remember very little, and it is almost certain that we have taken this learning for granted. Did it just happen, or was it something which we gained after long and painful experience?

It is not easy to go back over our lives to those early years, but, to be able to do our work well, we must try to understand the difficulties which a child finds when starting to learn about number. We must try, somehow, to put ourselves in the place of the child.

Let us see whether we can do this. Let us see whether we can get some idea of the difficulties which a child may meet when he first deals with numbers up to ten.

Obviously it cannot help our understanding of these difficulties if, at grown-up level, we deal with a number system which we already know. So let us, for this purpose, suppose we have new names for the numbers from one to ten. For example, we may have:—

Yuh, Nye, Ted, Nay, Shons, Kee, Lee, Man, Jah, Roh;
instead of 'one', 'two', 'three', etc.

Now, imagine that you are a child. You have just started school and everything is strange to you: the schoolroom, the desks, the discipline, the teachers, and even some of the children. You are one of the children who cannot yet count properly. You have heard your brothers and sisters counting and your parents using words which seem to mean groups of things. You have probably heard all the words from *Yuh* to *Roh* used, but not in order, and you may even think that *Nye* and *Ted* mean groups as shown here; but you yourself cannot count.

Nye [::]

Suppose your teacher, without fully under-standing your lack of suitable experiences, proceeds to teach you and the rest of the class to count mechanically from *Yuh* to *Roh*. He starts by getting you and the rest of the class to repeat after him:—*Yuh, Nye, Ted, Nay, Shons, Kee, Lee, Man, Jah, Roh.** You say the words again and again, and per-haps the teacher allows you to count on your fingers. After a time, you will be able to say them in the correct order. (The reader MUST TRY to do so, if he is to under-stand what follows.)

Ted [∴]

The teacher now starts to ask you questions like these: 'What comes after *Nay*?' 'What comes before *Jah*?' (Can you, the reader, answer these questions without looking at the series of names? Did you have to start chanting the numbers from the beginning? †)

Soon the teacher asks you to think of these number-names not only as having a position in a line from *Yuh* to *Roh*, but also as describing groups of objects. For example: 'Pick out *Jah* beads from a box.' (Can you do this?) Then: 'Pick out *Shons* sticks', and 'If we put *Shons* sticks and *Nye* sticks together, how many have

---

* The reader should make a serious attempt to learn these names. It may be easier when they are recognized as the syllables of U—NI—TED NA—TIONS and KI—LI—MAN—JA—RO.

† Have you, as a teacher, noticed that many children have to 'chant' before they can answer your questions?

we?' (Did you find the last question easy? Or did you, as a child does, find yourself having to translate the number-name into a number of things and laboriously count them out? Like this: '*Shons . . . Yuh, Nye, Ted, Nay*, SHONS; *Nye . . . Yuh*, NYE. Now altogether . . . *Yuh, Nye, Ted, Nay, Shons, Kee*, LEE. There are LEE sticks altogether.')

The time comes when the teacher shows you the number-symbols. Here they are:

$$\Omega \quad \square \quad \wp \quad \perp \quad \Phi \quad \angle \quad \wedge \quad \eth \quad \oplus \quad \triangledown$$

(Do you find them rather confusing? It is no worse for you than for the child. You have seen most of these shapes before, just as the child may have seen 5, 8, 3, etc., without giving them a definite meaning.)

The teacher then gets you to point to the symbols in order, and say their names. He may show you a chart like this:

$$\square \quad \wp \quad \perp \quad \Phi \quad \angle \quad \wedge \quad \eth \quad \oplus \quad \triangledown \quad \square\Omega$$

Yuh Nye Ted Nay Shons Kee Lee Man Jah Roh

He may also make you draw the symbols, and put a number of dots under each, like this:

$$\square \quad \wp \quad \perp \quad \Phi \quad \angle \quad \wedge \quad \eth \quad \oplus \quad \triangledown \quad \square\Omega$$

Later, you are given some of the symbols in a different order and asked to put in the correct number of dots; for example:

$$\Phi \quad \eth \quad \triangledown \quad \wp \quad \perp$$

Soon the teacher goes on to talk about simple addition and subtraction, with examples of this type:

$$ \Phi + \wedge = \square \Omega, \quad - \perp = \Phi $$

(This is what the early number combinations may look like to a child when he first meets them. Try to do these examples quickly *without* first changing the symbols into those which you normally use.)

We will stop here.

Have you found these exercises somewhat confusing and unreal? Do you feel that too much ground has been covered far too quickly, without giving you a chance to get used to the new ideas, names and symbols? *If so you are beginning to find yourself in the same position as many children* when their early number ideas are introduced too quickly and in a rigid and meaningless manner.

The purpose of Chapter IV is to give methods of introducing children to these early number ideas in a more natural way. We must try to let the children's knowledge and understanding of the number-names and -symbols grow out of their own personal experiences, so that they will develop a healthy mental attitude towards number. They will then have the necessary basis for success in their further work in arithmetic, and eventually in mathematics.

CHAPTER IV

THE CHILD'S FIRST IDEAS OF NUMBER

A—*The need to study children and how they learn*

It has been rightly said that teachers do not teach unless children learn. This is a short way of saying that the process of educating a child depends mainly upon the reactions of *the child* to all the people (including teachers) and things around him. It does not depend, except secondarily, upon the amount or weight of material which *the teacher* puts before him. In fact a great deal of what the child learns does not depend upon direct teaching at all. He learns to walk and talk, to eat the proper things, to be sociable and to live in his community, mainly through his own observations and experience and through his unconscious imitation of others.

The emphasis in the education of children today is not upon the teacher teaching but upon the child learning. The desire to learn must come from the child. The teacher's job is to present material in such a way that the children are able to learn for themselves. No one will deny, of course, that it is possible to teach children to perform certain actions like tame animals, or to say words and numbers like a parrot. But this is not teaching —it is training. Such children have not learned because they have not properly understood: they are unable to apply the things they can say or do to new situations.

Looking back at the tasks given in the section before this chapter, we remember that, while we could learn new number-names and their symbols in parrot fashion (*Yuh, Nye, Ted, Nay,* etc.), we found great difficulty in using them to solve problems until we could give them meaning in concrete form (for example, that *Nay* meant 4 things).

In the same way we can easily get children 'to learn' in parrot fashion the names of numbers, and even abstract facts, like $2 + 3 = 5$, but unless they understand the reality behind the abstraction they are unable to use the knowledge in any further process. Until the child has previously had the experience of handling, and dealing with, numbers of concrete objects, classifying them and counting and grouping them, it is folly to ask him to deal with symbols like $2 + 3 = 5$. Indeed, it may cause him to have difficulties in arithmetic for the rest of his life.

It is becoming increasingly clear, then, to teachers and educationists in general, that the effective teaching of any subject depends upon the teacher getting to know the child he is going to teach. It is only when the teacher understands *how* the child learns (or why he fails to learn) that he is able to select the best way of teaching (that is, the best way of presenting material so that the child can learn for himself). It is only when the teacher knows his children as individual personalities, with individual difficulties and individual capacities, that he is able to help them learn to the best advantage.

B—*The child's 'readiness' for learning*

The study, in recent years, of children's development throughout the world has thrown some light, amongst other things, on:—

(a) How children learn.

(b) What they are individually capable of learning.

(c) What they learn without any direct teaching.

(d) What is the best time (or age) to begin learning new subject matter.

In this and succeeding chapters we shall be concerned with all four of these aspects. Let us discuss here the question of readiness for new learning.

Results of research seem to show that there are times in every individual's life when he is particularly 'ready' for new experiences. What do we mean by the term 'ready'? Let us think of it in terms of grown-up persons: for instance, ourselves.

We, as grown-ups, have all had the experience of trying to learn something new and failing to do so. But, after an interval, when perhaps we have forgotten the subject at which we failed, we come back to it and find very little difficulty with it. We appear to have matured in some way during the interval, so that our minds can now cope with the work. In other words we are 'ready' for learning it.

For example, many young students, attempting to learn academic psychology, find great difficulty in understanding the ideas involved in such a study. They are too young, too intellectually immature. They have not had sufficient experience of observing human behaviour. They have not watched children closely enough nor with sufficient interest. They are not 'ready' for learning this subject. Five years later, the same students are often 'ready' for a course in psychology. The necessary basis of experience has been acquired, and they themselves are more mature people. They have observed more closely their own and other people's behaviour, and have met children in various environments. Psychology has more meaning for them, and they read about it with much less difficulty.

The same is true of children learning about numbers and how to perform arithmetical processes. They, too, need to be 'ready' for each piece of work at any particular stage. They do not learn a new process properly until they have had the necessary previous experience, and until they have developed the physical and mental powers needed to understand it.

If, therefore, we teachers are to find out which are the best ways of teaching arithmetic, we have to study children much more closely, to watch how and what they learn, and how they 'pick up' information about numbers from all that is going on around them. We shall then be more likely to know when they are 'ready' for new learning and what to introduce at any particular stage. We should not, of course, make the mistake of thinking that all we have to do is to sit back and wait for children to be 'ready'. We teachers can help, where necessary, to make them 'ready' by giving them the right kind of early number experiences in school—particularly when children come from homes with a somewhat limited background.

C—*The child's experiences before starting school*

Let us see how most children get their ideas of number before they start school, how they learn to give meaning to number-names and symbols, how they gradually make themselves 'ready' for formal arithmetic.

(*a*) *Hearing*—A child's first contact with number-names is through hearing the general conversation of the home. He hears numbers referred to by his parents, brothers, sisters, and other adults, and he picks up the words in exactly the same way as he learns his other speech, by imitation. They mean very little to him at this early stage. If he uses number-words at all (for example, in his play) it is largely imitative. He hears his father come home from the pasture and say 'Two sheep have died', or 'It took twelve oxen to drag that dead hippo from the river'. His mother watches a hen sitting on eggs and says 'Last year we only got eight chickens from ten eggs'. An older brother announces 'It will take me two days and a night to reach the town'. Gradually the child himself begins to use these number-words and many other words and phrases which contain arithmetical ideas, for example, 'many', 'more', 'a lot', 'a few', 'big', 'little', etc. And gradually, as the child gets experience, these words begin to have meaning, but the meaning is not very clear for a long time.

(*b*) *Seeing*—At the same time, the things the child notices through his sight also help to enlarge his understanding. Quite early in his life he notices that some objects, people or animals, which look alike to him, appear to come together in groups: for example, he notices people who look like his mother. Then he notices groups of animals, pots, pans, and, in the towns, cars and other vehicles. He notices that he has two legs, that a dog has four, etc. Gradually, he becomes able to see the differences between groups (remembering that groups are collections of similar objects). He sees that one group is larger than another but he does not *yet* know by how much. As his mind develops, this power of differentiation spreads to other qualities in intricate patterns. He sees groups of big black pigs, little white pigs, tall men who are old, tall men who are young, etc.

(*c*) *Doing*—The child's understanding of numbers in groups also grows appreciably as he learns, in his play, how to sort the various objects in his environment. He puts all the small stones together, all the large stones, all the red beads, all the large beans, all the small white beans, and he is experiencing the properties of numbers by handling these things. But we cannot expect him yet to be able to tell us how many there are in a particular group. That ability comes later, as we shall find.

This *handling* of materials of all kinds is of very great importance in helping children to develop a sense of number. There are some teachers and parents who say that young children are wasting their time by 'playing' with bricks, clay, beads, beans, etc. But this is not so: it is most important that children should have experience of handling and counting objects of all kinds.*

(*d*) *Counting*—Soon (how soon depends upon his environment) the child begins to count. That is, he begins to try to say the number-names in series, in the correct order. He is helped in this by learning number rhymes and by number games in his play, the rhythm helping him to get the right order. Here are two counting rhymes, in English. Teachers may make up similar rhymes in the children's own language:

> One, two; what shall I do?
> Three, four; sit on the floor;
> Five, six; pick up sticks;
> Seven, eight; we'll all be late;
> Nine, ten; run to the den.

> One, two; three, four, five,
> Once I caught a fish alive;
> Six, seven; eight, nine, ten,
> Then I put him back again.

The child finds great help in using his fingers as he counts, though he may not yet fully realize what the words he is saying

* In a school for 'spastic' children the teachers have found that many of the children, who are quick to learn and can soon read easily, are backward in arithmetic. ('Spastic' children suffer from a disease known as 'cerebral palsy' which makes it difficult for them to use various parts of their body like ordinary children.) It is suggested that possibly these children lack the number sense of the average child because, from their early childhood, they have never been able to *handle*, play with and count groups of everyday objects as the ordinary child does.

represent. The number five, for example, may mean to him the fifth finger, or the name of the number that comes after four in the series. It may be some time before his counting enables him to realize that each number-name stands for all the objects already counted, that is, that the number five also represents five objects. When he has played at counting and sorting all kinds of objects, this becomes clearer to him.

D—*The child's first arithmetic in school*

(1) Informal activities to give more experience of number language and ideas

The ideas about number, which the child has formed so far, have come through the use of spoken words and by his own seeing and handling of objects and groups of objects. The next big step forward in his arithmetical learning, and understanding of ideas about number, comes through his introduction to the number-names * which represent the varying groups of objects he has been using. This is a step which rarely takes place until the child comes to school. Unfortunately, some teachers expect the child to take this step before he has successfully passed through the previous stages. There is no doubt that many children fail to progress in arithmetic because they have been introduced too soon (that is, before they are 'ready') to abstract ideas of number.

Where this 'readiness' does not exist (that is, in the early years at school) teachers can do a great deal to give children the necessary experiences to get them 'ready'. This involves encouraging the children to take part in all kinds of play activities. Much of the work is informal, but the teacher should keep a careful record of what happens with each child.

Here are some suggestions for such activities:—

(i) Sorting trays—Shells, seeds, stones, nuts, etc. are sorted for size and colour (Fig. 1). The teacher says: 'Put all the black seeds in here, all the red ones in here', 'Put all the big shells in here, all the little ones in here', etc.

---

* *Note*—At this stage the children are not using written symbols. These are introduced later (see pages 30-37).

(*ii*) *Collecting*—Articles such as sticks, feathers and leaves are collected and tied in pairs, in threes, in fours, etc.

(*iii*) *'Playing house'*—The children play at making houses with any materials available. Tins, pieces of wood, shells, etc., can be

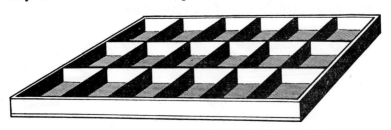

FIGURE 1.—A number-tray. (For sorting small objects, e.g. shells, nuts, pebbles, etc., into groups according to size or colour, etc.)

Suitable dimensions: 12″ × 9″ × ¼″, but it is also useful to have one or two larger trays for group work

used for bowls and plates. 'Food' can be 'made' from clay or fruit seeds. The children must make sure they have enough 'food' and enough plates for the number of people in their 'family'.

(*iv*) *Arranging*—The children are given a number of sticks and rods of varying lengths and are asked to arrange them according to their sizes. (There are no markings on these sticks to indicate

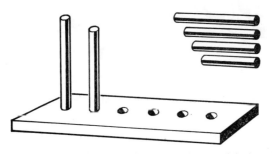

FIGURE 2.—A peg-board. (For arranging pegs or sticks in order of length)

length.) The children can either lay the sticks flat on the ground (or desk) or they can arrange them in order in a peg-board (Fig. 2).

(*v*) *'Posting-box'*—The children are given pieces of wood or cardboard of varying shapes, which should be distinct and not too small. These have to be 'posted' in their proper holes in the box (Fig. 3), which may be of any convenient size.

(*vi*) *Inset-tray*—This is similar to the 'posting-box', but the shapes are to be fitted, lying flat, into their correct places (Fig. 4).

(*vii*) *The daily 'news'*—The children are asked, individually, to stand up and tell the rest of the class of any 'news' which con-

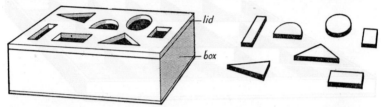

FIGURE 3.—A posting-box. (To help a child in recognizing shapes)

tains reference to numbers. For example, a child may say: 'Ten little pigs were born this morning'; another: 'My father caught two hares last night'.

(*viii*) *Threading beads*—The children are given some beads and are asked to thread them on pieces of wire or string. The teacher says: 'Put *three* beads on each of your pieces of string. Now take them off. Now put *four* beads on each piece of string', etc.

(*ix*) '*I spy*'—This is a game in which one child says, for example:

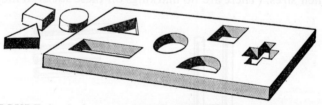

FIGURE 4.—An inset-tray. (Another aid to the recognition of shapes)
Suitable size: 12″ × 8″

'I spy with my little eye something with four legs.' The other children guess what the object is: it may be a chair, table, cow, dog, etc. (Note: the object chosen must be in view of the whole class.) The child who guesses correctly now has a turn and says, for example: 'I spy with my little eye a picture with five animals on it', and the game continues.

(*x*) *Counting parts of the body*—Each child in turn points to different parts of his body and says, for example: 'I have one nose, two eyes, two ears, two thumbs, eight fingers, ten toes', etc. They then consider a particular animal's body in the same way.

(*xi*) *Number songs, rhymes, etc.*—*In the child's own language* the teacher uses rhymes and songs which bring in numbers. (Two examples in English are given on page 21.)

(*xii*) *Dance rhythms*—The children dance to a given rhythm and call out the numbers as they dance. For example:—

(Slowly) One, two—one, two—one, two.
(Quickly) One, two, three—one, two, three—one, two, three.
(More difficult) One, two; three, four, five—one, two; three four, five.

The teacher may beat a drum (or play a note on any suitable local instrument) to help the rhythm, or the children can beat their own drums whilst they count.

(*xiii*) *Out-door games*—Many of the games used in the physical education lesson help children to get a number sense. For example, any game where the class is divided into teams adds to the child's arithmetical ideas of grouping and dividing. Examples of such games are: '*Fox and goose*', '*Oranges and lemons*', '*Chain tag*'.

In all these and many similar activities children gradually begin to use the vocabulary of arithmetic in real situations: for example, when they have raced across the playground they say: 'I was quickest', 'I came first', 'You were second', 'He was last', etc.

Sometimes the activities are spontaneous, sometimes suggested or required by the teacher, but always we should make use of every opportunity to give children arithmetical experience. It is wise to remember here that children are preparing, by their own constructive play (often where there is no obvious connexion with number), the groundwork for a great deal of their later mathematical work. For example, the child who gets bamboo sticks and leaves, old boxes, tins, etc., and proceeds to 'build' a 'house', however unrecognizable, is experimenting with his own ideas of size, weight, shape and length. It is invaluable experience, and we should provide as much material as possible for this kind of make-believe play in the child's early years at school. Such material may include:—

(*a*) Pieces of wood of various shapes and sizes; scrap paper; old kitchen-utensils; tins of various sizes for measuring.

(b) Materials for 'playing at shops': for example, seeds, wool, coconut shells, fruits, beans, stones; anything common, well-known and easily obtained by the children; home-made scales.

(c) A log or strong plank for playing see-saw. Children gain many of their early ideas about balance and weight from this.

(d) Swings; ropes from trees.

(e) Stepping stones. (Children count as they step from stone to stone.)

(f) Sand-pit.

(g) Water and small vessels of different shapes and sizes.

(h) Materials for 'playing at house'.

(j) Nature table: children bring collections of interesting objects and display them.

(2) *Further work on oral counting*

The children have now reached the stage when they are ready to proceed to a wider experience of counting. So far, they know something, from their play activities, of numbers up to four or five, but with regard to higher numbers, their ideas and language are not very accurate. Some of the work in counting continues to be informal, but there are other activities which we can organize for a special purpose.

(a) *Everyday happenings*—The ordinary class routine, and day-to-day happenings, are made use of, by the teacher, to increase the children's counting ability. Here are a few situations which lend themselves to counting:—

(i) The number of children present in class.

(ii) The number of children absent from class.

(iii) The number of children who come to school by various routes.

(iv) The number of children in various teams and play-groups.

(v) The number of chalks (pencils, pens) in a box.

(vi) The number of small cups (or other containers) which can be filled from a large jug or bottle.

(vii) The number of handfuls of soil (or sand) which are needed to fill a tin.

(*b*) *Counting activities organized by the teacher*—Some of these activities take place in the class room, others in the playground.

(*i*) *Striding* across the playground and counting the number of steps. Guessing, and then pacing out, the length of the class room, etc. Counting number of 'feet' (*heel to toe*) in the width of the class room, etc. *Jumping and hopping* given distances.—Who takes the least number of jumps?

(*ii*) *Rhymes and counting games* are popular. These should bring in objects which are familiar to the children such as stones, sticks, eggs, hens, pigs, etc. The teacher should make up rhymes in the children's own language. Here are two simple examples in English:—

> Here are stones
> All in a ring.
> We will count
> While we sing.

(A child walks round and picks up the stones one by one, putting them in the centre of the ring. The rest of the class sing the numbers as the stones are collected. Now another child puts them back in the form of a circle. The counting goes on.)

> We've got sticks
> To build a pen
> Let us count them up to ten:
> One two three four,
> Five, six, seven,
> Eight—nine—ten.

(The children each collect a bundle of sticks which they put in front of them. When the rhyme has been sung, they all count out the sticks one by one.)

FIGURE 5.—Playing skittles. (For counting)

(*iii*) Playing *skittles*. The children take turns in knocking down as many skittles (or other suitable objects) as possible, by rolling or throwing a ball from a fixed line (Fig. 5).

All the children count the number knocked down by each child. The skittles may be of any handy size. (Sticks may be used, provided that they are pushed only lightly into the ground and are easily knocked down by the ball.)

(*iv*) *Quoits* is a game in which the children have a large ring or hoop made of wood or thick rope. In turn they throw the ring

FIGURE 6.—The game of quoits. (For counting. It is better to have all objects the same: e.g. pebbles or match-boxes or small milk tins.)

over a group of small objects placed a short distance away (Fig. 6). All the children count the number of objects which lie inside the ring when it comes to rest.

(*v*) *Marbles*, also enjoyed by children, is a game similar to skittles. The marbles, made from clay, are placed in a circle and the children in turn throw a larger marble and try to knock as many marbles as possible out of the circle.

(*vi*) The *sorting tray* (see Fig. 1, page 23) may now be used by the children in another way. They put given numbers of objects into its various sections. The teacher says, for example: 'Put nine shells in each little box. Make sure you have the right number.'

(*vii*) A *classroom picture*, particularly if it shows a scene familiar to the children, can be used to help them to count. For example, the teacher asks: 'How many cows can you see? Let us count them in the picture. Now how many trees?'

(*c*) *Counting activities leading to recognition of groups*—A stage is reached when children are able to recognize small numbers of objects grouped together without counting them one by one. For example, they are able to recognize groups of twos and threes without counting. Here are some activities which encourage this ability:—

(*i*) The children are given *pattern-cards* (Fig. 7) on which there are groups of dots. Each card is given a number-name and children practise recognizing the number of dots on each card. In general a child cannot recognize a group of more than three or four objects unless they are arranged in a regular pattern. It is difficult for a grown-up to say straight away how many strokes there are here ////////////. If, however, they are grouped into fives like this ///// ///// // it is obvious that there are twelve. The arrangement of dots in Fig. 7 is recommended, since it makes use of the child's ability to recognize such simple patterns as lines, squares and triangles.

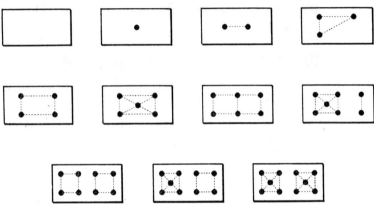

FIGURE 7.—Pattern-cards. (For recognizing groups. The dotted lines are shown here merely to indicate the 'pattern')

Suitable sizes: 2¼" × 1½" for children; 6" × 4" for a teacher's use with the class

However, it is important for later work in arithmetic that children should not rely always upon dots to enable them to recognize number groups. The next two activities help children to recognize other groupings.

(*ii*) The children are given '*bead-bars*' (Fig. 8) and thus get practice in recognizing the smaller numbers. For example, the

FIGURE 8.—Bead-bars. (For recognizing groups. The 'beads' may be nuts or any suitable objects, threaded on thin wire, cane, stiff reed, etc.)

teacher says: 'Holds up your four bead-bar. Now your six bead-bar', etc.

(*iii*) The children are given varied lengths of *cardboard strips* which are marked as in Fig. 9. They count the spaces and give

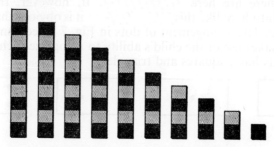

FIGURE 9.—Marked strips. (Another help in recognizing number groupings)
Suitable size: 1″ strips, marked off in inch lengths

each strip a number-name. Next they arrange them in order of size from one to ten. The teacher says: 'Hold up the four strip. Put it back. Now hold up the six strip', etc.

E—*Introducing the number-symbols*

Up to this stage the children have not used number-*symbols* in any of their activities, though they have used number-*names*. Many of the children have, of course, seen number-symbols in school and in their everyday activities, though very few are able to draw them or to give them much meaning.

The stage is now reached when the teacher can introduce the use of the figures which stand for the numbers (of objects) with which the children have been dealing in their early activities.

Remembering the difficulty which we ourselves experienced in recognizing the symbols in the section before this chapter, it is clear that we must approach the work for children in easy and understandable stages. It is suggested that the work should include the following:—

(*a*) Teaching the child to recognize the number-symbols in connexion with their *names*.

(*b*) Teaching the child to recognize the symbols in connexion with their *values*.

(c) Teaching the child how to write (or 'draw') the symbols and at the same time to know their names *and* their values.

It should be realized that the learning of number-symbols and their meaning is a big step for young children. Moreover, real understanding is necessary for a child's future success in arithmetic. Many difficulties found in later stages have been traced back to lack of understanding at this early stage. It is worth while to spend time on this work, until the child realizes not only the value of particular numbers but also has some idea of their relationship to each other. This comes to him best if he is given the opportunity to use a variety of apparatus and take part in number games and activities where he is using printed and written symbols. A few such activities are suggested in the following paragraphs.

(a) *Introducing the symbols with their names*—This should be done gradually, so as not to confuse the children. For example, it is wise not to introduce more than three or four of the symbols (figures) at a time.

(i) *Rhymes* help the children to get to know the figures. The teacher draws a figure 2 on the blackboard (or holds up a cut-out figure). The children are taught to say:—

> 'This is a 2
> For me and for you.'

(The teacher should invent rhymes in the children's own language, of course.) Here are two more in English: –

> 'This is a 3
> For Jill, Jack and me.'

> 'This is a 4.
> Stick it on the door.'

(ii) The figures are cut out *from sand-paper* (that is paper with a rough surface) and stuck on card. The children look at the figures and get to know their shapes by going over the rough surface with their hands. Whilst doing so, they say what each figure is. Next they repeat this with their eyes closed, and then try to recognize figures by their sense of touch.

The figures may also be made from clay or other material so that they stand up above the surface of the card.

(*iii*) *Inset-trays*, with number shapes instead of squares and rectangles (see Fig. 4), can be used to make the number-figures more familiar. The teacher says: 'Pick up the figure 2. Put it in its proper place in the tray. Now pick up the 3', etc.

(*b*) *Giving meaning to the symbols*—These activities are intended to help children link the symbols with numbers of things.

(*i*) *Matching-trays.* Number-trays (Fig. 1, page 23) may be used in various ways for matching:—

(I) The teacher puts number-cards into one row of sections of the tray. The child has to put the correct number of objects (beads, seeds, etc.) into the next row of sections of the tray (Fig. 10).

(II) The teacher puts picture-cards (numbers of fish, goats,

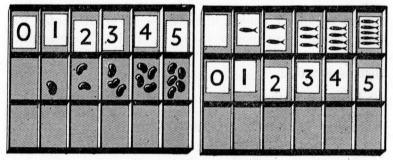

FIGURE 10.—Number-tray (see Fig. 1), used to match figures with numbers

FIGURE 11.—Number-tray, used to match figures with picture-cards

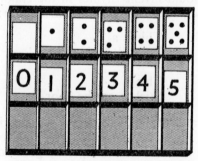

FIGURE 12.—Number-tray, used to match figures with number-pattern cards

Suitable size for number-cards: 2″ × 2″

eggs, sheep, etc.) into one row of sections and the children put in the correct symbols (Fig. 11).

(III) The child has to match number-cards with pattern-cards (Fig. 12).

As the children become more proficient the teacher can re-arrange the cards so that they are not in numerical order.

(*ii*) The children *thread beads* on a string (or on thin wire) as in previous activities, but this time they also attach the correct number-card (Fig. 13).

FIGURE 13.—Bead-bars (or strings of beads) with number-cards

(*iii*) The children *collect various things* (feathers, sticks, leaves, etc.) into bundles, and tie the correct number-card to each bundle.

(*iv*) The children play *skittles* (Fig. 5) as before, but now they also select the number-card corresponding to the number of skittles knocked down. (The number-cards should be in full view of all the children so that they can see whether the correct card has been chosen.)

(*v*) The children make *flags* with sticks and paper. Then they build a 'castle' of earth or sand and stick the flags on it. They then count the number of flags and put a number-card in front of the 'castle' to show how many flags it has (Fig. 14).

FIGURE 14.—Flags on 'castles', and number-cards

(*vi*) The children are given *number-cards* from '0' to '10'. The teacher claps his hands a number of times. The children listen carefully and then hold up the correct number-card. (To give practice with the nought-symbol, '0', the teacher prepares to clap his hands but does *not* bring them together to make a sound.)

(*vii*) The *figures* are made from wood or cardboard, and in each figure are cut a number of holes corresponding to the value of the figure: a '2' has two holes, a '3' has three holes, etc. (Fig. 15).

FIGURE 15.—The number-symbols as 'cut-outs' (with holes for pegs)
Minimum size: 2¼". Match-sticks may be used as pegs

The child has the cut-out figures before him and a box of small sticks or pegs. He looks at a figure, decides its value, then takes the correct number of pegs from the box and inserts them into the holes in the figure.

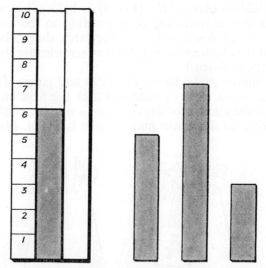

FIGURE 16.—The '10' number-slide (unmarked strips, of exact lengths, are used)
This apparatus is described on page 469

(*viii*) The children work in pairs. They are given a *number-slide*, ten inches long (Fig. 16), and several strips of cardboard, each an exact number of inches. These strips have no marks on them.

One child picks up a strip, looks at it, and guesses its 'number'. The other child then takes the strip and tests whether the guess is correct by placing it on the number-slide.

(*ix*) A *wall 'number-board'* (or *'matching-board'*) is made from wood or thick cardboard, as in Fig. 17. Three narrow strips of wood are nailed across the board to make ledges on which cards can be placed. One method of using this apparatus is for the teacher to place number-pattern cards along the top row. The

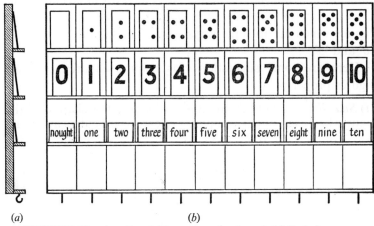

(*a*)   (*b*)

FIGURE 17.—A wall matching- or number-board: (*a*) End view,
(*b*) Front view

Suitable size: 4′ × 2′ 3″

children, in turn, then come out and place the correct number-symbol cards underneath them. (At the proper time, the written number-words are also introduced.) Hooks are fastened along the bottom so that children can hang groups of small objects corresponding to the number-cards.

(*c*) *Writing the number-symbols*—Some children learn to draw the figures well without very much help. But the majority need considerable guidance from the teacher in the early stages. The teacher should bear in mind that:

(1) Children find it much more difficult than grown-ups to draw small figures. In the early stages they should be allowed to make their figures big. The emphasis should be on the *shape* of the figure rather than on its *size*. The children are helped by having *large* crayons, pencils or chalks, and a *large* surface, such as a

blackboard, on which to write. (It is sometimes better to let the child draw with the blackboard flat on the ground.)

(2) The children need guidance about where it is best to begin the figure and where best to finish it. For example, the figure '5' should start with a down stroke and should be completed with the stroke from left to right at the top. The figure '3' should *start* at the top with a horizontal stroke. Some children have difficulty in writing figures because they have acquired bad habits.

(3) Children should be given help so that they do not confuse figures which are in some ways alike, for example, '6' and '9', '5' and '3'.

Here are some suggestions for helping children to draw figures properly:—

(*i*) *Stencils* are made from thin cardboard, the shapes of the figures being cut out. The amount of cardboard cut away should leave room only for a pencil or thin crayon to be inserted

FIGURE 18.—Stencils for the number-symbols
Suitable size: one-inch figures on two-inch cards

(Fig. 18). It will be noticed that the figures '0', '8', '9' require complete circles to be cut out. The children are told to draw round the edge of the circles in the stencils.

(*ii*) *Sand* (or other suitable material) can be used as a surface on which children can draw the figures with their fingers. This activity is popular and very effective, since the children can quickly smooth the surface and continue practising.

(*iii*) A whole class may practise forming figures in the activity known as '*sky writing*'. In this the children extend one arm and 'draw' the figure in the air.

(*iv*) Pieces of *tracing paper* are placed on top of printed number-cards and the children trace over them with a pencil. Then they take off the paper and compare what they have drawn with the printed figure.

(*v*) When children have reached the stage of drawing figures without help from the teacher, they should be given *paper marked off in squares*. The squares should be large to begin with (for example, one inch) and later should be reduced in size (Fig. 19).

This chapter has described some of the ways in which children's number experience can be enlarged so that they are 'ready' for more formal arithmetic. The examples given should be

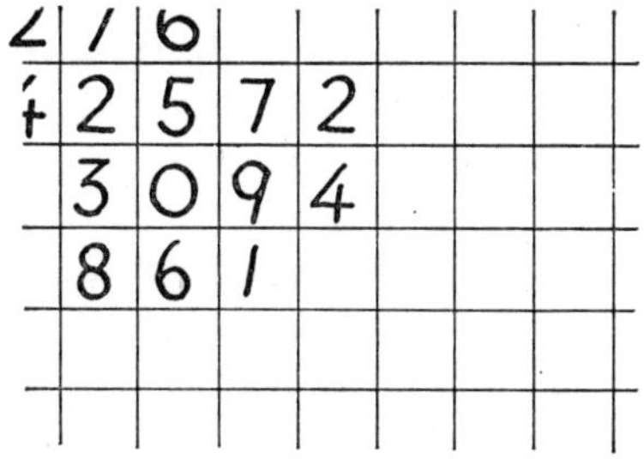

FIGURE 19.—Squared paper for children's drawing of number-symbols

adapted to the conditions and situations of the teacher's own class: that is, they must not only be understandable but 'real' and 'alive' for the children concerned. It cannot be too strongly emphasized that this kind of number experience is essential if children are to go on easily to learn about addition, subtraction, multiplication and division. Methods of introducing these processes are discussed in the next four chapters.

CHAPTER V

INTRODUCING CHILDREN TO ADDITION

A—*The idea of addition*

The idea of addition begins to come to a child through the number situations which he meets in everyday life and through the early number-activities at school (e.g. those described in Chapter IV).

For example, a child 'sees' that two or more small groups of beans or marbles can be combined to make one larger group. He also 'sees' that two short sticks may be joined to make a longer stick. These two examples illustrate two aspects of addition with which we must be concerned.

In the early stages a child adds two small groups of objects by dealing with the separate objects in each group; he puts them together and then counts the number of objects in the whole group. For example, he adds three and two by putting together three objects and two objects and then counting the whole group.

The child needs much experience of this nature, but we must not delay experiences which lead to the idea of adding two groups *without counting* the separate items in each group. For example, the child adds three and two by putting together a three-strip and a two-strip in the number-slide (Fig. 16, page 34) and 'seeing', without counting, that they are equal to a five-strip.

Our aim is to enable the children eventually *to add quickly and accurately*. This means that there comes a stage when they need to be able to add without counting.

B—*The language of addition*

(1) Words and phrases which mean 'add'
Children should meet all the words which mean 'add' while dealing with situations which they know. For example, we

should introduce little problems in discussion and invite the children to make up their own little 'sums', such as:—

(*i*) There are three fruits in this basket and four in that. How many will there be if we put them all into one basket? Let us do it. Now let us count them all.

(*ii*) You have two oranges, your brother has one. How many oranges are there altogether?

(*iii*) Let us put the five-strip and the two-strip together. We have made a longer one now. How long is it?

(*iv*) You caught five fish and your friend three. How many fish were caught in all?

(*v*) This hen laid four eggs last week and five this week. How many eggs is that equal to?

(*vi*) What do two and three make?

Although this work is oral at first, the teacher should put the figures on the blackboard to represent the number of things being discussed.

(2) *The addition sign*

When the words and phrases which indicate that adding must take place are understood, the sign, '+', is introduced. The teacher should describe the card showing '+' as 'the adding

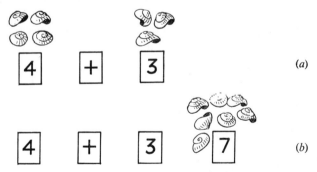

(*a*)

(*b*)

FIGURE 20.—Addition, using objects and number-cards
Suitable size for number-cards (as in Fig. 10): 2″ × 2″

sign'. It is also known as 'the plus sign'. The work is still oral and practical, but the children can represent the addition activities by using number-cards. For example, the children can put two little piles of shells on the desk or floor, placing the number-cards underneath (Fig. 20(*a*)). The shells are then put together in one pile at the right-hand side of the original piles; the children count 'one, two, three, four, five, six, seven', and place the correct number-card against them (Fig. 20(*b*)).

Pictures of familiar objects may also be used. The children put the pictures together and (Fig. 21) count the total number of fish.

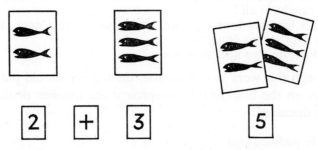

FIGURE 21.—Addition, using pictures and number-cards

(3) The 'equals' sign

The 'equals' sign is best introduced during activities with shells, picture-cards, etc., as described for the '+' sign. Its use enables the activity to be represented fully by number-cards. In the above examples the finished activities are shown as:

4 + 3 = 7 and 2 + 3 = 5

The teacher should describe the card showing '=' as 'the equals sign', but should also use other phrases such as 'make-up', 'are altogether', etc.

(4) Recording the addition

When the children have had enough practice in the use of number-cards for showing the result of their addition activities, they should begin to record the activities on paper.

In the early stages the groups of objects are drawn and the symbols from the cards are copied underneath them. Later the symbols only are written down. To start with, the setting down should follow the pattern of the cards, that is, $4 + 3 = 7$. Later, however, the method of setting down the figures under each other should be introduced. For example, instead of $4 + 3 = 7$, the addition is written as shown here.*

$$\begin{array}{r} 4 + \\ 3 \\ \hline 7 \end{array}$$

The children should be given practice in writing these 'sums' in both ways.

C—*Giving further experience of addition*

(*1*) *Totals up to ten*

When the children understand the idea of addition and know how to record their results, we can start to give them experiences of a wider range of examples of addition. It is wise to work to a plan and, as a start, it is suggested that the examples should be such that the total is not more than ten. List I on page 42 gives *all* the examples of this kind.

Note—The children, at this stage, get *experience* of the 'facts': they do not yet make any conscious effort to memorize them. In List I *all* the facts are given to help the teacher to ensure that *all* are dealt with by the children.

---

* *Note*—In examples of this kind many teachers and mathematicians prefer to put the sign in front of the lower figure, as shown here. They say that this follows more naturally from the equation, $4 + 3 = 7$. They say that '2 +' has no meaning, while '+ 2' has and later leads a child to appreciate what is meant by '— 2'. *There is no right or wrong in this matter:* it is simply a question of convenience. Teachers in any school should *stick to the same system*, whichever is adopted, and it is an advantage when all schools in a district use the same system.

$$\begin{array}{r} 4 \\ + 3 \\ \hline 7 \end{array}$$

In this book the sign is put on the right of the top figure as it is regarded merely as an instruction to the child to perform a certain operation: that is, it is regarded as an abbreviation for 'add these numbers'. Thus it can be used when more than two numbers are to be added. Moreover, a child is more likely to see the instruction at once when it is put on the top line, and there is no risk of the sign becoming mixed up with the tens or hundreds columns. The advantage of this is more obvious when we have to deal with examples of the addition of money and weights and measures.

$$\begin{array}{r} 2 + \\ 4 \\ 3 \\ \hline \end{array}$$

LIST I

THE SIMPLE ADDITION 'FACTS' (TOTALS NOT GREATER THAN 10)

Each fact is printed as a vertical addition (top number, added number with +, rule, and total). The facts shown are:

9 +1 = 10	8 +1 = 9	7 +1 = 8	6 +1 = 7	5 +1 = 6	4 +1 = 5	3 +1 = 4	2 +1 = 3	1 +1 = 2	
	8 +2 = 10	7 +2 = 9	6 +2 = 8	5 +2 = 7	4 +2 = 6	3 +2 = 5	2 +2 = 4	1 +2 = 3	
		7 +3 = 10	6 +3 = 9	5 +3 = 8	4 +3 = 7	3 +3 = 6	2 +3 = 5	1 +3 = 4	
			6 +4 = 10	5 +4 = 9	4 +4 = 8	3 +4 = 7	2 +4 = 6	1 +4 = 5	
				5 +5 = 10	4 +5 = 9	3 +5 = 8	2 +5 = 7	1 +5 = 6	
					4 +6 = 10	3 +6 = 9	2 +6 = 8	1 +6 = 7	
						3 +7 = 10	2 +7 = 9	1 +7 = 8	
							2 +8 = 10	1 +8 = 9	
								1 +9 = 10	

| 9 +0 = 9 | 8 +0 = 8 | 7 +0 = 7 | 6 +0 = 6 | 5 +0 = 5 | 4 +0 = 4 | 3 +0 = 3 | 2 +0 = 2 | 1 +0 = 1 | 0 +0 = 0 |
| 0 +9 = 9 | 0 +8 = 8 | 0 +7 = 7 | 0 +6 = 6 | 0 +5 = 5 | 0 +4 = 4 | 0 +3 = 3 | 0 +2 = 2 | 0 +1 = 1 | |

We should try to give the children experiences which cover *all* the examples in the List. For at this stage the children should be getting a real understanding of these various addition examples, so that later, when they have to *begin to memorize* the results, they will be helped by being able to think back to this early work.

It will be noticed that the list of examples has been arranged in two groups. This is because many of the examples occur in pairs, as in the example here. The answer is the same in both cases. We should give the children plenty of experiences which help them to see this, for they will often use the idea in their later work. We should demonstrate the principle: for example, when adding the two fish and the three fish we can change the pictures round so that the example becomes three fish plus two fish.

$$\begin{array}{c} 2\,+ \\ 3 \\ \hline 5 \end{array} \qquad \begin{array}{c} 3\,+ \\ 2 \\ \hline 5 \end{array}$$

(2) Addition activities

The teacher should use activities which are best suited to the conditions in his school. A few suggestions are given below.

(*i*) *Two strings of beads* are given to a child and he is told to put all the beads on to one string. He then sets out the number-cards (Fig. 22). Next, he draws what he has done in his book and then writes down the 'sum' in either of the ways shown here.

$$3 + 4 = 7 \quad \text{or} \quad \begin{array}{c} 3\,+ \\ 4 \\ \hline 7 \end{array}$$

(*ii*) *Skittles* (or '*Ninepins*') may be played to practise simple addition. For example, a child takes two balls; he throws one

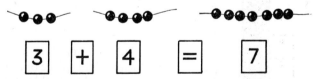

FIGURE 22.—Addition, using strings of beads and number-cards

ball and knocks down three skittles. So he takes the '3'-card. With the second ball he knocks down two skittles, so he takes the '2'-card. He copies these two numbers into his book and

adds them in either of the ways shown. The sticks are then replaced and another child has a turn.
(It is important that there should be a number of nought-cards ('0'), so that children who fail to knock down sticks with one ball may record properly, for instance, $3 + 0 = 3$.)

$$\begin{array}{r} 3\ + \\ \underline{2} \\ 5 \end{array} \quad \text{or } 3 + 2 = 5$$

(iii) Numbered strips of cardboard are most helpful in giving children experiences of adding in groups instead of by counting.

FIGURE 23.—Skittles: using number-cards for addition

(I) *The number-slide.* The children work singly or in pairs. They take two strips of card, numbered according to size, and slide them into the groove. They can then 'read off' the total size of the two strips (Fig. 24). The 'sum' is then written into their books as shown here.

$$\begin{array}{r} 5\ + \\ \underline{3} \\ 8 \end{array} \quad \text{and } 5 + 3 = 8$$

FIGURE 24.—The '10' number-slide, with numbered strips, for addition
The apparatus is described on page 469

(II) *The 'number-story' apparatus.* This piece of apparatus is used to enable children to find out for themselves how any particular number may be made up from two other numbers. In this way children are helped to get a clear idea of addition and subtraction at the same time.

A number of strips of thick card, preferably in a box, are given to the child. He is then asked to 'tell a number-story'. Fig. 25 shows the material for 'telling the story of the number five'. The strips are plain on one side and are numbered on the other. The child first uses the strips with the plain side upper-most. As he puts the strips together into the box the child says what he is doing (that is, tells the story):

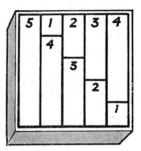

'Five and no more make five;
Four and one make five;
Three and two make five;
Two and three make five;
One and four make five.'

FIGURE 25.—A 'number-story' apparatus—for 'the story of five', showing the strips with numbered side uppermost. (Similar boxes are used for all the numbers up to ten)

Then the child takes the pieces apart, each strip in turn and says:

The strips are one inch in width

'If I take the one from the five it leaves the four,
If I take the two from the five it leaves the three,
If I take the three from the five it leaves the two,' etc.

Each number (up to ten) is dealt with in the same way.

In the next step the child turns the strips over, to show the back, which is numbered. The child now writes down the story of five.

$$5 + 0 = 5$$
$$4 + 1 = 5$$
$$3 + 2 = 5$$
$$2 + 3 = 5 \text{ etc.}$$

and

$$5 + \quad 4 +$$
$$\underline{0} \quad \underline{1}$$
$$5 \quad 5$$ etc.

(*iv*) *Number-tops* (Fig. 26) may be used by individual children, pairs or groups. A child spins the top. When it comes to rest,

FIGURE 26.—'Number-tops'. (For practice in addition)
The construction of these tops is described on page 471

the number on the edge touching the ground is noted and the child selects a card showing the same number. He then has a second spin and takes a second number-card. He records the two numbers and adds them together. This game is also useful for introducing children to the idea of adding more than two numbers (see page 49).

(*v*) *The fishing-game* can be played by two or more children. The children take turns to 'catch' the fish (Fig. 27). Each time they land a fish they write down the number written on it, and when they have caught two (or more) they find their total catch by adding the two (or more) numbers together. Details of the construction of the apparatus are given on page 471.

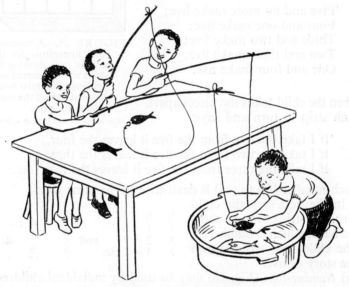

FIGURE 27.—The 'fishing-game'. (Where magnets are unobtainable, a child hooks the 'fish' on to the lines)

(*vi*) *Class activities.* Most of the work so far described is individual or concerned with small groups of children. This means that the teacher must continually move around the class, supervising the activities and giving help and encouragement.

There is also a place, at this stage, for the whole class to take part in oral work on addition. Here are some examples of the kind of oral work the teacher can do.

(I) *Addition rhymes.* It helps to strengthen children's memory of numbers being added together if they learn a few addition rhymes. The teacher should invent rhymes in the children's language (mother tongue). Here are two in English:—

Three little cowries and one more:
Put them together—that makes four.

Six long tobacco leaves hanging on a line;
Bring another three—that makes nine.

(ii) *Hand-clapping*. The teacher says: 'Listen, I am going to clap my hands several times to the right, then several times to the left. Listen carefully. I want you to tell me how many times altogether I clap my hands.'

(iii) *Everyday examples*. The teacher should make use of any opportunity which may occur during the day for drawing the children's attention to real addition examples. For instance, there may be three girls in the class dressed in red and four boys in red shirts. The teacher should bring these children together and make the occurrence into an example of addition, saying to the class: 'How many children are dressed in red?' Such opportunities occur frequently in dealing with team or individual marks: for example, 'This team got five team points this morning and two this afternoon. How many for the day?'

(*vii*) *Other activities* may be devised from the various examples of games given in Chapters IV and XV.

(3) The use of apparatus to work addition exercises

Up to this stage the children's examples of addition consist of writing down their own adding activities. We should now reverse the process by putting examples on the blackboard. The children now have to work out the addition by using the kind of apparatus they have used before (number-slide, counters, beads, etc.). This stage enables us to make sure that all the examples given in List I are practised by the children.

$$6 + \quad 5 + \text{etc.}$$
$$\underline{2} \quad \underline{4}$$

We cannot be certain that at previous stages *all* the examples have arisen in the children's own activities. It is therefore most important that List I should be used for this purpose.

We do not, of course, give the examples exactly in the order that they are given in the list.

(4) Adding numbers up to 9 + 9

When the children have had sufficient experience with the

addition examples given in List I they should extend their work to cover the addition of the remaining pairs of numbers up to 9 + 9. These are given in List II.

The children gain experience of these examples through

LIST II

FURTHER SIMPLE ADDITION 'FACTS'
(TOTALS FROM 11 TO 18)

			$\begin{array}{r}2+\\9\\\hline 11\end{array}$					$\begin{array}{r}9+\\2\\\hline 11\end{array}$
	$\begin{array}{r}3+\\8\\\hline 11\end{array}$	$\begin{array}{r}3+\\9\\\hline 12\end{array}$					$\begin{array}{r}8+\\3\\\hline 11\end{array}$	$\begin{array}{r}9+\\3\\\hline 12\end{array}$
	$\begin{array}{r}4+\\7\\\hline 11\end{array}$	$\begin{array}{r}4+\\8\\\hline 12\end{array}$	$\begin{array}{r}4+\\9\\\hline 13\end{array}$			$\begin{array}{r}7+\\4\\\hline 11\end{array}$	$\begin{array}{r}8+\\4\\\hline 12\end{array}$	$\begin{array}{r}9+\\4\\\hline 13\end{array}$
$\begin{array}{r}5+\\6\\\hline 11\end{array}$	$\begin{array}{r}5+\\7\\\hline 12\end{array}$	$\begin{array}{r}5+\\8\\\hline 13\end{array}$	$\begin{array}{r}5+\\9\\\hline 14\end{array}$		$\begin{array}{r}6+\\5\\\hline 11\end{array}$	$\begin{array}{r}7+\\5\\\hline 12\end{array}$	$\begin{array}{r}8+\\5\\\hline 13\end{array}$	$\begin{array}{r}9+\\5\\\hline 14\end{array}$
$\begin{array}{r}6+\\6\\\hline 12\end{array}$	$\begin{array}{r}6+\\7\\\hline 13\end{array}$	$\begin{array}{r}6+\\8\\\hline 14\end{array}$	$\begin{array}{r}6+\\9\\\hline 15\end{array}$			$\begin{array}{r}7+\\6\\\hline 13\end{array}$	$\begin{array}{r}8+\\6\\\hline 14\end{array}$	$\begin{array}{r}9+\\6\\\hline 15\end{array}$
	$\begin{array}{r}7+\\7\\\hline 14\end{array}$	$\begin{array}{r}7+\\8\\\hline 15\end{array}$	$\begin{array}{r}7+\\9\\\hline 16\end{array}$				$\begin{array}{r}8+\\7\\\hline 15\end{array}$	$\begin{array}{r}9+\\7\\\hline 16\end{array}$
		$\begin{array}{r}8+\\8\\\hline 16\end{array}$	$\begin{array}{r}8+\\9\\\hline 17\end{array}$					$\begin{array}{r}9+\\8\\\hline 17\end{array}$
			$\begin{array}{r}9+\\9\\\hline 18\end{array}$					

Note—These further facts are also listed in full to help the teacher make sure that the children deal with them *all*. The children are still gaining *experience* and do not yet begin to memorize deliberately.

activities similar to those already described for the earlier work. (The 'ten' number-slide is, of course, replaced by a 'twenty' number-slide.)

Again we must take care to cover *all* the examples.

(5) *Adding three numbers together*

At this stage, too, the children should be given practice in adding three numbers together, provided that the total of the 'sum' is not more than twenty.

But we must remember that a few children find difficulty in adding more than two numbers at once, because they have to learn to add a figure which they cannot see—as in the example 6 + 3 + 2. They say: 'Six and three make nine. Nine and two make eleven.' The 'nine' has to be remembered while they are adding, since it is not written down.

There are several activities which give opportunity for recording the addition of three figures. For example, adding three *bead-bars*; adding three number-strips when using the '*20*' *number-slide* (page 469); adding the score when three balls are thrown at *skittles*; adding the score when three *number-tops* come to rest.

(6) *Using '10' as a land-mark*

It is suggested that, at this early stage, the teacher should not go into the question of 'place-value'.* The number ten (10) should be regarded, for the present, as a symbol in its own right, and so should the other numbers up to nineteen. It is probable, however, that the children themselves will begin to see that the number ten is a kind of land-mark in their arithmetic. They begin to realize that when writing figures above ten they are really 'starting again':—

11 is 10 and 1 more;
12 is 10 and 2 more;
13 is 10 and 3 more; etc.

Games, such as 'the changing-game' (see the next paragraph), and suitable practice-cards (see page 58), can help to give these ideas a more definite form. Such experiences prove invaluable when it becomes necessary to explain to children the idea of 'place-value'.

The 'changing'-game. Here the children play in pairs. Each

* For example, in the number 22 the right-hand figure 2 denotes two units, the left-hand figure 2 denotes two tens. Thus the 'place' or position of a figure determines its 'value' (see page 147).

player has a pile of number-strips of varying sizes from 1 to 10. The first player picks up two strips (for example, the '8' and the '7') and says to his partner: 'Please change these for me.' The partner must give him a ten-strip and a five-strip, and must say: 'Yes, here are fifteen.' If he is right he scores a point. Where there is any doubt the two children refer to the '20' number-slide.

D—Learning the 'primary addition facts'

(1) What is an arithmetical 'fact'?

In order that a child may make good progress in arithmetic it is necessary for him to be able to deal with the easy examples of addition without having to work them out by counting and using practical materials. This is also found to be true in subtraction, multiplication and division. He must know (i.e. understand *and* remember) the basic arithmetic 'facts'.

An arithmetical 'fact' may be defined as the complete statement showing the result when two numbers are associated in a particular way. For example, the numbers 6 and 3 may be considered as being associated in the following four ways:—

$$6 + 3 = 9$$
$$6 - 3 = 3$$
$$6 \times 3 = 18$$
$$6 \div 3 = 2$$

Each of these four statements is an arithmetical 'fact'.

(2) The primary addition 'facts'

At this stage in their work the children have had experience of dealing with a considerable number of addition 'facts': simple ones, like $1 + 3 = 4$; more difficult ones, like $13 + 5 = 18$; and some with a nought, like $5 + 0 = 5$.

It is convenient to divide these facts into two groups. First, there are the *primary* 'facts'; that is 'facts' which arise from the addition of two numbers each less than ten. For example, $7 + 6 = 13$ and $5 + 4 = 9$ are primary facts.

Secondly, there are 'facts' like $17 + 6 = 23$, and $27 + 6 = 33$. We are not concerned with these at this stage, but later we shall find that a knowledge of the primary 'facts' is necessary in order to deal with them quickly.

LIST III

THE HUNDRED PRIMARY ADDITION FACTS

'Twin' facts

(36)

$$2+1=3$$
$$3+1=4 \quad 3+2=5$$
$$4+1=5 \quad 4+2=6 \quad 4+3=7$$
$$5+1=6 \quad 5+2=7 \quad 5+3=8 \quad 5+4=9$$
$$6+1=7 \quad 6+2=8 \quad 6+3=9 \quad 6+4=10 \quad 6+5=11$$
$$7+1=8 \quad 7+2=9 \quad 7+3=10 \quad 7+4=11 \quad 7+5=12 \quad 7+6=13$$
$$8+1=9 \quad 8+2=10 \quad 8+3=11 \quad 8+4=12 \quad 8+5=13 \quad 8+6=14 \quad 8+7=15$$
$$9+1=10 \quad 9+2=11 \quad 9+3=12 \quad 9+4=13 \quad 9+5=14 \quad 9+6=15 \quad 9+7=16 \quad 9+8=17$$

(36)

$$1+3=4 \quad 1+4=5 \quad 1+5=6 \quad 1+6=7 \quad 1+7=8 \quad 1+8=9 \quad 1+9=10$$
$$2+3=5 \quad 2+4=6 \quad 2+5=7 \quad 2+6=8 \quad 2+7=9 \quad 2+8=10 \quad 2+9=11$$
$$3+4=7 \quad 3+5=8 \quad 3+6=9 \quad 3+7=10 \quad 3+8=11 \quad 3+9=12$$
$$4+5=9 \quad 4+6=10 \quad 4+7=11 \quad 4+8=12 \quad 4+9=13$$
$$5+6=11 \quad 5+7=12 \quad 5+8=13 \quad 5+9=14$$
$$6+7=13 \quad 6+8=14 \quad 6+9=15$$
$$7+8=15 \quad 7+9=16$$
$$8+9=17$$

Facts without a 'twin'

(9)

$$1+1=2$$
$$2+2=4$$
$$3+3=6$$
$$4+4=8$$
$$5+5=10$$
$$6+6=12$$
$$7+7=14$$
$$8+8=16$$
$$9+9=18$$

The facts involving nought (19)

$$0+1=1 \quad 0+2=2 \quad 0+3=3 \quad 0+4=4 \quad 0+5=5 \quad 0+6=6 \quad 0+7=7 \quad 0+8=8 \quad 0+9=9$$
$$0+0=0$$
$$1+0=1 \quad 2+0=2 \quad 3+0=3 \quad 4+0=4 \quad 5+0=5 \quad 6+0=6 \quad 7+0=7 \quad 8+0=8 \quad 9+0=9$$

Let us look at the primary addition 'facts'. (They are shown in Lists I and II.) Altogether there are a hundred of them. We see that many of them occur in related pairs: for example, $1 + 2 = 3$ and $2 + 1 = 3$. For convenience, let us call these *'twin'* facts. (Some 'facts', such as $3 + 3 = 6$, have no 'twins'.)

The grown-up, of course, accepts these 'twin facts' without question. To him '$2 + 7$' and '$7 + 2$' are the same thing. But it should not be taken for granted that the same understanding comes naturally to children, so the earlier teaching and activities in addition should be directed towards making this idea clear (see pages 38–47).

Once the children understand the idea, the learning of the facts is easier for them. When they learn, for example, $5 + 3 = 8$, they realize at the same time that $3 + 5 = 8$ and, by constant use, gradually begin to apply the principle without thinking about it.

Thus we help the children to learn the primary addition facts more quickly and with less trouble. The hundred facts in Lists I and II are combined in List III, page 51.

(3) Arranging the facts in sets

Listing the hundred primary facts in this manner is helpful when we begin to consider in what order the children should learn them. (So far children have been gaining experience of the facts; now they have to learn them.) If we accept the idea, as we should, that a fact and its twin are memorized at the same time, then the fifty-five facts on the left of List III cover all the child's needs. (That is, he is then in a position to know all the hundred facts in the List.)

We cannot expect the children to learn all these facts at the same time. We have to arrange them into suitable sets, each containing about ten facts. The children should deal with all the facts in one set before going on to the next. We should provide throughout for regular revision of the facts already dealt with.

It is *not* advisable to work through List III as it stands, starting with $1 + 1 = 2, 1 + 2 = 3$, etc., and finishing with $8 + 9 = 17$,

$9 + 9 = 18$, because this puts all the easy facts first. Thus the early facts tend to be revised and practised most, whilst the more difficult facts come last and are practised least.

A better plan is to arrange the sets in such a way that each includes easy facts, difficult facts, twin facts, non-twin facts, and 'nought' facts. This can be done in many ways according to the teacher's own ideas. A specimen arrangement of the facts in sets is given in List A.

In this plan (List A) there are nine sets with eleven facts in each, making a total of ninety-nine facts. (The fact $0 + 0 = 0$ has not been included. This fact can be dealt with as the need arises.)

Further different sets may be obtained from this List if the facts are looked at in columns instead of rows. These sets, however, tend to be random, rather than selected, arrangements, and 'twin' facts do not occur in the same set.

(4) Activities to help the children in memorizing the addition facts
In the early stages it is most important that the work should be as individual as possible, and that we should keep a careful record of each child's work, noting where he has failed.

(a) Addition practice-cards—These are cards of addition examples (see Figs. 29 to 33) through which the children work.

In making up these cards it is suggested that the teacher may well use the sets of facts in List A, page 54.* This ensures that *all* the facts are adequately covered. Each card should be marked with a reference letter and number.

To start with, each child in the class is given a different card to work through. He works through every card in a series, and eventually through all the series, thus getting plenty of practice in dealing with *all* the facts.

The teacher marks each card as it is finished and the child corrects his mistakes. A record is kept of each child's progress and of his special difficulties.

A record book with one page devoted to each child is perhaps the best way to do this. A specimen page of such a book is given

* By using vertical columns as well as horizontal rows, the teacher may prepare twenty different cards from List A.

LIST A

THE PRIMARY ADDITION FACTS * ARRANGED IN NINE
SELECTED SETS †

(for practice-cards, flash-cards and other activities)

Set 1	2 + 9	7 + 3	0 + 3	4 + 5	7 + 7	9 + 2	2 + 1	3 + 7	3 + 0	5 + 4	1 + 2
Set 2	7 + 1	5 + 1	4 + 8	6 + 9	1 + 5	7 + 0	8 + 4	1 + 7	9 + 6	0 + 7	2 + 2
Set 3	4 + 0	2 + 5	6 + 3	0 + 4	9 + 7	8 + 2	3 + 6	6 + 6	7 + 9	5 + 2	2 + 8
Set 4	4 + 9	8 + 0	3 + 3	1 + 3	6 + 4	7 + 5	4 + 6	0 + 8	5 + 7	3 + 1	9 + 4
Set 5	0 + 1	1 + 8	6 + 5	9 + 3	5 + 3	9 + 9	1 + 0	3 + 5	8 + 1	3 + 9	5 + 6
Set 6	6 + 2	1 + 1	9 + 0	2 + 4	8 + 7	6 + 7	0 + 9	7 + 6	4 + 2	7 + 8	2 + 6
Set 7	9 + 8	7 + 4	8 + 6	5 + 5	0 + 6	4 + 1	6 + 8	4 + 7	1 + 4	6 + 0	8 + 9
Set 8	4 + 3	9 + 5	3 + 4	7 + 2	8 + 3	0 + 5	3 + 8	5 + 9	4 + 4	2 + 7	5 + 0
Set 9	3 + 2	0 + 2	1 + 9	8 + 5	6 + 1	2 + 3	8 + 8	2 + 0	5 + 8	9 + 1	1 + 6

    * *Note*—The 'result' or 'answer' of each addition, normally a part of the full statement of the *fact*, is omitted in this List, as the teacher does not need it when using the sets for oral testing, the making-up of practice-cards, etc.

    † *Note*—As described on page 52, the teacher may arrange similar sets. He may also use the eleven vertical columns of the above List, though these will tend to be 'random' rather than 'selected' sets of facts and they do not contain twin facts'.

in Fig. 28. Each child should be shown his record from time to time to encourage interest in the work being done.

NAME: JOHN KAMONO

		SET 1	2	3	4	5	6	7	8	9	10	11	12	13	14	15	16	17	18	19	20	Facts not well known (to be given further practice later)
ADDITION	First working (pictorial)	√	√	√	√	√	√	√	√	√	√	√	√	√	√	√	√	√	√	√	√	6 + 9, 8 + 5, 7 + 8
	Second working	√	√	√	√	√	√	√	√	√	√	√	√	√	√	√	√	√	√	√	√	
	Third working	√	√	√	√	√	√	√	√	√	√	√	√	√	√	√	√	√	√	√	√	
	Fourth working	√		√		√	√	√			√	√	√	√				√	√	√	√	
SUBTRACTION	First working																					
	Second working																					
	Third working																					
MULTIPLICATION (Early facts)	First working																					
	Second working																					
	Third working																					
DIVISION (Early facts)	First working																					
	Second working																					
	Third working																					

FIGURE 28.—A specimen page from a teacher's record book

The work with the cards should be carefully graded so that a child can progress steadily from the stage when he needs to use apparatus to that where he can add quickly without any aids. Here is a suggested order of working:—

(*i*) The first series of practice-cards should be of the *pictorial type*, as in Fig. 29. This forms a useful link with the earlier

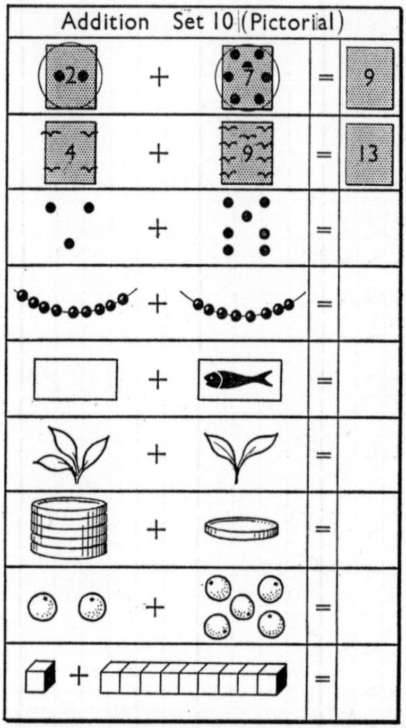

FIGURE 29.—A practice-card—pictorial, for addition. The child puts a number-card on top of the picture of each group of objects

Suitable size: $4\frac{1}{2}'' \times 3''$

work and helps the children to get used to the cards. As a child works through an example he places a number-card over each number-pattern or group of objects. He then selects his 'answer' number-card and puts that in its place. In this way he makes up an addition fact. He writes down this fact in his book. Each child works through all the cards (twenty, say) in this manner. (*ii*) The next series of practice-cards does not have pictures, *only figures being used* (Fig. 30). The children write down each example in their books and work it out with the help of apparatus.

(*iii*) This second series of cards is worked through again, but this time, after writing the examples in their books, the children write down the answer *without the use of apparatus.* (Less able children are allowed to count, if they wish, but they should be encouraged to stop using 'aids' as soon as possible.) It has been

Addition		Set	1	○
2	+	7	=	
8	+	1	=	
4	+	6	=	
5	+	3	=	
0	+	9	=	
1	+	1	=	
9	+	0	=	
3	+	5	=	
6	+	4	=	
1	+	8	=	
7	+	2	=	

Addition		Set	2	○
4	+	9	=	13
5	+	7	=	12
2	+	8	=	
0	+	3	=	
6	+	1	=	
4	+	4	=	
1	+	6	=	
3	+	0	=	
8	+	2	=	
7	+	5	=	
9	+	4	=	

FIGURE 30.—A practice-card, for addition. (Children use apparatus if necessary, and write down each example in their notebooks)

FIGURE 31.—Another practice-card, for addition. (Children write the 'answers' only, on the slip of paper, on the back of which they put their names)

found useful on occasions to let children mark their own work by checking their answers with the number-slide.

(*iv*) The same series of cards is again worked through, but this time the children write down *the answer only*, without setting out the sum. A convenient way of doing this is to attach to the right-hand side of the card a slip of paper (Fig. 31), on which the child writes his answers, after putting his name on the back for the purpose of the teacher's marking.

(*v*) Some teachers find other types of practice-card helpful in giving further understanding and in 'fixing' knowledge of the facts. Here are two suggestions:—

(I) *Number-story* practice cards (Fig. 32). These give practice in seeing how any number can be made up.

(II) *Changing-game* cards (Fig. 33). These should be given to the children for practice after they have played the 'changing

The Story of Ten			O
10	=	5 +	
10	=	9 +	
10	=	7 +	
10	=	2 +	
10	=	6 +	
10	=	0 +	
10	=	3 +	
10	=	1 +	
10	=	4 +	
10	=	8 +	

FIGURE 32.—A practice-card, for addition, of a type for 'telling the story of a number'

(Cards for 'the story' of other numbers are similar)

game' (page 49). The cards help the children with their first ideas of place-value.

(*b*) *Self-corrective flash-cards*—These are cards made up as in Fig. 34. (For details see page 472.) Each card has, on the front, two numbers to be added, and, on the back, the addition is completed. Their purpose is to give quick practice in the addition facts. They can be used with individual children in the same way as with a whole class. The 'question' side of the card is 'flashed' to the children (that is, for about two seconds) and they are expected to give the correct answer without hesitation. The card is then turned over for all the children to see the full correct 'fact'. The less able children are thus helped to remember this fact when it is shown again. These cards can be used in many popular, interesting and useful games, such as the three described in Chapter XV, pages 247–8.

(*c*) *Oral class-activities*—The children find it stimulating if the

The Changing Game			O
9 + 4	=	10 +	3
6 + 9	=	10 +	5
8 + 8	=	10 +	6
5 + 7	=	10 +	
3 + 9	=	10 +	
9 + 7	=	10 +	
9 + 9	=	10 +	
7 + 6	=	10 +	
4 + 8	=	10 +	
2 + 9	=	10 +	
9 + 5	=	10 +	
8 + 3	=	10 +	
7 + 7	=	10 +	
8 + 9	=	10 +	
6 + 6	=	10 +	
5 + 8	=	10 +	
7 + 4	=	10 +	
7 + 8	=	10 +	
6 + 5	=	10 +	
8 + 6	=	10 +	

FIGURE 33.—A practice-card, for addition—the 'changing-game' type. (Children write the 'answers' on the strip of paper pinned on the right-hand side of the card and their names on the back of the slip)

teacher sometimes takes the class as a whole for oral questioning, in order to find out their knowledge of the addition facts.

For example, we may spend a few minutes at the beginning of the arithmetic lesson in quick questioning. 'What are five and four?' 'What are four and five?' 'Give two numbers which make

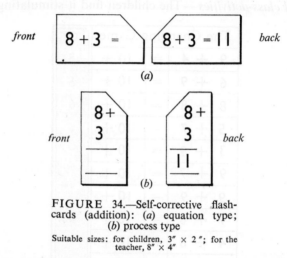

front   8 + 3 =   8 + 3 = 11   *back*

(*a*)

front   8 + 3   8 + 3   *back*

                                11

(*b*)

FIGURE 34.—Self-corrective flash-cards (addition): (*a*) equation type; (*b*) process type

Suitable sizes: for children, 3″ × 2″; for the teacher, 8″ × 4″

up nine.' There are numerous class-activities of this kind (see Chapter XIII, page 193, and Chapter XV, page 249, for some details).

E—'*Problems*'—*the importance of words as well as figures*

In our everyday lives we meet, and have to answer, all sorts of questions and problems. Some of these include numbers,* which are often spoken, written or printed as words and are not shown to us as figures. Further, the problem, expressed in words, seldom tells us directly what process we have to use in finding the answer. Thus we need not only knowledge of numbers and of the simple arithmetical facts and processes, but we must understand how to change the words of a problem into the right figures set down in the right way: that is, we must be able to see what process is needed for finding the answer to a problem stated in words. (This becomes even more important if ever we come to study a subject like science.)

* For example: questions which may happen to concern us about numbers of people or things, money and prices, lengths and distances, times, sizes, weights, and so on.

The sooner children get used to hearing, and then reading, little 'problems' the better. If they start young, they soon gain confidence, speed and accuracy.

Unfortunately, many children have difficulty, throughout their schooldays, in working out arithmetical examples given in the form of problems. Indeed, many adults have the same trouble all their lives. Yet most of the children and adults can 'do' the actual arithmetic of their 'problems': their difficulty arises because they do not understand what they have to do—they cannot see how to use the information given in words so that it may be expressed in figures and arithmetical processes. There are several possible reasons for difficulty of this kind:

(*i*) Lack of experience of little 'problems' when young.

(*ii*) Insufficient practice with oral and written statements.

(*iii*) Failure to understand the words, phrases or sentences of the problem.

(*iv*) Inability to apply and use arithmetical processes in real situations.

Clearly, we can do much to help children to avoid such difficulties:

(*a*) By making sure that, from the earliest stages, children get used to the language of arithmetic. They must hear plenty of suitable questions, and then, as they learn to read and write, should have little problems set for them on the blackboard. At first, the problems may be as drawings, with the words spoken. Later, the words are written (Fig. 35). Thus children learn to understand the meaning of phrases like: 'add up', 'how many in all?' 'altogether', 'find the total', etc.

(*b*) By giving plenty of practice with little problems at this very simple level, both orally and in writing. The teacher should regularly devote short periods, with the whole class, to this kind of work. At times the arithmetic lesson becomes a reading lesson, helping children to understand the meaning of exact statements put in simple words.

(*c*) By taking pains to see that the problems are always suitably and clearly expressed in a form which the children can grasp.

(*d*) By making the problems 'real': that is, by basing them on everyday happenings and things familiar to the children. There are many opportunities of drawing attention to little problems concerning numbers outside the actual arithmetic lesson, and these should never be missed.

(1) Put these beans in a bag. How many have you altogether?

(2) Here is a tree. Draw it. Draw two birds on one
    branch and four on another.
    How many birds are there in all?

(3) Draw a dish with fish on it like this.
    Now put on two more.
    How many fish are there now?

FIGURE 35.—Blackboard 'problems' for young children

Using such methods from the start, we help the child to grow up unafraid of problems, prepared to meet them and able to answer them.

This chapter shows how children can learn what addition means, and how they can deal with the simple examples which occur during their play and other activities. The children are introduced to simple apparatus, which helps them to understand and to add more quickly. They also have practice in working out and learning the primary addition 'facts'. If this work is well done, it leads easily to the later addition process described in detail in Chapter XI.

CHAPTER VI

INTRODUCING CHILDREN TO SUBTRACTION

A—*The idea of subtraction*

Subtraction comes to have full meaning for a child only when he has the real experiences which involve it. Some of these experiences occur before he comes to school, that is, in the home and at play. From the people around him he 'picks up' a vocabulary which later gives meaning to the symbols of subtraction he learns in school. For example:—

(*i*) He goes to collect the hens' eggs. He drops and breaks some of them and finds there are fewer than when he started.
(*ii*) He wants to play a game for four players. One child has to go away. Three are left and they cannot play the same game.
(*iii*) He has a number of coins. He uses some of them to buy things at the store and finds that he now has fewer coins than when he started.

Any comparison made by him (or by the people around him) of lengths, sizes, weights or numbers may bring in the idea of subtraction in some form or another. For example:—

(*i*) One tree is taller than another. It will need more foot-holds if he is going to climb it to get nuts or fruit.
(*ii*) He discusses his age with his brother and with other children; for example, 'I am five years old. My brother is seven. Next year I shall be six and he will be eight.' 'He is two years older than I am.'
(*iii*) He talks about his height in comparison with that of others: 'I am taller than you.' 'My father is bigger than yours.'
(*iv*) He makes claims about what he can do: 'I can run faster than you.' 'I can jump higher than all the other children.'
(*v*) At meal-times he compares sizes of dishes: 'My brother has been given a bigger dish than I have.'

B—*'Comparing' and 'taking away'*

There are two aspects of subtraction, as may be noticed in the two sets of examples given above. There is the aspect of subtraction which involves 'taking away', and that which involves 'comparison'. Two further examples may illustrate the point more clearly:—

(*a*) '*Taking away*'. 'Mother has a basket of twelve oranges. She finds that five are bad and throws them away. Seven good ones are left.' Here the five is contained in the twelve. It is a straightforward 'take away' example. If the child is doing this in his early arithmetic he merely removes the five from the twelve and counts what is left.

(*b*) '*Comparing*'. 'You knocked down three skittles. I knocked down five. I won. I knocked down two more than you.' Here the five and the three are separate quantities which are being compared. The three is *not* contained in the five.

There is no need in the early stages to worry children about these two aspects of subtraction, but we ourselves should always be aware of them. We can then be sure of arranging work which includes examples of both types.

C—*Early school experiences*

(*1*) *Subtraction activities*

As in the work on addition, we enlarge on the ideas with which the child comes to school, and arrange all kinds of activities and apparatus, so as to give further experience of subtraction. These activities are oral to begin with and are later associated with number-symbols.

Here are a few such play activities, and many more can be invented. Some may be organized by the teacher and others made up by the children themselves.

(*i*) The children play a game like '*man eater*'. A group of children (say ten) are placed in a 'village' (a circle drawn on the ground). Another child, acting as the 'lion', approaches from the 'jungle' and 'captures' children from the circle. Another child acting as the 'hunter' chases the lion away and tries to catch him before he reaches the 'jungle'. If the 'lion' escapes, the 'hunter' returns to the 'village' and counts the number of children left and decides how many were 'eaten'.

(*ii*) *Skittles*—see pages 27 and 43–4.

(*iii*) The children act a little scene: for example, '*having visitors*'.

A plateful of 'cakes' is made and placed ready for the meal. A naughty boy comes in and takes some of them. The 'mother' counts the cakes and decides there are not enough for the 'visitors'.

(*iv*) At the end of games like '*Oranges and Lemons*' the children form groups behind their two leaders. Each group is counted and the larger group is declared the winner.

(*v*) Subtraction *rhymes* are very valuable as a means of introducing subtraction through counting backwards. If the children 'act' the rhyme they understand the idea more quickly.

Teachers should invent rhymes in their own language. Here are some simple examples in English: —

> (I) Ten little school-boys standing on a line;
> One boy moved backwards. Then there were nine.
> Nine little school-boys sitting on a gate;
> One boy fell off. Then there were eight.
> Eight little school-boys went down to Devon;
> One boy fell in the sea. Then there were seven.
> Etc.

> (II) *Ten* green bottles hanging on a wall;
> If one green bottle should accidentally fall,
> There'd be *nine* green bottles hanging on the wall.
> *Nine* green bottles hanging on the wall;
> If one green bottle should accidentally fall,
> There'd be *eight* green bottles hanging on the wall.
> Etc.

> (III) Five big coconuts at the top of a tree:
> A monkey knocked down two —
> Then there were three.

The children may be encouraged to make up their own subtraction rhymes out of school.

(*vi*) The '*number-story*' apparatus, described in Chapter V (pages 44–5), provides an excellent link between addition and subtraction. The children have in front of them strips of cardboard which make up the 'story of five'. They see that the various pairs of strips each make up 5. Then they 'tell the story' in subtraction form as they 'take away' various strips. For example: —

> 'If I take *one* from five I have *four* left.
> If I take *two* from five I have *three* left.
> If I take *three* from five I have *two* left.
> If I take *four* from five I have *one* left.
> If I take *five* from five I have *none* left.'

(2) *The language of subtraction*

In all these, and in other activities such as scoring games, the child either compares one amount with another or sees that when one quantity is taken from another there is a smaller quantity left. Thus he gets the idea and vocabulary which help him to understand and, in due course, to deal with the subtraction process. He begins to know what it means to ask: 'How much bigger?—taller?—heavier?' 'How many are left?' 'How many more?' 'What is the difference between?' 'What must I add to?' He also begins to understand instructions such as: 'Take away', 'Take from', 'Subtract'.

(3) *Children's records of subtraction activities*

The children should now be 'ready' to record the results of these activities, firstly by the use of number-cards (as in addition), and secondly by copying the figures down on paper.

They are introduced to the sign '−' which indicates the process of 'taking away'. (It is also known as the 'minus sign'.) The teacher refers to the sign '+' which they already know.

The skittle game is perhaps the best activity to record first. The child sees how many skittles are standing up (nine) and he gets a '9'-card to represent that number. He then throws his ball, notices how many he has knocked down (e.g. three), and gets a '−'-card and a '3'-card. He then counts how many skittles are still standing and gets a card for that (a '6'-card). He then sets down what he has done, like this:

$$\boxed{9} \quad \boxed{-} \quad \boxed{3} \quad \boxed{=} \quad \boxed{6}$$

This is then copied down on paper as $9 - 3 = 6$. Later he writes it in another way as shown here.* It is important to have 'nought'-cards available so that children learn the idea of subtracting 0 from another number (for example, $9 - 0 = 9$), and subtracting a number from itself (for example, $9 - 9 = 0$).

$$\begin{array}{r} 9 \ - \\ 3 \\ \hline 6 \\ \hline \end{array}$$

The same procedure is used for other activities, such as 'number-stories'.

* See footnote on page 41.

LIST IV

64 PRIMARY SUBTRACTION FACTS (WHERE THE SUBTRACTION IS FROM 10 OR LESS)

1 −	2 −	3 −	4 −	5 −	6 −	7 −	8 −	9 −	10 −
1	1	1	1	1	1	1	1	1	1
0	1	2	3	4	5	6	7	8	9
	2 −	3 −	4 −	5 −	6 −	7 −	8 −	9 −	10 −
	2	2	2	2	2	2	2	2	2
	0	1	2	3	4	5	6	7	8
		3 −	4 −	5 −	6 −	7 −	8 −	9 −	10 −
		3	3	3	3	3	3	3	3
		0	1	2	3	4	5	6	7
			4 −	5 −	6 −	7 −	8 −	9 −	10 −
			4	4	4	4	4	4	4
			0	1	2	3	4	5	6
				5 −	6 −	7 −	8 −	9 −	10 −
				5	5	5	5	5	5
				0	1	2	3	4	5
					6 −	7 −	8 −	9 −	10 −
					6	6	6	6	6
					0	1	2	3	4
						7 −	8 −	9 −	10 −
						7	7	7	7
						0	1	2	3
							8 −	9 −	10 −
							8	8	8
							0	1	2
								9 −	10 −
								9	9
								0	1

0 −	1 −	2 −	3 −	4 −	5 −	6 −	7 −	8 −	9 −
0	0	0	0	0	0	0	0	0	0
0	1	2	3	4	5	6	7	8	9

Note—Children are first given experience with *all* the facts in this List.

LIST V

THE OTHER 36 PRIMARY SUBTRACTION FACTS

11 − 2 9							
11 − 3 8	12 − 3 9						
11 − 4 7	12 − 4 8	13 − 4 9					
11 − 5 6	12 − 5 7	13 − 5 8	14 − 5 9				
11 − 6 5	12 − 6 6	13 − 6 7	14 − 6 8	15 − 6 9			
11 − 7 4	12 − 7 5	13 − 7 6	14 − 7 7	15 − 7 8	16 − 7 9		
11 − 8 3	12 − 8 4	13 − 8 5	14 − 8 6	15 − 8 7	16 − 8 8	17 − 8 9	
11 − 9 2	12 − 9 3	13 − 9 4	14 − 9 5	15 − 9 6	16 − 9 7	17 − 9 8	18 − 9 9

Note—The primary subtraction facts are listed in full to enable the teacher to cover them *all*. Only when children are familiar with *all* the facts in Lists IV and V do they begin to make a deliberate attempt to memorize them.

D—*Subtraction examples set by the teacher*

The children now pass from recording their own activities to working out examples set by the teacher. As explained for addition, in Chapter V, we must be sure that the children are having practice in *all* the subtraction 'facts'. These 'facts' may not arise in the number games which the children play on their own. Thus it is necessary, at this stage, for us to organize the work so that *all* the 'facts' are covered.

The hundred primary subtraction 'facts' are given in Lists IV and V. List IV deals with the sixty-four 'facts' where the subtraction is from ten or less. When the children have had plenty of practice with *all* the facts in List IV, they may be given the examples in List V. (This deals with the next thirty-six 'facts' up to $18 - 9 = 9$.)

We use these lists when writing examples on the blackboard for the children to work out. As before, the children use apparatus such as number-slides, counters, etc., to help them carry out the subtraction.

E—*Learning the primary subtraction 'facts'*

As with the addition facts, there comes a stage when, having had experience of all the primary subtraction 'facts', the children must memorize them so that they know them without having to think. They must be able to do this so that they will not be hindered when they come to more difficult work.

Following the plan for addition, the primary subtraction facts should be arranged in selected sets so that adequate practice is given on each individual fact.

A suggested arrangement is given in List B, built up as described for List A, page 54. This gives nine sets for learning (omitting the fact $0 - 0 = 0$, which can be dealt with separately). The teacher may build up similar sets, or use also the vertical columns of List B (though these tend to be 'random' rather than selected sets).

The learning of the facts in each set is most effective if the teacher follows the plan recommended for addition.

(a) *Subtraction practice-cards*—These are made up so that each contains a set of facts from List B (Fig. 36(a)). First the children work through all the cards,* using apparatus if necessary, and writing down the examples in their books.

Next, the cards are worked through again, but this time without apparatus.

Finally, the series is worked through without writing down the

Subtraction Set 5			o	
11	—	4	=	
8	—	2	=	
3	—	3	=	
10	—	5	=	
13	—	9	=	
14	—	8	=	
11	—	7	=	
8	—	6	=	
3	—	0	=	
13	—	4	=	
14	—	6	=	

Subtraction Set 6			A6	
13	—	5	=	
10	—	3	=	
7	—	1	=	
8	—	4	=	
6	—	4	=	
12	—	9	=	
13	—	8	=	
10	—	7	=	
7	—	6	=	
6	—	2	=	
12	—	3	=	

(a)   (b)

FIGURE 36.—Practice-cards, for subtraction: (a) Children use apparatus if necessary, and write out the examples in their note-books—*facts from Set 5, List B*; (b) Answers only are written on a slip of paper (with the child's name on the back)—*facts from Set 6, List B*

As before, a suitable size for these cards is 4½″ × 3″

examples. The answer only is written on a slip of paper (Fig. 36(b)), the child having first written his name on the back for purposes of marking.

It is again most important that the teacher should keep a

* Twenty cards may be made up from List B if the eleven vertical columns are used as well as the nine horizontal rows.

LIST B

THE PRIMARY SUBTRACTION FACTS * ARRANGED IN NINE SELECTED SETS †

Set 1	17 − 9	9 − 8	7 − 7	6 − 5	5 − 2	17 − 8	9 − 1	7 − 0	6 − 1	5 − 3	4 − 2
Set 2	4 − 3	16 − 9	8 − 8	11 − 6	7 − 5	4 − 1	16 − 7	8 − 0	11 − 5	7 − 2	18 − 9
Set 3	16 − 8	3 − 1	15 − 9	13 − 7	10 − 6	5 − 5	3 − 2	15 − 6	13 − 6	10 − 4	5 − 0
Set 4	9 − 3	2 − 1	4 − 4	14 − 9	15 − 8	12 − 7	9 − 6	4 − 0	14 − 5	15 − 7	12 − 5
Set 5	11 − 4	8 − 2	3 − 3	10 − 5	13 − 9	14 − 8	11 − 7	8 − 6	3 − 0	13 − 4	14 − 6
Set 6	13 − 5	10 − 3	7 − 1	8 − 4	6 − 4	12 − 9	13 − 8	10 − 7	7 − 6	6 − 2	12 − 3
Set 7	11 − 2	12 − 4	9 − 2	6 − 0	7 − 4	12 − 6	11 − 9	12 − 8	9 − 7	6 − 6	7 − 3
Set 8	2 − 2	10 − 1	11 − 3	8 − 1	9 − 5	2 − 0	6 − 3	10 − 9	11 − 8	8 − 7	9 − 4
Set 9	8 − 5	5 − 4	9 − 0	10 − 2	1 − 1	8 − 3	5 − 1	1 − 0	9 − 9	10 − 8	14 − 7

* *Note*—The 'result' of each subtraction, normally a part of the full statement of the fact, is omitted in this List, as the teacher does not need it when using the sets for oral testing, the making-up of practice-cards, etc.

† *Note*—As described on page 52, the teacher may arrange similar sets. He may also use the eleven vertical columns of the above List, though these will tend to be 'random' rather than 'selected' sets of facts and they do not contain 'twin acts'.

detailed record of the children's progress and mistakes (see suggestions on page 53).

(*b*) *Relating subtraction and addition facts*—It has already been suggested that there should be some linking of subtraction facts with addition facts. The child's memory of both is helped if he understands that each subtraction fact is related to an addition

front					back				
Subtraction Set 3			O		Addition check Set 3			O	
16	−	8	=		8	+	8	=	
3	−	1	=		2	+	1	=	
15	−	9	=		6	+	9	=	
13	−	7	=		6	+	7	=	
10	−	6	=		4	+	6	=	
5	−	5	=		0	+	5	=	
3	−	2	=		1	+	2	=	
15	−	6	=		9	+	6	=	
13	−	6	=		7	+	6	=	
10	−	4	=		6	+	4	=	
5	−	0	=		5	+	0	=	

FIGURE 37.—A practice-card, for subtraction, with addition check. (The child removes the slip of paper and checks his answers by turning the card over and comparing them with the first column of figures on the back.   Similarly he may check his additions against the first column of the subtraction side of the card)

fact which he already knows. For example, if he knows that:
$$9 + 8 = 17, \quad \text{and} \quad 8 + 9 = 17,$$
he is helped in learning that:
$$17 - 9 = 8, \quad \text{and} \quad 17 - 8 = 9.$$
Practice-cards should be made up which give children experience in dealing with these related facts (Fig. 37). Children can mark their own answers if it is pointed out to them that the first figures on the left-hand side of the 'addition' part of the card

are the answers to the examples on the 'subtraction' part of the card (and vice versa).

(*c*) *Self-corrective flash-cards*—As described in Chapter V (page 58), flash-cards (Fig. 38) are used to give the children further pleasurable repetition of the facts, through games and other activities (see Chapter XV).

We should use this opportunity for putting right the mistakes commonly made by the children. For example, we should arrange for the children to play flash-card games using the facts of which they are uncertain (as shown by our record book).

(*d*) *Oral class-activities*—Most of the ways of learning so far described have been individual, but throughout all this work we

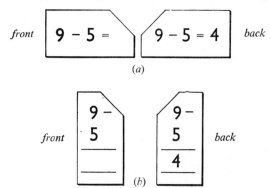

FIGURE 38.—Self-corrective flash-cards (subtraction): (*a*) equation type; (*b*) process type
As before, a suitable size for these cards is 3″ × 2″

should make use of the stimulation which often comes from taking the class as a whole. This should only be for short periods at a time, however. For a minute or two at the beginning of a lesson, for example, the children may be questioned, orally, on a particular set of facts.

We must also make use of any happening during the day which may be thought of as an example of subtraction. For instance, in the physical education lesson each team-leader is asked to find out how many children in his team are away from school. One leader reports, for example: 'I should have nine in my team. I only have seven. So two are away.'

D

F—*'Problems'—the importance of words as well as figures*

Oral work with the class is also important because it gives children the opportunity to make correct statements about subtraction, and to understand statements made by someone else. Correct use of the language of subtraction is the basis for later ability to deal with oral and written 'problems'. Thus the teacher should help children to hear and 'see' a simple fact, like $5 - 2 = 3$, expressed in various ways, such as:

'Three is two less than five.'
'Two needs three more to make five.'
'Five is bigger than three by two,' etc.

The learning of arithmetical facts loses its value and children have great difficulty in dealing with problems unless they have plenty of experience of this 'arithmetic in words'.

It is advisable, from the start, to give short, but regular, periods of practice in carrying out directions requiring that subtraction should take place. At first this work should be oral; later, it should be in written form. Examples:—

(*i*) 'Here is a strip of paper. Draw twelve crosses in a row on it. Tear off three crosses. How many are left? Put down what you have done in figures in your note-book.'
(*ii*) The teacher says: 'There are ten books on my table. John, please leave three and put the rest away in the cupboard. Close the cupboard door. Now, how many books did John put away?'
(*iii*) The teacher strides across the room, the children counting the number of strides. Now Mary strides across and the children count again. The teacher asks the class: 'How many more strides did Mary take than I did?'

The teacher is recommended to read again the section on problems in addition (pages 60–62), as it applies equally to subtraction. It is most important that the work should relate to everyday happenings, to familiar objects inside or outside the class room, or to things which the children can draw. It must be remembered, too, that suitable examples often occur during lessons on other subjects, or in play-time. We should always show how a suitable 'problem' can be written down in figures as an instance of subtraction.

This chapter suggests ways of helping children to understand the idea of subtraction, whether expressed in words or figures. It shows how children may be introduced to methods of dealing, on paper, with simple examples. To do this they first use apparatus and then learn the primary facts through practice-cards and flash-cards. They learn, too, the important principle that addition and subtraction 'facts' are linked and can be remembered together.

If this work is done thoroughly, so that the children really understand it, they go on with confidence, and much less difficulty, to the subtraction process described in Chapter XII.

CHAPTER VII

INTRODUCING CHILDREN TO MULTIPLICATION

A—*The idea of multiplication*

In everyday life multiplication is probably the most used of all the four common arithmetical processes. It is therefore very important that the child's introduction to multiplication should be thorough and well understood. Speed and accuracy in multiplying are essential for later mathematical work, and depend upon thorough learning in the early stages.

The children should be introduced to the idea of multiplication *after* they can add, easily and correctly, up to totals of about twenty. It is better to postpone the introduction to this stage because understanding of multiplication depends upon the child's previous understanding of addition.

A child's *early* number experiences rarely include situations where he needs to be able to multiply. It may seem, therefore, that the process is more difficult to teach, since the basis for it appears to be lacking. But, if we think of the process as a quick and convenient method of adding a series of the same numbers, we see that most children do, in fact, have the necessary experience upon which to build the idea of multiplication.

Children begin quite early to notice groups of objects which look alike. Soon they begin to see that some groups look alike because they are made up of equal numbers. They notice pairs of things very early: legs, eyes, birds' wings, shoes, bicycle wheels. They may notice that certain plants have leaves set in threes. Groups of four come within their experience from observing the number of legs of some common animals, from looking at tables and chairs, and from noticing the wheels of cars, trucks or lorries. Fives and tens they observe from their fingers and toes. Groups of six may occur to the child as an extension of the 'threes' grouping, but he may also notice groups of six if he counts the legs of an insect, or the points of a 'star' on a badge, flag or other emblem. He may also notice, perhaps, that in some countries certain coins have six sides, and that in some games the 'board' is constructed of holes grouped in sixes. Groups of seven may be experienced through counting on the calendar, when he notices that a week occupies a line of seven days from Sunday to the following Saturday.

It is doubtful whether larger groupings suggest themselves until they are met in connexion with measurement and money (for example, groups of twelve inches, or twelve pennies). But we are here concerned only with the *early* grouping as a foundation upon which to build *the idea* of multiplication.

B—*Early grouping-activities*

It has been recommended that young children should not start multiplication until they are proficient in the early work of addition. It is further strongly recommended that multiplication should be preceded by plenty of activities which involve grouping into twos, threes, fours and fives. This not only helps the child to understand multiplication but also proves very useful in the work to be done in division.

Here are a few such activities:—

(*i*) The children collect beans, seeds, marbles, etc., and put equal numbers of them into sections of the *sorting-tray*, according to

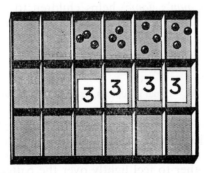

FIGURE 39.—The number-tray, used for equal groupings and number-cards.
(See Fig. 1)

the number asked for by the teacher. The children then put the appropriate number-card into each section of the tray (Fig. 39).

The teacher then asks: 'How many threes (or fours, etc.) have you?'

(*Note:* There is *no multiplying yet*, no asking for a total. The child is merely getting the idea of recurring groups of numbers.)

(*ii*) The children play '*Noah's ark*' with wooden or clay-moulded animals. They pair them off, two by two. The teacher asks: 'How many twos (pairs, couples) have you?'

(*iii*) The same number of flags, made of paper and sticks, is stuck into each of several '*castles*' (heaps of sand or soil—see Fig. 14, page 33). The teacher asks: 'How many fours have you?'

FIGURE 40.—Equal groupings, using model bird-nests and eggs

(*iv*) Models of *bird-nests* are made from grass. The same number of model eggs, made from clay or mud, is put into each nest. The teacher asks: 'How many nests have you with five eggs in each?' (Fig. 40).

(*v*) The children *thread beads* in twos (or threes). After each group they thread a number-card (Fig. 41). The teacher asks: 'How many twos (threes) have you?'

(*vi*) The '*blind man's game*' helps children to recognize equal groups through their sense of touch. The teacher prepares cards

FIGURE 41.—Equal groupings, using beads and number-cards

(such as those in Fig. 92, page 245) on which the number-patterns are raised above the surface (for example, buttons). The children test each other in turn. One child closes his eyes and is asked by the other to feel lightly over the pattern on the card. The 'blind man' then has to answer questions like: 'How many fours on the card?'

(*vii*) The children make *models* of sheep (or other local animals) from clay or mud. These are put into pens made of sticks, six in each pen. They are supposed to be at the market. Each pen has a card bearing the number six. The teacher asks: 'How many sixes?'

(*viii*) These activities can be extended by telling *number 'tales'*. The stories are first of all made up by the teacher, and then later the children make up their own. The teacher begins: 'This is a tale of fours. Pick out the fours. "A *car* (four wheels) went fast down the road. It nearly ran into a *cow* which was being driven by a little boy who had a *dog* to help him."—How many fours? Yes—three fours.' (At first the teacher emphasizes the words in italics.)

'This is a tale of fives. Listen to the fives: "I held out my *left hand* when teacher asked me. Then he asked me to show the opposite, so I held out my *right hand*. Then I looked at my *right foot* because teacher said I had mud on it. I looked at the *left foot* and found it was clean." How many fives? Yes—four fives.'

'This is a tale of twos. Listen for the twos: "The bird perched with its *little feet* on the branch of a tree. Then it saw a cat coming. So it opened its *wings* and flew down to where a *man was walking* wheeling a *bicycle* in front of him."—How many twos were there? Yes—four twos.'

'This is a funny story of threes. Listen carefully for the threes. "A very fat man came into our house and sat on a chair. He was so heavy that *one of the legs broke off the chair*. He then sat on the table and *a leg broke off that too*. So we brought him *a three-legged stool*." How many threes? Yes—three threes.'

The above activities lend themselves to drawing so that children can add to their experiences by illustrating the various groupings which they meet.

C—*Counting in groups*

The work so far has been concerned with equal grouping only, so that the children have been able to say after each activity: 'I have four groups of two; I have three groups of four; I have five groups of three'; etc. There has so far been no direct request on the part of the teacher for the children to calculate totals from their grouping. Able children often make these calculations of their own accord, and grasp the idea of multiplication without any direct teaching. But the majority of the children need to be shown how to find the number of objects they have altogether.

They can, of course, count in ones, but the teacher should emphasize that it is quicker to learn to count in groups.

It is suggested that the activities like those previously described should be used to introduce this work For example:—

(*i*) The children make four 'nests' and put two 'eggs' in each. The teacher then says: 'Let us find how many eggs we have altogether. Let us count in twos. Ready! Two. Another two—that makes four. Another two—that makes six. Another two—that makes eight. Four groups of two make eight.' (The children write down, from the blackboard, '4 twos make 8'.)

(*ii*) The children put three beans into each of four sections of a matching-tray. The teacher says: 'Let us find how many we have altogether. Let us slowly count them in threes. Ready! Three. Another three—that makes six. Another three—that makes nine. And another three—that makes twelve.' (The children write down from the blackboard '4 threes make 12'.)

(*iii*) The children make five sand-castles and put four flags on each. The teacher says: 'How many flags altogether? Let us count them in fours. Ready! Four, eight, twelve, sixteen, twenty. Five groups of four make twenty.' (The children write down '5 fours make 20'.)

(*iv*) The '20' or '24' number-slide (see page 106) is used. The child takes, for example, three number-strips (size five, say). He puts them into the slide and finds that three fives make fifteen. This fact is then written down.

(*v*) The learning of suitable rhymes also gives facility in group counting. Here are some examples in English. Teachers should make up similar rhymes in the language in which they teach.

'Two, four, six, eight, ten; when shall we go home again?'
'Three, six, nine; they are all mine.'
'Twelve, fifteen, eighteen; please don't keep me waiting.'
'Four, eight, twelve; sixteen, twenty; fruit to eat—I like plenty.'

D—*Recording multiplication activities*

The children should now be ready to be introduced to the phrases and symbols which will eventually enable them to deal with multiplication facts.

(*1*) *Introducing the word 'times'*

This is best approached through some simple class-activity. For example, a number of shells (beans, stones or any common object) are put on the table at one end of the room. A child is told to go to the table and bring back *two* shells. 'Now go again and bring another *two*. Now go again and bring another *two*.' We then ask the class:

> 'How many times did he go?'—'Three times.'
> ('3 times' is written on the blackboard.)
> 'What did he bring each time?'—'Two.'
> (The blackboard now reads '3 times 2'.)
> 'And how many have we altogether?'
> The children count in two's—'Six'.
> So we have '3 times 2 makes 6'.

We go through this procedure with other 'facts' (up to a product of 24), and each time the children write down in their books what is happening. After the first stages, it is probably better to use pictures of objects instead of the actual things, since pictures are easier to handle and give a better idea of groups. So that, for example, when introducing the fact $5 \times 4 = 20$, we ask a child to go five times to the table and pick up each time a picture (Fig. 42) with four fruits (of a kind known to the children).

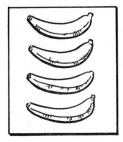

FIGURE 42.—A picture-card, for equal groupings, useful when introducing the word 'times'

This is also a convenient method for introducing the 'nought facts' in multiplication. For example, we ask a child to go to the table three times and bring nothing back each time.

> 'How many times did he go?'—'Three times.'
> 'What did he bring back each time?'—'Nothing.'
> 'What has he got altogether?'—'Nothing.'

The fact is then written up: '3 times 0 makes 0'.

(2) Introducing the multiplication sign

The teacher should then introduce the sign ' × ' to take the place of 'times', referring to the other signs which the children have already met in addition and subtraction. The word 'multiply' need not be introduced at first.

The previous work should now be repeated, but with the sign ' × ' instead of the word 'times'. Thus the children now record the facts like this: $3 \times 4 = 12$. (They are already familiar with the sign ' = '.)

At this stage the children should also learn, and have practice in setting down, the 'facts' in another way, as shown here.* This gives the opportunity for introducing the word 'multiply'.

	4	×
	3	
1	2	

(3) Working out the early multiplication facts

As in the early work in addition and subtraction we should decide what 'facts' the children are to deal with at this level, and then should make sure that *all* these facts are given adequate attention.

It is convenient to decide upon those facts which have a product of twenty-four or less. These facts deal with small numbers, so the children are not worried while they are still getting the *idea* of multiplication. Moreover, from these facts the full 'table of twos' † can be built up. All these facts are given in List VI.

We should use this list to give examples on the blackboard which the children can write down and work out, using apparatus if necessary. In this way they should gain experience of *all* the facts in the list.

E—Building up the early multiplication facts into 'tables'

It is advisable, now, to set down in the form of 'tables' (see the footnote below) the facts with which the children have been dealing. In this way they can see how the facts are related to

---

* See footnote on page 41.

† A multiplication 'table' consists of related multiplication facts listed in increasing order. Thus the 'table of twos' begins 'One two is two; two twos are four; three twos are six; . . .' and (usually) ends at 'Twelve twos are twenty-four'. In this form the facts are most easily repeated aloud and learned by rote.

EARLY MULTIPLICATION FACTS (WHERE THE RESULT OF THE MULTIPLICATION IS NOT GREATER THAN 24*)

1 ×	2 ×	3 ×	4 ×	5 ×	6 ×	7 ×	8 ×	9 ×	10 ×	11 ×	12 ×
1	1	1	1	1	1	1	1	1	1	1	1
1	**2**	**3**	**4**	**5**	**6**	**7**	**8**	**9**	**10**	**11**	**12**
1 ×	2 ×	3 ×	4 ×	5 ×	6 ×	7 ×	8 ×	9 ×	10 ×	11 ×	12 ×
2	2	2	2	2	2	2	2	2	2	2	2
2	**4**	**6**	**8**	**10**	**12**	**14**	**16**	**18**	**20**	**22**	**24**
1 ×	2 ×	3 ×	4 ×	5 ×	6 ×	7 ×	8 ×				
3	3	3	3	3	3	3	3				
3	**6**	**9**	**12**	**15**	**18.**	**21**	**24**				
1 ×	2 ×	3 ×	4 ×	5 ×	6 ×						
4	4	4	4	4	4						
4	**8**	**12**	**16**	**20**	**24**						
1 ×	2 ×	3 ×	4 ×								
5	5	5	5								
5	**10**	**15**	**20**								
1 ×	2 ×	3 ×	4 ×								
6	6	6	6								
6	**12**	**18**	**24**								
1 ×	2 ×	3 ×									
7	7	7									
7	**14**	**21**									
1 ×	2 ×	3 ×									
8	8	8									
8	**16**	**24**									
1 ×	2 ×										
9	9										
9	**18**										
1 ×	2 ×										
10	10										
10	**20**										
1 ×	2 ×										
11	11										
11	**22**										
1 ×	2 ×										
12	12										
12	**24**										

The facts involving nought

0 ×	0 ×	0 ×	0 ×	0 ×	0 ×	0 ×	0 ×	0 ×	0 ×	0 ×	0 ×
1	2	3	4	5	6	7	8	9	10	11	12
0	**0**	**0**	**0**	**0**	**0**	**0**	**0**	**0**	**0**	**0**	**0**
1 ×	2 ×	3 ×	4 ×	5 ×	6 ×	7 ×	8 ×	9 ×	10 ×	11 ×	12 ×
0	0	0	0	0	0	0	0	0	0	0	0
0	**0**	**0**	**0**	**0**	**0**	**0**	**0**	**0**	**0**	**0**	**0**
0 ×											
0											
0											

* The primary facts usually refer only to single figure multiplications, ending at 9 × 9 = 81. Multiplication by 10, 11 and 12 is included here because of its frequent use in the British system of money and measurement.

each other. Seeing and saying the facts in the form of tables helps children to memorize the individual facts.

In Chart I the facts (from List VI, page 83) are set down in the form of tables. This should be done *with the children*, starting with the 'table of twos'. (It is considered unnecessary to set down the 'table of noughts' at this stage since the facts should be learned by applying a general principle, and by inclusion in practice-cards, etc., which are used later. The 'table of ones' may also be omitted, according to the teacher's preference. Both tables are included at a later stage—see Chart IV, Chapter XV—for the sake of completeness.)

This chart should be put on strong paper or cardboard and left on display in the class room. It should be added to as the children learn new facts. Eventually the chart should contain all the tables which have been gradually built up with the children.

It should be pointed out to the children that most of the facts in the table of twos appear again, *in 'twin' form*, in the other tables. The same is true of the facts in the other tables. The ways in which children can be helped to understand and use this very important principle are fully described in Chapter XIII (pages 188–90).

F—*Learning the early multiplication facts*

As with the addition and subtraction facts, there comes a stage when the children must learn these multiplication facts so that they know them without having to think.

The facts should be arranged in selected sets so that adequate practice can be given for each individual fact. A suggested arrangement of sets, which may be used for practice-cards, etc., is given in List C.

(*a*) *Multiplication practice-cards*—These are made up so that each has a selected set of facts (Fig. 43(*a*)). The children first work through all the cards, using apparatus if

3 ×		1 ×		4 ×	
4		2		6	etc.
1 2		2		2 4	

CHART I

EARLY MULTIPLICATION FACTS (60), ARRANGED AS TABLES

(Product not greater than twenty-four)

1×1= 1	1×2= 2	1×3= 3	1×4= 4	1×5= 5	1×6= 6	1×7= 7	1×8= 8	1×9= 9	1×10=10	1×11=11	1×12=12
2×1= 2	2×2= 4	2×3= 6	2×4= 8	2×5=10	2×6=12	2×7=14	2×8=16	2×9=18	2×10=20	2×11=22	2×12=24
3×1= 3	3×2= 6	3×3= 9	3×4=12	3×5=15	3×6=18	3×7=21	3×8=24				
4×1= 4	4×2= 8	4×3=12	4×4=16	4×5=20	4×6=24						
5×1= 5	5×2=10	5×3=15	5×4=20								
6×1= 6	6×2=12	6×3=18	6×4=24								
7×1= 7	7×2=14	7×3=21									
8×1= 8	8×2=16	8×3=24									
9×1= 9	9×2=18										
10×1=10	10×2=20										
11×1=11	11×2=22										
12×1=12	12×2=24										

necessary, and writing down the examples in their books as shown.

Next the series is worked through again, but this time without apparatus.

Finally the cards are worked through without writing down the examples. The answers only are written on a slip of paper

Multiplication Set I		
3 × 4	=	
1 × 2	=	
4 × 6	=	
2 × 2	=	
1 × 1	=	
4 × 3	=	
6 × 4	=	
2 × 1	=	

Multiplication Set 15			O15
6 × 4	=		
3 × 1	=		
7 × 3	=		
5 × 2	=		
2 × 6	=		
1 × 9	=		
2 × 12	=		
3 × 7	=		

(a)　　　　　　　　　　　(b)

FIGURE 43.—Practice-cards, for multiplication. (a) With this type the children first use apparatus; later they do without, in each case writing out the examples in their note-books—*facts from Set 1, List C.* (b) Having written his name on the back of a slip of paper, the child pins it to the card and writes the answers only —*facts from the seventh vertical column of List C*

Suitable size (as before): 4½″ × 3″

(Fig. 43(b)), on the back of which the child first writes his name for marking purposes.

The teacher should keep a careful record of each child's progress and mistakes and, as described in Chapter V, pages 54–5, should arrange for further practice of facts not properly known.

(b) *Self-corrective flash-cards*—As in Chapters V and VI, flash-cards (Fig. 44) are used to give the children further pleasurable repetition of the facts through games and other activities. (See Chapter XV for some details.)

LIST C

EARLY MULTIPLICATION FACTS* (ARRANGED IN EIGHT SELECTED SETS†)

Set 1	3 × 4	1 × 2	4 × 6	2 × 2	1 × 1	4 × 3	6 × 4	2 × 1
Set 2	5 × 3	2 × 9	1 × 3	2 × 3	3 × 5	9 × 2	3 × 1	3 × 2
Set 3	1 × 8	3 × 3	4 × 5	8 × 1	3 × 7	4 × 4	7 × 3	5 × 4
Set 4	2 × 5	3 × 6	4 × 1	2 × 8	6 × 3	1 × 4	5 × 2	8 × 2
Set 5	6 × 2	1 × 11	3 × 8	8 × 3	1 × 7	11 × 1	2 × 6	7 × 1
Set 6	4 × 2	9 × 1	11 × 2	1 × 10	10 × 1	2 × 11	1 × 9	2 × 4
Set 7	5 × 1	2 × 7	7 × 2	6 × 1	12 × 2	1 × 6	2 × 12	1 × 5
Set 8	12 × 1	3 × 8	1 × 12	2 × 10	7 × 3	8 × 3	3 × 7	10 × 2

Note—(1) The facts 8 × 3 × 7 × 3 × are included twice in order to give
            3   8   3   7

the same number of facts in each set.

(2) The facts involving nought are not included at this early stage. (They are included in later charts and sets—see Chapter XV.)

* The 'answer' part of each fact is omitted here, as the teacher does not use it in making up practice-cards, etc.

† Further 'sets' may be taken from the vertical columns of the List.

We should arrange for the children to play games with flash-cards of the facts which they find hard to learn or which they do not remember.

(*c*) *Oral class-activities*—Throughout the day, we should make use of any events or situations which may serve as illustrations of multiplication facts. For instance, in a nature study lesson plants have been hung up in groups of four. The teacher says: 'Look at these, children. There are five groups of plants with four in each group. How many are there altogether?' There are many occasions when such opportunities occur, both indoors

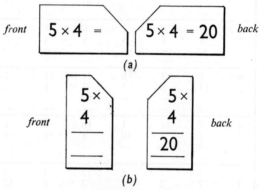

front　$5 \times 4 =$　　$5 \times 4 = 20$　*back*

(a)

front　$\begin{matrix} 5 \times \\ 4 \\ \hline \end{matrix}$　　*back*　$\begin{matrix} 5 \times \\ 4 \\ \hline 20 \end{matrix}$

(b)

FIGURE 44.—Self-corrective flash-cards (multiplication): (*a*) equation type; (*b*) process type

Suitable size (as before): 3″ × 2″

and out of doors, and in other lessons, including drawing, painting, hand-work, physical education, religious knowledge, etc. Whenever he has the chance, the teacher should refer to an arithmetical principle which the children are learning or have learned. Similarly he can give suitable practice (for example, as here, in grouping) and point out the applications of processes. Children enjoy the brief 'interruption' ('Do you remember?' 'How could we do that?' etc.), and it makes them realize that arithmetic is not a mere 'lesson' but something constantly used and useful in daily life.

From time to time the class should be taken as a whole, to say the tables, and for quick questioning on individual facts.

Chapter XV deals in detail with the learning of multiplication facts. The teacher is strongly recommended to use the ideas which are suggested there for stimulating the children's desire to learn.

G—'*Problems*'—*the importance of words as well as figures*

It is important that, from the earliest stage, children should begin to learn the 'language of multiplication'. Hence we should give them practice in hearing oral statements involving multiplication at a very simple level. As soon as they can read a little, simple written statements should be given. In this way children get to know the various words and phrases which mean that multiplication is necessary.

At the same time, and as in the case of addition and subtraction (see pages 60 and 74), very simple problems should be set: at first orally; later, on the blackboard. The whole class works together, to begin with, and each child illustrates the problem and writes down the results in his note-book. For example: 'Draw three flowers, each having five petals. How many petals are there altogether?' 'Here is a cart, with four wheels. Each wheel has five spokes. Draw the wheels. How many spokes are there in all?' It is only too easy to overlook this very important part of the work when trying to help children with facts, figures and processes.

As suggested already, such 'problems' should be based on things and events familiar to the children in their everyday lives. In this way children get used to, and gain confidence in dealing with, spoken and written problems.

This chapter suggests various ways of giving children the experience which helps them to understand the meaning of multiplication. Then we consider how they learn to write down and work out the early multiplication 'facts', which are later memorized through the use of practice-cards and flash-cards.

It is emphasized again that, throughout this work, the teacher should remain aware of the importance of children seeing and using multiplication in everyday activities. Similarly, we note that the importance of little 'problems' in words should always be kept in mind.

When children acquire a good knowledge of this work, they are 'ready' to go on to the further multiplication facts and processes discussed in Chapter XIII.

CHAPTER VIII

INTRODUCING CHILDREN TO DIVISION

A—*The idea of division*

Most teachers think that division is very difficult for children to understand. As evidence for this opinion they point to the undoubted fact that the division processes are usually performed less quickly and less accurately than any other process.

The apparent difficulty may be due to a number of causes, among which the following are perhaps the most important:

(*a*) Some teachers themselves do not have a clear idea of what is involved in the division process.

(*b*) The idea of division does not occur as easily and spontaneously to children through their normal activities as, for example, does the idea of addition (see page 38).

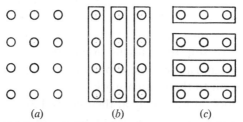

(*a*)   (*b*)   (*c*)

FIGURE 45.—An illustration of two meanings of '12 ÷ 3'

(*c*) The formal idea of division is often introduced too early for many children: that is, before they are 'ready' for it. This results in considerable confusion in the child's mind.

Let us look at these three points in turn.

If we put down twelve objects, as in Fig. 45(*a*), and write 12 ÷ 3, we may be required to think of the problem in one of *two different* ways—though, of course, the answer is the same (that is, 4) in both of them.

(*i*) 12 ÷ 3 may mean that we are asked to separate the 12 objects into 3 *equal* parts and the question is: 'How many objects are there in each part?'—as in Fig. 45(*b*). The answer is 4 *objects*.

(*ii*) 12 ÷ 3 may mean that we are asked to group the 12 objects into equal groups of 3. The question is: 'How many groups of 3 are there?'—as in Fig. 45(*c*). The answer is 4 *groups*. The answer is 4 in both cases, but what the 4 means depends upon what is asked in the problem.

It is important that we should understand the distinction between these two aspects of division, because, at a later stage, it affects children's understanding of how the division process is involved in written and actual problems. *It is, however, considered unwise to bring this distinction to the notice of children during the early stages.* At this level the child is mainly concerned with understanding the process of division, realizing when he needs to use it, recognizing the symbols for division, and making the appropriate calculation. This, of course, should always be based upon the handling of actual objects and other material and the practical carrying out of the division process.

Now let us take the next main reason for the difficulty involved in division as compared with other processes: namely, that the idea of dividing does not occur so easily or so frequently in the child's normal activities as do addition and subtraction. All the more reason, then, for us to give the child in school as wide a background as possible of practical experience of division before going on to the written work.

But if we look more closely at their general experience before they come to school we shall find that most children do see and hear a great deal of activity, on the part of their parents, brothers and sisters, which involves the idea of division in some form or another. From watching and listening to these activities they acquire a vocabulary which later helps them to give meaning to the terms used in division. It is upon this basis that we should build our teaching.

In most homes, for example, the child sees the sharing among the family of food and drink. This is not always equal sharing, it is true, but the mere fact that shares are sometimes unequal is sure to draw attention, and possibly cause argument! The child himself helps, perhaps, in the sharing of food and drink among domestic animals and birds, when phrases like 'share into four parts' are used. When the grown-ups and children return from fishing, the nets are emptied and the fish shared out, with much talking about quantities and shares. Other phrases, like 'We will have a quarter each (or a half each)', occur in play, or when the produce from a garden plot is harvested. When the family goes out collecting fish or crops, the child sees how piles of wood or fruits are divided up into bundles among the family to make it easier to carry them. He sees long pieces of rope being cut up into shorter lengths in order to tie up animals or goods. He watches and hears his parents and other grown-ups at the market, shop or store, reckoning the cost of one or more articles priced by the dozen or score. In some areas a child sees rituals and dances where groups of people divide off into smaller groups in order to perform separate parts of the ceremony.

Perhaps all this is understood very dimly by the child, and has little meaning as far as the division process is concerned. But gradually he is getting the ideas and, above all, the vocabulary connected with division. Slowly he comes to understand, through such experiences, the meaning of the words and phrases he is likely to meet in school: for example, share; divide into; how many are there in? grouping; split up, equal parts of, between, among; measure off; etc.

The third reason suggested for the apparent difficulty which children find in division is that they are often made to try formal written work before they have enough experience to understand what they are doing: that is, before they are 'ready'. The teacher's first job is to increase the child's pre-school experience, and then to adapt it to form a basis for later formal division. Suggestions for this kind of work, where the children share and divide by handling actual objects and apparatus, are described in the following section (B).

B—*Early division activities in school*

In the early stages of these activities no written symbols are used and no written work is done, but the vocabulary of division is used orally. Some of the work is individual; some is done by small teams of children under a leader, where the leader does the sharing. (Each member of a team takes turn to be leader.) In these various activities, the child sometimes *makes groups* of objects and sometimes *shares* things in order to do the division process. However, it is neither necessary, nor desirable, at this stage, to point out this distinction to the children.

(*a*) *Sharing with the number-tray*—In this exercise each child works alone. He is given a particular number of objects (beans, fruit stones, shells, coins, pencils, chalks, pictures), and told to share them equally between certain sections of the tray (Fig. 46).

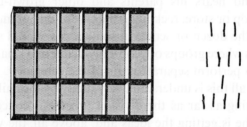

FIGURE 46.—The number-tray, for division (sharing). At a later stage the child puts number-cards with the objects in the sections of the tray. (See Fig. 1)

Note—Here the child is *sharing in ones* (not in groups), that is, putting the objects *one at a time* into each section. The question he is asked (or asks himself) is: 'How many in each section of the tray?'

(*b*) *Sharing and grouping small objects*—The leader of each team has a bag in which are a stated number (ten, say) of objects such as shells. He shares them between two other children. At first he probably gives them out one at a time and they get five each. But the teacher suggests that since he is giving shells to *two* people he should take out *two* shells at a time. Every time the leader takes two shells from the bag each child gets one. So that the number of times two shells are taken from the bag is also the number of shells each child gets. In this way the children get experience of division by grouping.

(*c*) *Folding and cutting paper*—The children are provided with a strip of paper upon which a number of equally spaced dots have been drawn. Alternatively, the paper strips may have holes punched in them. The children are asked how many dots there are.—Ten. They are told to fold over the paper after every two dots. 'Now, how many parts make up the whole strip? Count them.'—Five (Fig. 47(*a*)). 'How many lots of two make up ten?'—Five. (The children may cut up the paper, if the teacher thinks this is necessary.) A strip of paper, marked or punched in the same way, should then be used to enable the children to see that there are two fives in ten (Fig. 47(*b*)), that is, they are asked to halve the paper or 'fold it into two'.

Similar strips of paper, covering all the early division facts (List VII, page 100), may be made and used. In this activity again the children are making groups.

(*d*) *Playing at workmen on pay-day*—(*i*) One child has cardboard coins (all the same) and shares out the 'money' equally

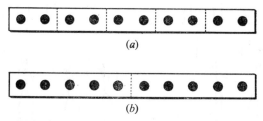

(*a*)

(*b*)

FIGURE 47.—Paper strips for folding (division)

among a number of other children. Here the question in their minds is: 'How much do we get each for the work we have done?'—that is, they are sharing.

(*ii*) The children have coins (for example, twenty, all the same kind), and are told that each workman must be given four coins for his wages. So they make piles, putting four coins in each. The question they have to answer is: 'How many workmen can be paid?'—that is, they are grouping.

(*e*) *Hoisting the flags*—The children are given a number of flags (for example, twelve). How many 'castles' can be built if each has three flags? (Here again the children are grouping.) The children take a flag each and group themselves into threes. Each group makes a 'castle' and puts in the flags (Fig. 48).

(*f*) *The 'division train'*—The children move the 'train' along the line to find how many 'signals' have to be passed on a particular journey (Fig. 49). (A 'signal' occurs every time the 'train' is moved forward its full length.) For instance: 'Take the "4" train. How many signals are there up to the number twenty on the line?' Here they are grouping by 'measuring off'.

(*g*) *The number-slide* (See pages 34, 44, Fig. 56 and page 469.)— The child takes a short strip, for example, of three inches, and is asked: 'How many times will this go to reach 12 (or 15, or 18)?' He tries it, marking with his finger where each strip ends, and counting the number of times it 'goes into' the given length. This is again grouping in the sense of 'measuring off'.

We arrange at the right time to introduce, into all such activities, situations where the children begin to get the idea that

FIGURE 48.—'Hoisting the flags': an experience in division

sometimes there is a remainder after the division has taken place. For example:—

(i) When sharing out shells between two children, the teacher arranges to have an odd number (for example, eleven) of shells

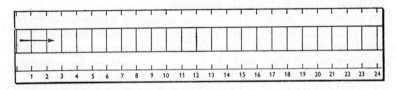

The '4' train

FIGURE 49.—The 'division train', another experience of division
(See page 473 for a description of the apparatus)

in the bag. The leader takes out two shells at a time. When the two children have five shells each, the leader dips into the bag again and finds only one shell. He cannot share this out. This one is 'over'.

(*ii*) When using the number-slide, the child is asked: 'How many times will the "3"-strip go into the 17?' He moves the '3'-strip along five times, and finds there are two spaces 'over', and which he cannot use.

In each case the bit left over should be commented upon by the teacher.

C—*Making use of everyday happenings*

We should also make use of incidental situations, inside and outside the class room, for giving children experience of division and of the vocabulary which goes with it. For instance:—

(*a*) In physical education lessons the class is often divided into a number of teams, with a certain number of children in each team. The teams must be equal in number for some games like relay races. (Sometimes there are children 'left over'.) Balls and other apparatus are often shared among the various teams.

(*b*) In dancing the children are sometimes arranged in equal groups.

(*c*) Attention may be drawn to the number of children in the class and how many can be seated at one desk or on one bench, and thus to the number of desks or benches needed.

(*d*) When discussing future plans, or coming events in the calendar, the teacher may bring in division by asking questions: 'Christmas will be here in 12 weeks time.—How many months (of 4 weeks) is that?' 'Holidays begin in 14 days.—How many weeks is that?'

(*e*) The learning of division rhymes may also help to fix ideas and to increase awareness of the process. *These rhymes may be invented by the teacher to suit the language of his own area.* Here are a few in English:—

'Six ripe mangoes hanging on a tree:
If two of us share them, we each have three.'

'Six red peppers shining and new:
If three of us share them, we each have two.'

'Eight little monkeys sitting on the floor:
Half of them were *brown*, the grey ones were four.'

'Ten little fishes, swimming all alive:
Catch two in each net: the fish-nets are five.'

D—*Recording division activities*

When the children are used to the idea of sharing and grouping, they begin to understand the meaning of the words used to indicate division: for example, share; divide; split up; how many are there in? etc. The teacher uses these words in organizing the activities and the children use them in talking about what they have done.

Now comes the time for them to do *the same activities* and *write down* what they do in drawing, words and symbols. The teacher shows them on the blackboard how they can put down on paper what they have done in their sharing activities.

(*a*) The children are asked to share twelve shells among three sections of the number-tray. They put four shells in each section, and then draw the tray with the shells in it.

Underneath the drawing the children (if they can) write down:

> '12 shells.
> 3 trays.
> 4 shells in each tray.'

The teacher then introduces the division symbol. (The children are already accustomed to the idea of using symbols in addition, subtraction and multiplication.) The children finish off the example by writing down: '$12 \div 3 = 4$'.

(*b*) The same example should later be repeated using thirteen shells, the result being written down like this:

> 13 shells.
> 3 trays.
> 4 shells in each tray, and 1 over.
> $13 \div 3 = 4$, and 1 over.

(*c*) Other activities can be recorded in the same way, but they do not all require drawing by the children. Gradually the children become able to write down the activity straight away in arithmetical form.

(*d*) We then introduce another way of setting down, by working out further examples on the blackboard with the children:
(*i*) Without remainder. 'Share eight pennies among four

children.' The teacher discusses the problem, writes down the question, and asks: 'How many fours in eight?' The children give the answer: 'Two'. The teacher shows where to put the answer.

$$\frac{2}{4)8}$$

(*ii*) With remainder. 'How many threes in twenty?' The teacher discusses the problem and writes down the question.

Each child gets 2 pennies

The children use the 'number-slide' to find the answer: 'It goes six times and there are two over.' The teacher shows how this is put down.

$$\begin{array}{r} 6 \\ 3)\overline{20} \\ 18 \\ \hline 2 \end{array}$$

The 'number-slide' helps the children to see that what is left over is the

$20 \div 3 = 6$, and 2 over

'difference' between 18 and 20; *that is, that subtraction must take place to find the remainder.*

E—*Division examples set by the teacher*

The division activities which the children have been working out and recording for themselves may not cover *all* the division 'facts' required at this stage. It becomes necessary, therefore, to select examples, for the children to do, covering *all* the facts. The early division facts are given in List VII. As in multiplication, numbers up to twenty-four only have been included at this early stage.

Each lesson the teacher puts a few examples from this list on the blackboard, and the children set them down and work them out, using apparatus if necessary. There should be included, each time, some examples which give a remainder of one or two. This practice helps the children to get used to the way of setting down the example and subtracting to find the remainder.

F—*Learning the early division facts*

A stage is reached when the children must learn the division facts so that they know them without having to think. Unless these facts are known *perfectly*, children are held up when they have to deal with more complicated processes. In many cases where children have difficulty with arithmetic, the trouble can be traced back to a faulty knowledge of the division facts.

LIST VII

EARLY DIVISION FACTS (WHERE THE NUMBER TO BE DIVIDED IS NOT GREATER THAN 24)

```
  0     0     0     0     0     0     0     0     0      0      0      0
1)0   2)0   3)0   4)0   5)0   6)0   7)0   8)0   9)0   10)0   11)0   12)0

  1     1     1     1     1     1     1     1     1      1      1      1
1)1   2)2   3)3   4)4   5)5   6)6   7)7   8)8   9)9   10)10  11)11  12)12

  2     2     2     2     2     2     2     2     2      2      2      2
1)2   2)4   3)6   4)8   5)10  6)12  7)14  8)16  9)18  10)20  11)22  12)24

  3     3     3     3     3     3     3     3
1)3   2)6   3)9   4)12  5)15  6)18  7)21  8)24

  4     4     4     4     4     4
1)4   2)8   3)12  4)16  5)20  6)24

  5     5     5     5
1)5   2)10  3)15  4)20

  6     6     6     6
1)6   2)12  3)18  4)24

  7     7     7
1)7   2)14  3)21

  8     8     8
1)8   2)16  3)24

  9     9
1)9   2)18

 10    10
1)10  2)20

 11    11
1)11  2)22

 12    12
1)12  2)24
```

Following plans like those for the other processes, the early division facts should be arranged in selected sets, so that adequate practice is given on each individual fact, and so that we can find out which children have difficulty with any particular fact. A suggested arrangement of the facts is given in List D. There are only eight sets, and only nine facts in each set. It is perhaps a good thing that the facts are fewer, since children have been found to require more concentration for the division process than for the others. (The teacher may obtain further sets, for practice-cards, etc., by using the vertical columns of the List, although these tend to be 'random' rather than 'selected' sets.)

LIST D

THE EARLY DIVISION FACTS* ARRANGED IN EIGHT
SELECTED SETS†

Set 1	2)12̄	4)0̄	3)21̄	6)6̄	6)12̄	7)21̄	1)1̄	12)0̄	1)6̄
Set 2	4)8̄	3)24̄	5)0̄	1)7̄	2)8̄	2)4̄	1)0̄	8)24̄	7)7̄
Set 3	3)12̄	1)8̄	2)24̄	6)0̄	3)9̄	3)0̄	4)12̄	8)8̄	12)24̄
Set 4	2)0̄	10)20̄	9)9̄	4)16̄	7)0̄	6)18̄	2)20̄	1)9̄	3)18̄
Set 5	10)10̄	3)15̄	3)3̄	2)18̄	1)10̄	8)0̄	5)15̄	9)18̄	1)3̄
Set 6	11)22̄	11)11̄	4)20̄	1)5̄	2)22̄	1)11̄	9)0̄	5)20̄	5)5̄
Set 7	2)6̄	1)2̄	2)16̄	6)24̄	3)6̄	2)2̄	8)16̄	10)0̄	4)24̄
Set 8	7)14̄	2)10̄	1)12̄	4)4̄	2)14̄	5)10̄	12)12̄	1)4̄	11)0̄

* *Note*—The 'answer' of each division, normally a part of the complete statement of the *fact*, is omitted in this List, as the teacher does not need it when making up groups of practice-cards, etc.

† Nine further sets are available by making use of the vertical columns of the List, though these tend to be random rather than selected.

There are many ways in which List D may be used by the teacher to ensure that the facts are perfectly known. Here are some of them:—

(*a*) *Division practice cards*—These are made so that each contains one of the sets of facts (Fig. 50(*a*)). First the children work through all the cards* using apparatus if necessary and writing down the examples in their books in the way they have been shown.

Next the series is worked through again, this time without apparatus.

Finally the cards are worked through without writing down

Division		Set 8	
14	÷	7	=
10	÷	2	=
12	÷	1	=
4	÷	4	=
14	÷	2	=
10	÷	5	=
12	÷	12	=
4	÷	1	=
0	÷	11	=

Division		Set 3	
12	÷	3	=
8	÷	1	=
24	÷	2	=
0	÷	6	=
9	÷	3	=
0	÷	3	=
12	÷	4	=
8	÷	8	=
24	÷	12	=

(*a*)   (*b*)

FIGURE 50.—Practice-cards, for division: (*a*) using apparatus if necessary, the child works out the examples and writes them down in his note-book—*facts from Set 8, List D*. (*b*) The child writes his name on the back of a slip of paper, on which he then puts down the 'answers' only—*facts from Set 3, List D*

Suitable size (as before): 4½″ × 3″

the examples. The answer only is written on a slip of paper (Fig. 50(*b*)), on the back of which the child puts his name.

Again it is most important that we should keep a detailed record of each child's progress and mistakes (see the suggestions on pages 53–5).

(*b*) *Relating division facts with multiplication facts*—The children already realize that there is a close connexion between the learning of division facts and a previous knowledge of multi-

* There are seventeen cards altogether, if the teacher uses the nine vertical columns of List D as well as the eight horizontal rows.

plication. For example, when using the number-slide for division they 'count in groups' as they do in multiplication. The understanding of this relationship helps the children to memorize the multiplication and division facts together. For instance if they know $3 \times 4 = 12$, they should realize that they also know that:

$$4 \times 3 = 12$$
$$12 \div 4 = 3$$
$$12 \div 3 = 4$$

We should bring this to the children's notice frequently, till the relationships occur to them of their own accord.

front   *back*

Division		Set 9		o
12	÷	2	=	
8	÷	4	=	
12	÷	3	=	
0	÷	2	=	
10	÷	10	=	
22	÷	11	=	
6	÷	2	=	
14	÷	7	=	

Multiplication check		Set 9		o
6	×	2	=	
2	×	4	=	
4	×	3	=	
0	×	2	=	
1	×	10	=	
2	×	11	=	
3	×	2	=	
2	×	7	=	

FIGURE 51.—A practice-card, for division, with multiplication check—*facts from the first vertical column of List D*. (The child, having written his name on the back of the slip of paper, pins it to the card and puts down his 'answers'. He then removes the slip, turns the card over, and compares his figures with those of the first column on the back. Similarly, he may check his 'answers' in the multiplication facts by comparison with the first column of numbers on the division side of the card)

Practice-cards should be made up which give experience in dealing with related multiplication and division facts (Fig. 51).

The children can correct their own answers by turning over the card, if it is pointed out that the answers to the examples on one side of the card are the first numbers in the examples on the other side.

(c) *Practice-cards with remainders*—To give the children further

Division			Set 21
Sometimes there is a remainder			
24	÷	5	=
7	÷	2	=
16	÷	8	=
10	÷	3	=
20	÷	9	=
14	÷	2	=
13	÷	4	=
9	÷	2	=

FIGURE 52.—A practice-card, for division, including remainders

Division by Two			
10	÷	2	=
6	÷	2	=
12	÷	2	=
8	÷	2	=
0	÷	2	=
2	÷	2	=
4	÷	2	=
14	÷	2	=
20	÷	2	=
18	÷	2	=
24	÷	2	=
16	÷	2	=
22	÷	2	=

FIGURE 53.— A practice-card, for division related to a particular
multiplication table

practice in learning the facts, and in setting down the working when a remainder occurs, special practice-cards should be made up. (These can still be based on the sets in List D, but some of the numbers to be divided should then be increased so that a remainder sometimes occurs.) Each card should contain a mixture of examples with and without remainders (Fig. 52).

The '20' Division Card			
20	÷	4	=
20	÷	5	=
20	÷	2	=
20	÷	10	=

FIGURE 54.—A grouping-card—a practice-card for division of certain numbers into equal groups in different ways

(*d*) *Other practice-cards*—There are other practice-cards which may be used for particular purposes:—

(*i*) Cards such as that in Fig. 53 can be made up, relating the division examples to a particular multiplication table. In the example shown, the 'table of twos' has to be remembered, if the division examples are to be done quickly.

(*ii*) Grouping-cards (Fig. 54) can be made, giving further emphasis to, and practice in, recognizing related facts (see

Use the '24' Slide			
	Size of strip		
24	÷	4	=
24	÷	6	=
24	÷	2	=
24	÷	12	=
24	÷	3	=
24	÷	8	=

FIGURE 55.—A 'measuring-card', for use with number-slide and measuring-strips

E

page 102). At this stage five cards only of this kind are appropriate, namely the '12', '16', '18', '20', '24'. From this practice the children begin to realize that certain numbers can be split up into equal groups in a variety of ways. For example twenty objects can be split up into: 5 groups of 4; 4 groups of 5; 2 groups of 10; 10 groups of 2.

(*iii*) Measuring-cards (Fig. 55) make use of the 'number-slide'

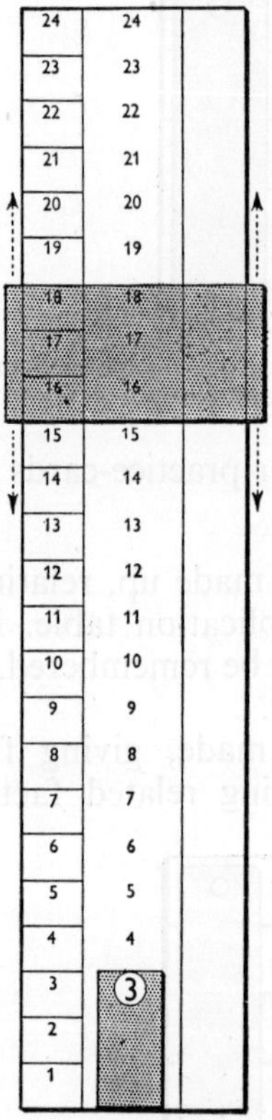

FIGURE 56.—The '24' number-slide, with runner and measuring-strip. (The runner, or cursor, may be moved up or down the slide to cut off the number series at any given place. Here it is shown cutting off the '15', and the child's problem is: 'How many 3's "go into" 15?')

See page 469 for a description of the apparatus

(Fig. 56 shows the '24'-slide), and numbered strips of various sizes, to give a similar kind of practice in recognizing related facts. The child decides which number the card is asking him to consider for dividing in various ways. (In Fig. 55 it is the number 24.) He then finds the right size of measuring-strip and 'measures off' along the number-slide. (For the number 24, the child does not need the runner of the slide, but for smaller numbers he uses it as shown in Fig. 56.)

(e) *Self-corrective flash-cards*—Exactly as in addition, sub-traction and multiplication, flash-cards (Fig. 57) are used to give the children further pleasurable repetition of the division facts through games and other activities, such as those des-cribed in detail in Chapter XV.

The teacher should use this opportunity for putting right the mistakes commonly made by the children. For example, he arranges for children to play flash-card games, using the par-ticular division facts of which they are not sure.

(f) *Oral class-activities*—Regular short periods when the whole class responds to the teacher's quick questioning on the division

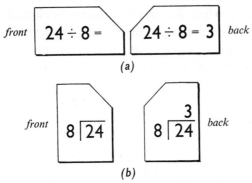

FIGURE 57.—Self-corrective flash-cards (division): (*a*) equation type; (*b*) process type

Suitable size (as before): 3″ × 2″

facts are valuable as a means of revision. But we should re-member that, when taking oral work with a whole class, there is often a tendency to overlook some of the 'facts', while others are practised unnecessarily. *All* the facts should be given attention.

We should also make good use of anything that happens during the day which may be thought of as an example of division. For instance, the class may be splitting up into sets of four for ball-play. We say: 'There are twenty-four children in the class. How many balls do we need? We have to divide twenty-four by four?' An actual example from a class room further illustrates the point. (The children had begun to deal

with higher numbers.) A box had broken open at the side
showing six layers of crayons. The lid of the box indicated that
there were seventy-two crayons in the box altogether. The
teacher showed this to the class and said: 'Look, there are six
layers and there are seventy-two crayons in the box altogether.
Who can tell me how many crayons I shall find in the top
layer?'—'Twelve?'—'All right, let us see. You are right. How
did you find out?'

G—'*Problems*'—*the importance of words as well as figures*

Some children are able to divide numbers accurately, yet find
great difficulty when the division process is clothed in words;
that is, when it occurs in 'problem' form. The remarks about the
other three processes (pages 60, 74 and 89) apply equally here.

The ability of children 'to do division in words' depends to a
considerable extent upon whether, *from the beginning*, they
understand and become used to the language of division. The
experiences described in this chapter help them to get the necessary understanding, since they talk and write about, and deal
with, actual situations involving division.

We should make sure that these experiences are continued
throughout the work, particularly at the stages where much of
it is of a mechanical nature. Regular practice should be given,
through talking, drawing and (a little later) writing and reading,
so that the children get plenty of opportunities to interpret the
words and phrases which indicate that they must divide.

Hence, from the start, we should give little 'problems', at first
orally and later through drawing and writing. For example:—

(*i*) Take twelve counters from your box. Split them into three
equal groups. Now draw what you have done. Write it down in
figures.
(*ii*) There are fifteen fish in a pot. Draw three small dishes and
put an equal number of fish in each. Write down what you have
done in figures.
(*iii*) I have twenty-four young fruit trees. Draw a garden with
the trees planted in four equal rows. Write down what you have
done in figures.

At first, of course, the teacher works through such examples with the class.

The 'problems' should be real to the children, so we should try to take our examples from everyday affairs and things the children know. We should miss no chance of pointing out an example which may arise during other lessons or activities.

This kind of constant practice helps children to get the idea of dealing with spoken or written problems systematically. They begin to see what method they should adopt and what arithmetical process they must use to find the answer.

In this chapter some reasons are put forward for the fact that many children seem to have greater difficulty in grasping the idea of division than they have with earlier work. Ways of helping them to understand are discussed, and suggestions are made for increasing their experiences of division. It is shown how, through varied activities, children meet, work out and learn the early division facts, and then relate them to the early multiplication facts.

The teacher is advised, throughout, of the importance of giving children practice in the use of division facts in everyday situations and in little 'problems' put into words.

The value of thorough knowledge and understanding of the work at this stage becomes obvious when children go on to the division process described in Chapter XIV.

CHAPTER IX

BEGINNING TO DEAL WITH MONEY

A—*The child's first ideas of money*

For most people money has value only in terms of the goods it can buy. It is therefore natural that a child's first ideas of coins as money come through shopping activities. (Some children, of course, have the opportunity to handle coins before they know anything about their value. Perhaps they play with them, as counters which make a pleasant tinkling noise when shaken together.)

Coins are sometimes used in the home to help the child with early counting activities, but it is not till later that the child realizes that they have value in terms of goods and services. He finds that his parents, or older brothers and sisters, can get many necessary and sometimes exciting things by handing over coins to somebody in a shop or in the market place. In some places the child begins to realize that by giving up a coin he can go for a ride in a train, bus, lorry or car. He may sometimes watch workmen being paid in coins for the work they have done.

He notices later that, in exchange for a coin, the grown-ups sometimes get several other coins in addition to the goods they are buying. He learns that this is called 'change'. Through this experience he gradually comes to realize that coins have value in terms of other coins and he is led to notice the differences between the various kinds: in size, colour, shape, pattern, weight, and kind of metal.

B—*Early experiences with money in school*

We must build upon these pre-school experiences by providing many and varied activities in which money can be used and discussed. In some areas the work will be much easier for teacher and children because the coinage is simple. In countries which use dollars or francs, for example, there should be no great difficulty. In other countries (for example, Britain) the coinage is complicated and requires very careful teaching at the early stages. British coinage is therefore taken as the example in the whole of this chapter. But the same principles and ideas should apply in areas where other coinage is used. (The sole difference is that their *application* is much easier!)

(1) The need for a practical approach

The business of earning and spending money is a very important part of the life of most communities. It affects people's work, leisure and games, their possessions, their thinking and their expressed opinions. Teachers get the best response from children when the work in school is linked closely with the life of the community outside the school, in village or town. If children are to get a proper understanding of how to deal with money, *the early work must be practical.* Class-room 'shops' should be arranged, so that the children can imitate the grown-ups by 'playing shop'. It is best to use real coins, but, as this is often impossible in school, model coins are essential. Money calculations on paper have no meaning unless the children have begun to see that the numbers represent actual coins which can be used to buy things.

Here are descriptions of various types of class-room shops.

(a) The open market—The 'goods' are arranged on the floor and the shopkeeper sits among them (Fig. 58).

(b) Simple models of shops in town or village—(*i*) The 'goods' are displayed on a table. Wooden pieces are fixed to the sides to act as a frame for a coloured or painted screen (Fig. 59), which may be made of cloth or paper.

(*ii*) In the folding-frame ('clothes-horse') type (Fig. 60(*a*)), a piece of wood (or a number of poles) is fixed across the two hinged ends to act as the shop counter. This type of 'shop' is readily folded up and so can be stored easily. If no counter is available, hooks may be fitted into the woodwork (as in Fig. 60(*b*)). The 'goods' can then be hung from the hooks.

(c) Large pictures of shops—Sometimes the class room is too small to hold a 'shop'. If this is so, a 'shop' can be drawn and painted on stiff cardboard (Fig. 61). Slots are cut in the card, and the pictures of 'goods' are placed in these, with prices

attached. When children come to 'buy', the shopkeeper (another child) takes a picture from the slot and 'sells' it.

(d) *Display of goods or pictures of goods*—This is often a suitable arrangement if there is plenty of room for the children to walk

FIGURE 58.—The 'open market', for children's 'shopping' activities. (Objects and prices must be suited to the neighbourhood of the school)

around. Before the lesson the teacher, helped by some of the children, puts the 'goods', with prices attached, in various parts of the class room. Some 'goods' or pictures may be placed on

FIGURE 59.—The 'table shop'. (Articles and prices should be suitable for the children)

a shelf, some in an empty corner; others may be hung on hooks on the wall, or pinned to the back of the door.

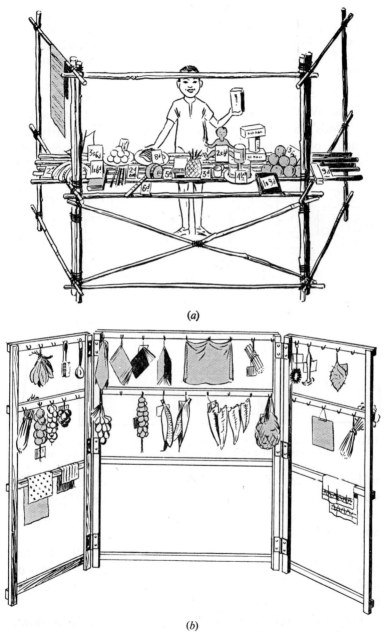

(a)

(b)

FIGURE 60.—The 'folding-frame shop': (a) with a counter; (b) with hooks

When the lesson starts each child is given a card bearing the name of an article (or articles) that he must 'buy', and some money (real or model). Each child then moves around the class room, finds the article or picture, takes it to the teacher, and 'pays' the proper price for it.

It is wise to make 'shopping' as attractive as possible to the children. We should try to give variety and interest by changing the 'goods' in the 'shop' as soon as they become dirty, un-attractive or out-of-date. Sometimes the children themselves can make the articles which are 'for sale'. They can make models

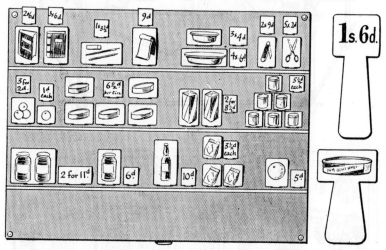

FIGURE 61.—The 'slotted-picture shop'. (The 'shop' is drawn or painted, and pictures of common articles at suitable prices are fitted into the slots)

of bread, pieces of meat, and sweets, for example, from clay suitably hardened and painted. They can make simple toys from wood, and wrap up packets of sand to resemble sugar, grain, or any local foodstuffs.

There is great educational value, too, in allowing the children to set up the 'shops' themselves and to act as shop-keepers or assistants. In this way they increase their vocabulary and their experience of number.

The articles to be bought, and the prices to be paid for them, in market-place or shop, vary greatly from country to country, district to district, season to season, and so on. We should always make sure that our examples are suitable. The articles mentioned must be familiar to the children: that is, they must be the kinds of things which can be bought locally. The prices mentioned must be, as nearly as possible, those which are being charged at the time of the lessons. Otherwise children are likely to regard the examples as silly, and so pay little attention to them, or even to find them meaningless. Thus the examples given here (or, for that matter, in any book) should be changed to suit the particular school and neighbourhood—though, of course, the level of the work should remain exactly the same. This means that the teacher must constantly revise the examples he uses, while making sure that they illustrate the principle he is teaching and that they are at the right level. Only in this way are the children likely to develop real understanding, so that, later on, they become able to apply their knowledge to situations with which they may not be familiar.

(2) Using the 'shops'

(*a*) *Recognition of coins*—We should make sure that the children are able to recognize, eventually, the names and values of all the common coins in use in their area. But we cannot expect this recognition all at once. The children gradually come to it through experience in 'shopping'. (Children who, from an early age, are used to real markets or shops, learn very quickly.)

In the very early stages the children use only one type of coin to make their 'purchases', so that they get plenty of practice in recognizing it and using it. Real coins are best, of course, but, if these are not available, good cardboard imitations should be bought, or made, by the children. Another way to help children to recognize coins by their shape and markings is to show them how to make coin-rubbings. A real coin is placed under 'yellow' or 'silver' paper, and the children scribble over it in pencil. Then they rub gently till the markings of the coin show through. The 'rubbing' is later labelled with the name of the coin. When the children have met several different coins, they should be given matching activities with the matching-tray

(Fig. 62). Coins are placed in one row of sections of the tray and the children have to find the correct symbol-card and name-card for each coin.

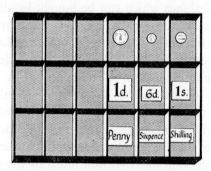

FIGURE 62.—The number-tray, used for coins with symbol- and name-cards. (See Fig. 1, page 23)

(*b*) *Recording purchases*—To begin with, the children 'go shopping' for one article only. They take the exact number of coins, or a card on which this number of model coins is pasted. They make the 'purchase', and then go to their seats and draw what they have done in their note-books (Fig. 63). Later they are asked to 'buy' two articles and to find how much money

FIGURE 63.—The child's exercise-book record of 'shopping' activities

they need. They draw the two articles, with the price by the side of each, and *add up* to find the total money required to 'buy' them (Fig. 64). In these 'purchases' they always use the same kind of coin. They do *not* use a mixture of different kinds of coins.

(*c*) *Buying with 'mixed' coins*—When the children have been introduced to another type of coin, and know its value, they should begin to make 'purchases' with two different coins. For

FIGURE 64.—The child's first recordings of addition of money

example, they may be given a sixpence and a penny and told to go and 'buy' one article which costs sevenpence. These 'purchases' are put down in their books in the usual way (as an addition), but the total amount, at this stage, should not exceed two shillings.

(*d*) *The idea of 'getting change'* —The previous work should have given the children some experience of thinking of the value of coins in terms of other coins. For example, the name 'sixpence', and the purchases made with additional pennies, should have given them the idea that the sixpence (though probably smaller in *size* than a penny) is equal in value to six pennies. These ideas become more obvious when the children begin to make 'purchases' of 'goods' whose price is less than the value of the coin. That is, when they begin to get 'change'. For example, they take one sixpence to 'buy' something priced at fourpence. They find that, in addition to the article, they get two pennies 'change'. The transaction is again recorded in their books, this time as a subtraction example (Fig. 65). This means they have to learn exactly what each coin is worth in terms of other coins. The children can be helped to learn this not only through 'shopping' experiences, but by other activities, arranged by the teacher, such as the following:—

(*i*) The children each have a *box of coins* (real or imitation), and they use *the matching-tray* to carry out the teacher's instructions. The teacher says, for example: 'Put a shilling in each part of one row in your tray. Now, find three different ways to make up a

FIGURE 65.—The child's first record of 'getting change' (i.e. a simple example of subtraction in money)

shilling, first using pennies, then three-penny pieces and then sixpences (Fig. 66).

(*ii*) The children are given boxes of *coins and individual cards* (Fig. 67). They have to make up the various amounts stated on the cards, using the coins available.

(*iii*) Two children take charge of *the class 'bank'*. They have a

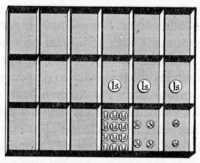

FIGURE 66.—The number-tray, used for equivalent coins. (See Fig. 1)

pile of money in front of them on a table. The other children each come in turn with a coin to get it changed. They then write down what they have done, for example, 'I changed a shilling for two sixpences.'

As the children become accustomed to the idea of getting change, they should be encouraged to set down their work as simple subtraction examples.

(*e*) *Simple multiplication*—During the shopping activities opportunities will arise for 'buying' a number of articles at the same

Put the coins on the line					
7d.	6d	1d			
1s. 4d.	1s	1d	1d	1d	1d
1s. 10d	1s	6d	1d	1d	1d	1d
9d.	3d	3d	3d		
1s.	6d	6d			
11d.	6d	3d	1d	1d	

FIGURE 67.—A 'money-card'—the use of 'mixed' coins to make up
given totals

Suitable size: about 10″ × 10″

price: for example, 'five eggs at twopence each'. This leads to
simple multiplication examples which are set down as shown
here.

(*f*) *Simple division*—Similarly,
'shopping' activities can be arranged so that the children get
experience of division of money.
They go to the 'shop' and find
that certain articles are marked at
'4 for a shilling'. They have to

$$\begin{array}{r} d \\ 2 \times \\ \underline{5} \\ 1\,0 \end{array} \qquad \begin{array}{r} d \\ 3 \times \\ \underline{4} \\ 1\,2 \end{array}$$

'buy' only one of these articles, so they must work out the price
for one. They do this in their books *before* making the purchase
(Fig. 68).

(*g*) *Use of shopping-lists and practice-cards*—As with the learning of number-facts (Chapters V to VIII) we should organize
the children's practice in dealing with money so that all possible
amounts (up to two shillings) are covered. It therefore becomes
necessary to prepare shopping-list cards and practice-cards, so
as to direct the children's experience. Some suggested types are

shown in Figs. 69 and 70. They are used in the same way as those described in previous chapters.

FIGURE 68.—The child's first record of division of money

In this early work on money the children are getting the idea of using money in shopping activities. They gradually come, through this experience, to realize that different coins have different values. Later they are introduced to the idea that some coins can be 'changed' for numbers of other coins and they learn how to make the simple kind of calculation needed in shopping.

In Chapter XVI it is shown how the children can make use of the ideas and information they have gained to work out examples in which larger sums of money are involved.

Note—The principles of this chapter apply to *any* system of *currency*. As stated in section B, the British system is more complicated than most. This makes it comparatively easy for a teacher to adapt the details and examples of the principles and methods to the money of his own country.

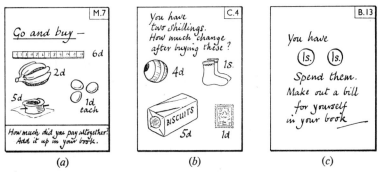

FIGURE 69.—'Shopping-list' cards, for practice in money: (a) addition; (b) addition and subtraction ('change'); (c) making out a simple bill

Addition of Money | A.10

- 2d + 5d
- 1d + 8d
- 6d + 3d
- 4d + 7d
- 1d each + 6d
- 3d 3d + 2d 2d

Subtraction of Money | S.6

I had	—	I spent	Change
6d	–	5d	
1s	–	9d	
6d 3d	–	4d	
2/-	–	1s. 6d	
1s 6d	–	8d	

Multiplication of Money | T.5

How much in all ?

- 5 at 2d each
- 4 at 3d each
- 8 at 2d each
- 12 at 1d each
- 6 at 3d each
- 2 at 9d each
- 3 at 4d each
- 7 at 3d each
- 9 at 2d each

Division of Money | D.9

How much for one ?

- 6 pineapples cost 1s. 6d.
- 8 pencils cost 1s. 4d.
- 1 dozen eggs cost 2s.
- 3 pens cost 1s.
- 4 coconuts cost 8d.
- 5 rubbers cost 1s. 3d.
- 2 cups of flour cost 1s. 6d.

FIGURE 70.—Practice-cards, for 'money': the four processes at the easiest level

Suitable size: about 8″ × 4″

CHAPTER X

LEARNING TO MEASURE*—LENGTH, WEIGHT, CAPACITY, TIME

A—*Pre-school experiences*

Before children begin their schooling they may have acquired a good deal of information about measures and measuring. In the ordinary everyday happenings of the home, in town or village, they meet situations, and listen to words, indicating that measurment of some kind is involved. It is upon these experiences that we eventually build the children's ability to measure, and to calculate measurements in, length, weight, capacity and time. Teachers should therefore know about these pre-school experiences of their pupils.

In the home, and when going about with parents and brothers and sisters, the child may come across the use of actual measurements of *length*. For example, he may see workmen on a building, hear them discussing the length of timber needed for a particular job, and then see them cutting it to the right length. But the language he hears is usually concerned with comparisons, not with actual measurements. He learns the meanings of 'long', 'short', 'longer', 'shorter', when sticks, planks, distances or animals are being compared: 'That snake is longer than the other.' He learns the meaning of the words 'high' and 'low' when the grown-ups talk about the levels of the river at various seasons, about the height of mountains, buildings and trees. When his parents and elders talk about going on a journey he begins to understand the meaning of the words 'near' and 'far away'. He is personally interested in discussions about his own height as compared with that of other children.

He sees the cow or goat tethered to a post and hears his father say that the rope must be made shorter because the animal is

---

* In this and later chapters on measurement, the measures described and dealt with are British. In areas where measures are different, the teacher should make the necessary changes to apply the principles, which remain the same.

wandering too far away. He knows then that by cutting or breaking the rope it can be made 'shorter'. He finds, too, that things can be joined together and made longer. This is particularly important to him if he finds that with a longer stick he can reach something which has been previously 'out of reach'.

The child's pre-school experience of *weight* depends very much on the area in which he lives. In towns and places where there are shops and regular markets, the child learns from watching his mother or father do the shopping for the family. He may hear them ask for pounds, ounces, hundredweights, or similar weights of produce, and he may know what these weights look like in grain, food or metal. In some places he may see some of the standard weights used by the shop-keeper on the scales.

But in many areas a child's pre-school experience of weight is almost entirely limited to understanding the meaning of words used by his family: 'heavy', 'light', 'heavier', 'lighter'. He may hear the words 'too heavy' when loads, such as sacks of corn or cocoa, or bundles of wood, are to be carried or lifted. He may also hear his family talking about animals gaining in weight when they are healthy, or losing in weight when they are sick. He can only give meaning to these words of weight by using his own muscles to pick things up and carry them about. He finds that he cannot always trust his eyes to tell him whether a thing is heavy or light. His muscle-sense alone can tell him that. Gradually he comes to know the big thing which is light (such as an empty box) and the small thing which is heavy (such as a piece of metal).

Few children gain much knowledge of the standard measures of *capacity* until they have been at school several years. And yet from their earliest years children are fond of experimenting with all sorts of materials which *later help them to understand these measures*. They enjoy playing with water, mud, sand and clay, using any kind of container they can find. They spend long periods doing no more than pour liquid or dry material from one container into another. In their play they begin to use words which indicate capacity: 'tinful', 'bottleful', 'bucketful', 'spoonful', 'basketful', 'armful', 'half full', a 'few drops'. In many places where water supply is a very important matter, they hear a great deal of grown-up talk about wells, storage-tanks, water-pots, etc. Sometimes they may see 'sheep-dip' being prepared by an agricultural officer who talks about pints and gallons. Drums of kerosene or petrol, marked with a number of gallons or litres, may also be familiar in some areas.

Ideas about *time* come very slowly to young children. That is why most teachers delay teaching it in school until the other measures have been dealt with. (Perhaps it is also the reason why the study of history is not usually recommended for young children: they are unable to grasp the mental idea of time.) But it is as well to remember that, when we do teach children about time measures, and expect them to 'tell the time' and calculate time periods, we should still base our teaching upon understanding. This understanding depends upon the children's experience in the home and in their early school years. The child soon learns about day and night, and gradually he comes to know what his parents mean by 'wet season', 'dry season', 'summer', 'winter', 'monsoon-season', etc. He begins to notice the apparent movements of the sun and the moon. 'Yesterday' and 'tomorrow' are often confused at first, but he soon knows about meal-times and bed-times. He is aware of the regular comings and goings of his family in their work at certain times of the day. He cannot easily see the difference in the ages of the people he meets, but it is not long before he recognizes the difference between 'old' and 'young'. By the time he is ready to attend school he knows what is meant by 'quick' and 'slow'. The learning about measurement of time should be built up from such early knowledge.

B—*Learning to measure lengths*

(*a*) *Early activities*—In their early arithmetic activities in school children learn to count. This counting may sometimes take the form of counting the number of steps they take in crossing the class room or the playing-field. They gradually come to realize that the distance from one point to another can be thought of as a number of paces. Later the teacher introduces the children to the idea of using other ways to measure distances. For example the children may use their feet (from heel to toe), or they may use the span of one hand, as two convenient ways of measuring a short distance. They may be shown how to measure the length of a wall by using as a unit the distance from finger-tip to finger-tip when the arms are outstretched. This can be varied by using the distance from the tip of the nose to the finger-tip of one extended arm.

(b) *The need for standard units*—During these activities some of the children find that they get different results from each other, even when they are carefully measuring the same distance. For example, one tall child says that the length of the room is ten paces, while a smaller child says it is twelve paces. Again a small child is asked to measure a shorter distance (for example, between the teacher's desk and the door) by using the length of his own feet (heel to toe). The class count the number of 'feet' as he goes. Next another child with bigger feet measures the same distance. Their answers are found to be different.

The teacher should use these situations to show the children that, if quarrels are to be avoided, they must agree to use the same unit of measurement. They are told that men long ago had the same difficulty and came to an agreement to use the length of a man's foot. Since the man's foot was not always available, it was found necessary to use pieces of wood, sticks, metal, etc., of the same length as the man's foot.

(c) *The foot*—The children are now shown several pieces of wood, cardboard, etc., each measuring a standard foot and are told that each of them is the agreed length and is called a foot.

The children are now given an unmarked foot-stick* and told to measure lengths in and around the class room. When they are accustomed to handling the 'ruler' they should be required to write down in a 'measuring book' what they have done (Fig. 71). It is a good plan at this stage to introduce the

* It is unwise to let the children use an ordinary foot ruler, at this stage, because most types of school ruler are a little more than a foot long. Moreover, some children become confused by all the figures and sub-divisions on the ordinary ruler.

idea of 'guessing' a length before measuring it. The children enjoy this because they are competing against themselves. It also leads to an ability which later proves very useful in every-day measurement: to be able to estimate with some accuracy.

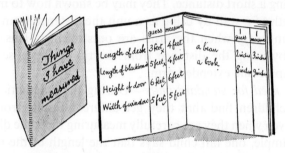

FIGURE 71.—A child's 'measuring book'

It is enough, in these early stages, if the children measure lengths 'to the nearest foot'. The teacher tells them not to worry, to begin with, if there is a bit over. He also tells them that if, for example, a length is nearly four feet, it should be counted as a full four feet.

(*d*) *The inch*—But it is not long before the children themselves begin to be dissatisfied with measurements to the nearest foot. They begin to complain: 'there is a bit over', or 'it is not quite long enough to be a foot'. *This is the time for the teacher to introduce a foot-stick with inch markings* (Fig. 72). If children

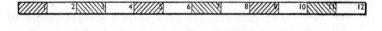

FIGURE 72.—'Foot-sticks' marked in inches: (*a*) in wood or cardboard; (*b*) in cane with notches

have already used the 'number-slide' for their early number activities (Chapters IV to VIII), they are already familiar with the idea of strips of various lengths representing numbers. The teacher now introduces the word 'inch' and the children discover by *counting* that there are twelve of them in the foot-stick. They now go on to measure smaller things to the nearest inch, making a record in their books (together with the measurement previously guessed).

Teachers often find that confusion is caused because the lengths chosen for measurement are not an exact number of inches. To introduce fractions of an inch, at this stage, may make matters worse. It is wise, therefore, to select, for the children to measure, objects which are an exact number of inches. If this is not possible, the teacher should prepare cards (sheets of paper will do), on which lines of selected lengths have been drawn. The children are required to guess the lengths of the lines and then measure them (Fig. 73). These cards are very

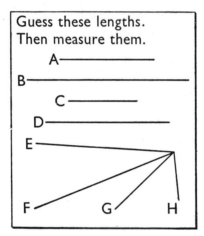

FIGURE 73.—A 'measuring card'. (Each line is a whole number of inches, so that the child does not have to worry about fractions)

convenient because the teacher can keep a list of the answers. Another valuable piece of apparatus, for measuring practice, consists of square and oblong pieces of cardboard (enough to give each child one piece). The cards are each marked by a capital letter and the children have to find the length and breadth of each piece in turn (Fig. 74). They can also find the distance round (we do *not* talk about the perimeter at this stage), by adding. This apparatus should be stored, as it is very useful when the children are introduced to area.

If children co-operate in groups, they can use their rulers to measure longer objects, afterwards writing down lengths in feet and inches. For example, they write: 'Length of desk = 2 feet 6 inches.' Three children working together and using rulers marked in inches may write down the length as '30 inches'. In

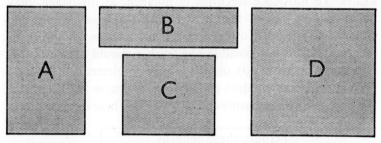

FIGURE 74.—Square and oblong cards, for measurements in inches

this way they begin to see, through experience, the relationship between two units of length-measurement, and to learn how to change one unit into another.

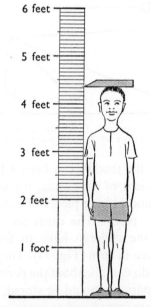

FIGURE 75.—A wall scale, marked in feet and inches. (Children find their heights to the nearest inch)

Children are very interested in the measurement of their own bodies. By working in pairs they can measure each other. The teacher should fasten a strip of marked paper or cardboard to the wall at a convenient height, so that the children may read off each other's height to the nearest inch (Fig. 75). The information should be kept in each child's personal book and added to as he grows older* (Fig. 76). The measurements may include, also, the length of the child's foot, and span of his hand, the distance from the finger-tip to finger-tip with arms stretched out sideways, the distance from the tip of the nose to the finger-tip of one arm extended sideways, the distance from the elbow to

FIGURE 76.—The child's record of his height (and other measurements)

the tip of the finger, the length of an ordinary step, the length of a stride, the measurements round the waist and the chest (using a piece of string or rope).

(*e*) *The yard*—When the children begin to measure longer distances, for example the length of a wall, the length of the playground, they find that the foot rule is not very satisfactory: the number of times they have to use it is so big that they forget the total. *This is the time for the teacher to introduce the yard measure.* A yard-stick made of wood (or cane) is shown to the children (Fig. 77(*a*)) and the teacher demonstrates how much more convenient it is for measuring longer distances. The yard-stick is then compared with the foot-stick and found to be three

* This information is very useful later for an introduction to graphs (see page 427).

times as long. It is also compared with the teacher's own stride and found to be about the same.

The children are given practice, as before, in measuring in yards and writing the work down in their books. (Attempts at accurate guessing should be made *before* each measurement.) Later the children find it necessary to measure the 'bit over' by using their foot rulers and perhaps to be even more accurate by measuring to the nearest inch, though this is neither necessary nor desirable for most children at this stage. The more able children may make an entry in their books like this: 'Length of room = 5 yards, 2 feet, 9 inches'; and some may make a folding

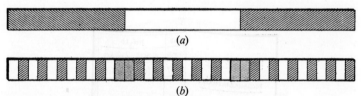

(a)

(b)

FIGURE 77.—Yard-sticks: (a) A stick, marked in feet only. (b) A folding type: three 'foot-sticks' (thin wood, or cardboard, strips) 'hinged' by cloth or soft leather; marked in inches

yard-measure by fastening three of their foot-sticks together with thin leather (Fig. 77(b)).

When longer distances are to be measured (for example, the school playground or compound) the teacher should show how a ball of string (or rope) can be made into a useful measuring instrument by firmly tying or sewing a piece of coloured material (wool or thin string) at every yard along the string. This apparatus also proves valuable for later measuring activities (see Chapter XVIII).

In all this work the children are learning, as before, through activity and experience, to see the relationship between the various units. They can now write down their longer measurements in two ways. For example:

'The length of a wooden pole is 4 yards *or* 12 feet'
'The length of the path is 5 yards and 2 feet *or* 17 feet'
'The width of a stream is 12 feet *or* 4 yards'
'The length of a fallen tree trunk is 37 feet *or* 12 yards and 1 foot'.

The teacher should, throughout, be helping the children to associate this work with the facts in the table of threes just as he associated inches and feet with the early facts in the table of twelves.

C—*Learning to measure weight*

The early work in school is concerned with giving further experience in learning what is meant by the words which indicate the idea of weight. Even in areas where the children do not get the opportunity to see shop-weights, they have heard the grown-ups discuss the weight (heaviness, lightness, etc.) of various things and they themselves have used 'weight' words when carrying things about.

The school has to help the child to make his own judgements about weight, so that he can use this judgement in his everyday life while at school and when he has left school. He is *not* helped to do this by being shown how to work difficult calculations in weight (an ability which is very rarely needed). He is helped by being given plenty of practice in comparing the weights of objects so that he can eventually make fine distinctions between them. It is suggested that this can be done in two ways:

(a) *By handling*—It must be remembered that our usual method of comparing the weight of two objects is to pick them up and use our muscle-sense to tell us which is the heavier or lighter. Children can practise this as a game, with their eyes closed, until they are able to 'feel' accurately even small differences in the weights of two objects. The game can also be played by guessing, and writing down which of a pair of objects is thought to be the heavier, by looking at them before picking them up to prove if the guess is right. Another game which children love to play is a 'pretending' game, in which they come in turn to the front of the class and show by the positions of their hands and arms, and by the looks on their faces, what kind of object they are pretending to carry. For instance one child may stagger around 'holding' a heavy bucket of water in one hand and an empty one in the other hand. Another child may pretend to have a feather on the palm of his hand and to blow it in the air. In this way they gain a greater sensitivity in the use of their muscles, which helps in guessing weight.

(b) *By using scales*—It is easy to make a pair of scales with which children can compare the weights of small objects. Every class room should have this simple piece of apparatus (see page 473 for details for making). With scales the children can 'see' which is the heavier of two objects, without all having to handle them. To begin with, they do not use standard weights. They merely 'weigh' one object (or group of objects) against another. Then they should be introduced to the idea of *'balancing'*. For example, they might put a stone in one scale and then try to 'balance' it with a quantity of sand or soil. They should be encouraged to do this with all kinds of material—grain, beads, clay, wood, etc.

They find that sometimes a very small piece of material (for example, metal) has to be balanced by a considerable quantity of other material such as paper or cardboard. This discovery eventually leads to the idea of standard metal weights, such as those used in shops, which can be used for weighing exact quantities of other materials. It is probably best with children to introduce the *pound** as the first standard measure. It has the advantage of being easy to handle and of being more widely used than ounces in trade and commerce, and therefore is more likely to be met in everyday life.

In towns where shops are plentiful we should try to get several metal pound-weights which the children can feel and handle. In other places we may have to make pound-weights, by using a small bag filled with the proper weight of beans, pebbles, sand, etc., and tied or sewn carefully so that the contents do not fall out when the bag is being used. The bag should be clearly marked with the sign '1 lb.'.†

* The pound, of course, is a British standard measure. In areas where measures are different, the teacher should decide which of his own weights he should introduce first. For example, in areas where the metric system is used, the kilogram may well be the first weight to be introduced.

† The short way of writing down one pound is '1 lb.'. In Roman times the words for this kind of weight were *libra pondo*. The modern word 'pound' comes from the second word of this phrase. The short form 'lb.' comes from the 'l' and the 'b' of the other word, *'libra'*.

The children should get plenty of practice in using these pound-weights with the home-made scales. They should measure out, by balancing, exact pounds of all kinds of materials. They enjoy the activity more if they can put the material in packets (made of paper or leaves), which can later be 'sold' in the class-room 'shop' (see page 111).

In this kind of activity the children soon come to a situation where they need to weigh objects less than a pound in weight. They may be 'selling' sweets or biscuits in the 'shop' and find that they need a smaller weight than the pound. *This is the time for the teacher to introduce the ounce-weights.* These should be of metal, if possible, but small bags (filled with beans, sand, etc.) weighing an ounce, and suitably marked '1 oz.',* may be used instead.

The teacher demonstrates, using the scales, that sixteen of these ounce-weights balance one pound. The children should practise this so as to establish the fact for themselves. All kinds of small objects should be weighed using ounce-weights. Later the children should be given opportunities to weigh objects using both pounds and ounces. They should write the work down in their books, as they did when measuring length. For example:

'The weight of a yam   = 1 pound, 13 ounces'
'The weight of a box of sugar = 2 pounds, 4 ounces'
'The weight of a parcel   = 8 ounces'
'The weight of five bananas   = 1 pound, 2 ounces'.

At this early level the children do little more than gain experience of the measuring of weight. They learn, through using them, about two of the important standard measures of weight, and they are now better able to guess and compare the weights of small articles and objects in their everyday lives. If *spring balances* are used in the school or neighbourhood, they should be demonstrated to the children.

The work described in Chapter XIX goes on to deal with fractions of a pound and the larger units of weight needed in

* The reason for the short form 'oz.' is discussed on page 323.

industry and agriculture: the stone, the quarter, the hundred-weight, and the ton.

D—*Learning to measure capacity*

As part of the play activities which should always be encouraged during the child's early years at school, some time is spent in filling and emptying various receptacles with water, sand and other materials. Grown-ups may think that in doing this the child is wasting his time. In fact he is getting very valuable experience, which later helps him with his ideas of number and in his ability to measure. The school should therefore encourage this kind of activity, by providing buckets, cans, pots, cups, bottles and tins (of all shapes and sizes). A plentiful supply of liquid and dry material should also be available in a place where the children can play (and make a certain amount of mess, without being scolded by the teacher!).

During these activities children often talk to themselves (or to each other) about what they are doing: 'Let us fill it up.' 'How many cups can I fill from this bottle of water?—one, two, three. Oh! there is a drop of water still in the bottle, but not enough for another cupful.' 'Here is some water in this wide jug. It only comes half-way up. Let us pour it into this narrow jug. Look what happens. The water comes right to the top in this one.' 'There is sand in all these tins. Pour it all into the bucket. There is not much, is there?'

From this kind of conversation, it can be seen that the child is making for himself all kinds of judgements about the measurement of quantities. He can use these judgements for an immediate purpose when he 'buys' from the class-room 'shop'. He may ask, for example, for some food which is served by the tin-ful. He soon comes to see the difference between 'heaped' and 'level' measures. The 'heaped' tin of food contains more than the one which is just full to the top of the tin. He must pay more for it, as the shop-keeper asks for a higher price.

It is in shopping activities that the children come to realize that it is better to have a standard measure of capacity (or a number of standards). They begin to find that they cannot rely on getting the same quantity of liquid, for example, if they or the 'shop-keeper' use a different size of tin each time a purchase is made. Moreover, they find that they cannot rely on the evidence of their eyes in this matter. A tall narrow jar is sometimes found to hold less than a wide short bowl.

To help in this difficulty, the teacher introduces the use of a standard-size tin or jug which, when full, holds exactly a pint of liquid.* If it is not possible to get several pint measures, any suitable size of container is satisfactory, provided the level, to which a pint of liquid reaches, is marked clearly inside the container (and if possible outside also). The container should also be clearly marked with the words 'One pint'.

The children are now encouraged to continue their experiments so that they can tell how many pints are required to fill larger containers. They are now '*measuring capacity*', using a standard measure (the pint), just as they were previously 'measuring length' by using a standard length (the foot).

At a suitable time the teacher should get the children to fill a container which holds two pints. This is labelled or marked as before with the words 'One quart', and this is also used as a standard measure. Later a tin or some other container is found which holds eight of the pint measures (or four of the quart measures) and this is labelled with the words 'One gallon'. This is a standard used for measuring larger quantities of liquid. The children in some areas may be familiar with tins or drums labelled, for example: 'Kerosene, 4 gallons', 'Petrol, 30 gallons', etc. These children have plenty of opportunity for experimenting with gallons and for estimating larger amounts of liquid. For example, they may have a four-gallon tin and fill it with water, using a pint or a quart measure.

In these sections on measuring, emphasis has been placed again, not on calculation, but upon the importance of children learning from their own experience about the need for standard measures and about the relationships which exist between these

---

* Again the British unit is used as an example. *Teachers must use their own local units.*

units. In Chapter XX the work extends to the ability to change the units quickly from one to another and so work out 'problems' in which these units are used.

E—*Learning to measure time*

Though time is something which is measured in the same way all over the world, it is found that in some areas the grown-ups at home do not need to measure time accurately. It seems that it is sufficient for them to know the approximate times of sunrise and sunset, so that they can arrange to make safe journeys during daylight. They also need to know the approximate time for the onset of the dry and rainy seasons so that sowing and harvesting can be prepared for. In some areas near the sea and in tidal rivers it becomes necessary to know something about the motions of the moon and the time of tides in order to go out in boats and catch fish.

In other areas, of course, people's lives (particularly in towns) are governed by the need to keep to a strict time-table. They have to be at work at a particular time. They have to do their business by meeting other people at a particular time. They must listen to the radio at certain times if they want to hear particular news-items or programmes. They must know exactly about the days, weeks and months of the year so as to plan their business and pleasure for the future. They cannot do this accurately by relying on the weather or changes in the moon.

But in almost every area the school-child is governed by a routine which means that he must have a good understanding of time, perhaps more than the grown-ups in his own area. He must eventually learn to 'tell the time', so that he can be punctual in his arrival and departure. He must be able to read time-tables, particularly the school time-table. He must know the times of all the regular happenings of the school day, and wants to know about the times and dates of special days and school holidays.

It is suggested that the early work in learning to 'tell the time' and in learning about days, weeks, months, etc., should go on together.

(1) Telling the time

The first approach to telling the time should come through an awareness of the times of regular happenings throughout the school day, linked with observation of the school clock. Times for arriving and going home, meal-times, playtimes, times for particular 'subjects', are written on a card (Fig. 78). The clock-faces and positions of the hands* at various times are discussed with the children, and the card is hung on the wall for reference. Alternatively one clock-face model, with movable hands, is put

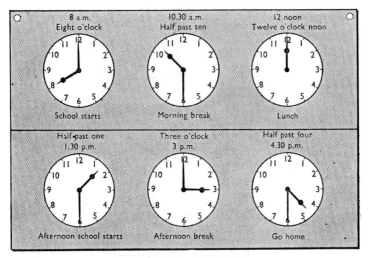

FIGURE 78.—A 'time-card': first steps in learning to 'tell the time'

in a suitable place: the children each day take turns in moving the hands at various times, and hanging up a card on which the time and the event are written (Fig. 79).

In this early approach to telling the time the child is learning to remember the various positions on the clock-face because the events associated with these times are important to him. Later, the teacher usually finds it necessary to teach the child the meaning of each position on the clock, first using the hour-hand, then the minute-hand, separately.

In Fig. 80 two clock-faces are shown. They are parts of the

* The *hands* of a clock are sometimes called '*fingers*'.

F

same clock-face when put together, but they are introduced separately to the children. First the teacher shows the hour-hand moving right round from twelve to twelve (Fig. 80(*b*)). The children are told that if the minute-hand is at the top (that is, pointing to the twelve) and the hour-hand is at the figure one the time is one o'clock. Similar illustrations are shown for the other hours. Then the children's attention is directed to the other clock-face showing the minute-hand only (Fig. 80(*a*)).

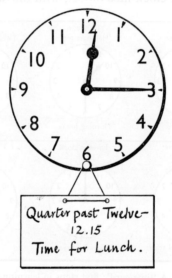

FIGURE 79.—Clock-face with movable hands. (At suitable times a child moves the hands and hangs up the proper card)

They are shown the minute-divisions on the right of the circle (there are thirty of them). The hand is pointed in turn to the positions '5 minutes past', '10 minutes past', '15 minutes past' (or 'quarter past'), '20 minutes past', '25 minutes past, '30 minutes past' (or 'half past'). The children are given practice in recognizing these positions on the right of the circle, which are indicated by the word 'PAST', that is 'past the hour'. When the teacher is satisfied that the children know these positions, he fixes on the small clock-face with the hour-hand, and gives the children practice in recognizing the time when both hands are present. He limits the position of the minute-hand to the *right* of the face only.

Next, the small clock-face, with the hour-hand, is again detached, and the children's attention is drawn to the positions on the left of the larger clock-face. The minute-hand is placed at '5 minutes to', and the children are asked: 'How many *minutes to* the *o'clock* mark at the top?' The children count the five minute-divisions. In the same way the positions of '10 minutes to', '15 minutes to' (or 'quarter to'), '20 minutes to', and '25 minutes to' are demonstrated separately, and the children

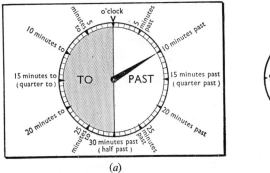

(a)

(b)

FIGURE 80.—The model clock-face, with separable parts, for learning 'to tell the time'. (a) The minute-hand and face (the 'Past' half is dealt with, then the 'To' half separately, in the early stages). (b) The hour-hand and face

(For description of apparatus, see page 474)

are given practice in quick recognition. The two clock-faces are again fixed together, so that the children can get practice in recognizing the time when both hands are present, but the position of the minute-hand to the *left* side only.

This method of dealing with the two hands separately, before dealing with both together, helps the children to get over the confusion which they feel when they hear a grown-up say, for example: 'Ten minutes past eight' when the minute-hand (which is the longer!) clearly points to the figure two.

The teacher should allow the children to see the workings of a clock if possible, and should show how the small hour-hand travels only a short distance while the larger minute-hand is going the full circle.*

It is also wise to show children later that some clocks have Roman numerals instead of the usual Arabic figures (see Fig. 81).

(2) Days, weeks, months, etc.

Time which is not measured by the clock is best approached through the school calendar, and through the simple diaries and

FIGURE 81.—The clock-face with Roman numerals

records kept by the children themselves. These relate again to events which are important to them and therefore worth remembering.

(a) *Class diaries.* These are filled in each day by a different group of children in turn. The group meets to discuss what is the important news of the day (referring often to future events), and one of the group is asked to write it. Another of the group makes a suitable drawing and colours it. This diary (Fig. 82(a)) is kept on display so that the whole class may read it.

(b) *Weather diaries.* These are also kept for and by the whole class. With young children they are simple and only contain a little information (Fig. 82(b)). Older children can use them for geographical as well as arithmetical information.

(c) *Personal diaries.* These are mainly simple drawings which bring in a reference to time and give the children an opportunity to record how they spend their days and weeks (Fig. 82(c)).

(d) *Time graphs.* These are simple graphs which can be filled in by individual children once a week. For example, the height of a

* The relative motion of minute- and hour-hands can be shown by using the cog-wheel mechanism from an old clock.

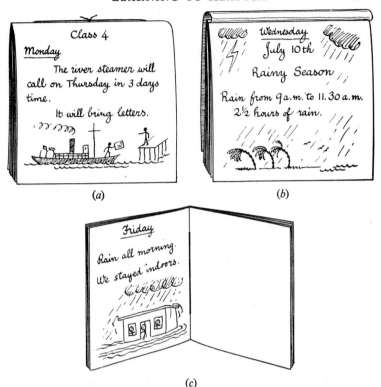

FIGURE 82.—Some 'time' records: (a) A class diary. (b) A weather diary.
(c) A personal diary

plant is marked on a sheet of cardboard, which is moved sideways each week to make a graph showing rate of growth (Fig. 83).

In this chapter a method of introducing children to learning to tell the time is described. It is shown how they may be given

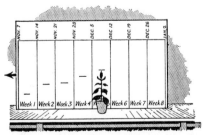

FIGURE 83.—Making a simple 'time graph' (to show the weekly increase in height of a growing plant)

activities in which they are learning through their daily experience the names of the days of each week, the number of days and weeks in each month, and the names of the months. The work in Chapter XXI shows how they go on later to extend these activities so that they see the relationships between all the units of time (seconds, minutes, hours, days, weeks, months, year). These time facts are then learned till they know them perfectly. They then use these facts in making calculations about time, reading travel time-tables, and solving simple 'problems' dealing with time.

SOMETHING TO THINK ABOUT—2

(*Addition*)

We grown-ups cannot easily remember how we ourselves learned to add. We did it so long ago, and since
then have had many other experiences, which have
tended to make our memories imperfect and unreliable.
Many of us, in any case, cannot give, in detail, the
stages by which we ourselves learned. We are inclined
to think 'it just happened'. Often it does 'just happen'
for the more intelligent child: he learns without being
taught. In general, teachers belong to the more intelligent section of the population, and this very fact makes
it more difficult to understand the problems our less
intelligent children find in learning. *We* understand—
why cannot *they*? How can we look at the addition process with the mind of a child, particularly the child of
average intelligence?

One of the chief difficulties which young children meet
in the addition process is the 'carrying' of numbers
from the units-column to the tens-column, etc., as in the
example shown. If children are to understand
what they are doing in a sum like this, they must
understand how our number system is arranged,
namely:—

$$\begin{array}{r} 54\; + \\ 28 \\ \hline 82 \end{array}$$

(*a*) It is based upon the numbers of our ten fingers
(or toes).

(*b*) We have a separate symbol for all the numbers
from nought to nine, that is:

$$0 \quad 1 \quad 2 \quad 3 \quad 4 \quad 5 \quad 6 \quad 7 \quad 8 \quad 9.$$

For writing down numbers greater than nine we have no
new figures but we make use of the figures we already
have. For example, if we want to write down the number
ten in figures we write 10, using the one (1) and the

nought (0). The *position* (or *place*) of the '1' means that it is different from one unit. Similarly, for the next higher numbers, we write 11 (1 ten and 1), 12 (1 ten and 2), 13 (1 ten and 3) ... 19 (1 ten and 9); 20 (2 tens), 21 (2 tens and 1) ... 99 (9 tens and 9). We then come to 10 tens. We call this a hundred and write it down as 100, the *new position* (*place*) of the '1' being used to show its new value.

These ideas are difficult for many children to grasp. Can we, as teachers, appreciate their difficulties?

Imagine you are a member of a race of people with only eight fingers and have no thumbs, so that your hands look like those in Fig. 84.

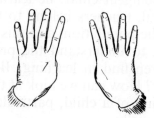

FIGURE 84.—Imaginary hands (without thumbs) as the basis of a number system

When you begin your number learning you learn to count on your fingers like this:

'Aye, Bee, See, Dee, Ee, Eff, Gee, Aitch.'

You then represent the numbers from *Aye* to *Gee* by the figures *1, 2, 3, 4, 5, 6, 7*, and also get to know the symbol for nought (*0*). For *Aitch* there is no new single figure (just as there is no single figure for ten in the number system based on ten fingers). We represent *Aitch* by using the one and the nought again and write it as *10*.

Set down in the form of a chart the system appears as in Fig. 85. For numbers above *Aitch* (*10*) you have number names and figures like this:

Aitch-Aye	*Aitch-Bee*	*Aitch-See*	...	*Aitch-Gee*
11	*12*	*13*		*17*

Then:

    Bee-Aitch   *Bee-Aitch-Aye* ... *Bee-Aitch-Gee*
      20   *21*   *27*

    etc., etc;

up to:

    Gee-Aitch   *Gee-Aitch-Aye* ... *Gee-Aitch-Gee.*
      70   *71*   *77*

Aitch-Aitch, the next number, is represented by *100*.

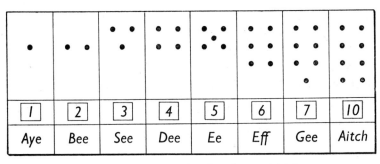

FIGURE 85.—A number-chart based on an 'eight' system

    Now, counting on your fingers, as children do, try to do these sums,* remembering that you only have *Aitch* fingers.

Units	*Units*	*Aitches*	*Units*	*Aitches*	*Units*	*Aitches*	*Units*
1 +	*4* +		*5* +		*4* +		*6* +
2	*2*		*3*		*6*		*6*
—	—		—		—		—
—	—		—		—		—

    Eventually, you realize that, if you want to avoid using your fingers, or counting by dots, you *must know* the addition number-facts; for example:

      $6 + 7 =$ *15*   in this system
    (*Eff* + *Gee* = *Aitch-Ee*)

* The answers, in this system, are:
    3 (See), 6 (Eff), 10 (Aitch), 12 (Aitch-Bee), 14 (Aitch-Dee).

Now try these examples:*

AU	AU	AU	AU
16 +	25 +	37 +	36 +
12	23	25	67
26	17	61	47

The first is worked like this. Starting with the *Units*. *Eff* and *Bee* make *Aitch* (*6 + 2 = 10*). And *Eff* makes *Aitch-Eff* (*10 + 6 = 16*). Put down the '*6*' in the *Units*-column of the answer and carry the '*1*' into the *Aitch*-column. Now deal with the *Aitch*-column, etc.

You may now appreciate one of the main problems which some children meet in the addition process, when trying to understand the idea of 'place-value' so that they can 'carry' from one column to another.

* The answers to the four examples are:
  56 (*Ee-Aitch-Eff*); 67 (*Eff-Aitch-Gee*); 145 (*Aitch-Aitch-Dee-Aitch-Ee*);
  174 (*Aitch-Aitch-Gee-Aitch-Dee*).

CHAPTER XI

LEARNING MORE ABOUT ADDITION

Chapter V is concerned with the *early* stages of teaching children the idea of addition. (At that level the children are expected to learn the primary addition facts and to be able to set down and work simple examples of addition.) The work in this chapter assumes that the early stages have been done properly, and is intended to extend the range of the children's experiences so that they have a full and accurate knowledge of the addition process.

At the end of the chapter there is a detailed analysis of the suggested stages and steps which may be followed in the teaching of addition. The teacher may find it helpful to look at this analysis before reading further. He will then be able to see how the various sections of this chapter fit into the general scheme.

A—*The idea of place-value*

The children have already learned to write 10, 11, 12, . . . 20 as number-symbols, but have not thought about the place-value of the figures. They have learned also, for example, that 13 is 10 and 3 more, again without necessarily thinking of place-value.

The stage is now reached when we should introduce the idea that the value of a figure in any number depends upon its position. This idea is not only necessary for full understanding of the addition process, but is invaluable when the child comes to learn about long multiplication, division and decimals.

(*1*) *Extending the children's ability to count*—Before we begin to deal with place-value we should make sure that the children are able to count, *with confidence*, at least up to one hundred. A great deal of the experience in counting comes through the children's own games and through their own love of repetition. But we should also arrange counting activities in school. For example:

(*i*) The children may count round the class, each child saying a number in sequence.

(*ii*) The teacher and children in turn call odd and even numbers of a sequence.

(*iii*) The teacher, during the counting, draws the children's attention to the fact that the numbers group themselves in tens. He shows how the numbers appear to 'start again' after every ten. For example, '. . . 27, 28, 29, 30—now we start again—31, 32, 33, 34 . . .' The children are encouraged to emphasize the last number of each group of ten (that is, 20, 30, 40).

(*iv*) The children count in tens, that is, 'ten, twenty, thirty . . . eighty, ninety, hundred'. Counting in tens is sometimes used by children in games like '*Hide and Seek*' where the 'seeker' covers his eyes and counts aloud in tens up to a hundred in order to give the others time to hide.

(*v*) The children start with a number like six and keep adding a ten, so that they count: 'six, sixteen, twenty-six, thirty-six . . . ninety-six'.

(2) *Helping children to understand our number system*—The children now progress to the writing down *on squared-paper* of the numbers, which they have been counting in tens. The teacher also writes down the numbers on the blackboard and shows the children how they can say these numbers in a different way. They point to the left-hand figures and say: 'One ten, two tens, three tens, four tens . . . nine tens.' From this the children see that the left-hand figure indicates the tens in each number. The teacher then suggests that this left-hand column should have a name. The children write the letter 'T' (to represent 'tens') at the top of the column.

1	0
2	0
3	0
4	0
5	0
6	0
7	0
8	0
9	0

The class now look at a series of numbers such as the one shown here. It is pointed out that 23 (20 and 3) is 2 tens and 3 ones. 24 (20 and 4) is 2 tens and 4 ones. 25 (20 and 5) is 2 tens and 5 ones.

The teacher suggests that a name is needed for the column of ones. The children probably suggest the letter 'O', but it is then pointed out that this may be confused with '0' for nought. Another word

2	3
2	4
2	5
2	6
2	7

which is often used for 'ones' is 'units'* and the column is headed with a letter 'U'.

The next step is to consider numbers like fourteen, fifty-seven, thirty-six, and ask the children how many tens and how many units there are in each number. They write down the numbers, using the tens and units notation.

The apparatus shown in Fig. 86(a) helps children to recognize

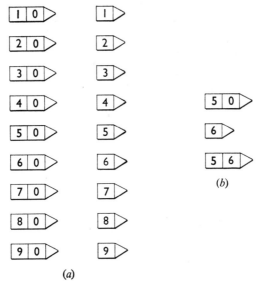

FIGURE 86.—Number-cards to help children understand the structure of numbers

numbers and understand their structure. Each child has nine cards for the tens (numbered ten to ninety) and nine cards for the units (numbered one to nine). The cards can be used in a variety of ways. For example, the teacher calls out a number: say, fifty-six. The children pick out their 'fifty' card and their 'six' card (Fig. 86(b)). The two cards are placed so that the pointers are together, and the children find they have made up the number 'fifty-six'.

This type of card can be used *later* to help children to recognize and write down hundreds and thousands. The activity

* 'Unit' comes from the Latin word (*unus*) meaning 'one'.

is particularly valuable in showing the structure of numbers which include noughts, such as 109, 210, 3007.

B—*The beginnings of addition using 'place-value'*
(*but no 'carrying'*)

(*1*) *Dealing with tens and units*—Since there is no 'carrying' in these early examples, the work consists mainly of the setting down of simple 'sums'. The children use their knowledge of the primary addition facts, their new knowledge of 'place-value', and the tens and units notation. The teacher should refer to the Analysis (page 161, stages D(2) and D(3)) for the detailed steps.

There are a number of important points which should be borne in mind during this work.

(*a*) Squared-paper is of very great help to the children's understanding and accuracy. Teachers are strongly recommended to use it.

(*b*) Standard phrases in working should be insisted upon. In the example given here the standard phrases used in the working may well be:

T.	U.	
4	1	+
2	4	
3	2	
9	7	

'First add the units.
Two and four make six; six and one make seven.
Put the seven in the units column of the answer.
Now add the tens.
Three and two make five; five and four make nine.
Put the nine in the tens column of the answer.
The answer is ninety-seven.'*

The purpose of insisting upon standard phrasing is not to get uniformity, but to make sure that the children are building up the right habits of working. Not only does this help the child to be accurate, but it also helps the teacher to find out when and why some children make mistakes. For example, a child may add the tens column before the units column. Unless the teacher occasionally hears the child using standard phrases he may not be aware of what the child is doing, because the right answer is obtained. Later, when the child gets a wrong answer,

---

* *Not* 'nine seven'.

because 'carrying' is involved, the teacher may not be aware of the true cause of the mistake.

(*c*) The teacher should decide whether the addition should start from the bottom or the top of the column. It is probably better to start from the bottom, as most teachers find that children are then less likely, at the later stage, to forget the 'carrying' figure in the tens and hundreds columns, etc. Whichever way is chosen the children should learn to check their answers by starting the addition from the other end of the column.

(*d*) The teacher should remember, throughout all this work, to give regular practice in examples set as 'problems'. These should be given orally and in written form. The words used should be varied, so as to give children experience of all the phrases which indicate that addition must take place.

(2) *Dealing with hundreds, tens and units*—The work with hundreds follows naturally when the children are confident in dealing with tens and units. The teacher should introduce 'H.T.U.' notation in a similar way to that for 'T.U.', using 'hundred' cards in the apparatus shown in Fig. 86, and should follow the progression of examples given in the Analysis (page 162, stage D(4)).

It is important that some of the examples are 'dictated' by the teacher (not copied from the blackboard or text-book). This gives practice in setting down figures in their correct columns. The children should also be given practice in setting down and working examples given in the following forms:

(*i*) '31 + 102 + 4 + 312 . . .'

(*ii*) 'Find the sum of thirty-one, one hundred and two, four, three hundred and twelve.'

C—'*Carrying*' *in addition*

It is wise to introduce 'carrying' by a revision of previous work, before going on to an actual example of 'carrying'. The new idea then follows naturally from what the children already know.

First, revision practice should be given in adding a column of numbers (each less than ten) where the total is greater than ten.

Much of this is revision of the primary addition facts. The children are asked to give the answer in tens and units, making use of their knowledge of 'place-value'. For example, if they are asked to add 5, 2 and 9, they give the answer as sixteen (1 ten and 6 units). Other examples should be revised where the total is twenty or more (for example, twenty-six) so that the children get the idea of giving the answer as 2 tens and 6 units.

T.	U.
	5 +
	2
	9
1	6

Secondly, the children should look at the figures in the examples they have done in previous weeks. The teacher should remind them that the highest number in any single column is never more than nine. As soon as a total is greater than nine, it has to be written down in 'tens' and 'units'.

(*1*) '*Carrying*' *to the tens-column*—An example of the type shown should be put on the blackboard. The children are asked to work it aloud, using the standard phrases to which they are accustomed. A child begins: 'First add the units. Eight and six make fourteen', and perhaps goes on: 'Put the fourteen in the units-column of the answer.' The teacher quickly carries out this instruction, expecting to be corrected, since the children know that they cannot have a number greater than nine in any one column. They tell him at once that fourteen is 1 ten

T.	U.
5	6 +
	8
6	4
1	

and 4 units; so the 14 is rubbed out, and they discuss what can be done. The teacher asks: 'Where do the 4 units belong?' 'Now where does the 1 ten belong? We must "carry" it to the tens-column but we do not write it in the answer straight away because there are more tens to be added. To make sure that we remember it when we add the tens, let us put it under the line in the tens-column like this.' Then the child goes on: 'Now add the tens. Begin with the one we are carrying. One and five make six. Put the six in the tens-column of the answer. The answer is sixty-four.'

When children understand the idea of 'carrying' they should

be given practice in working the different types of examples set out in the Analysis (page 164, stage E(1)).

(2) *'Carrying' to the hundreds-column*—If children understand the work so far they have little difficulty in extending the 'carrying' idea to the hundreds- and eventually to the thousands-column. The graded steps are set out in the Analysis (page 165, stages E(2) and (3)).

(3) *Helping the less able child to understand 'carrying'*—If there are children who still fail to get the idea of 'carrying', it is suggested that the teacher should go back to the stage where the children play the 'changing game' (Chapter V, page 49). They then realize that the 'change' for numbers which add up to more than nine always includes at least one ten. They may also be helped by using the '20-slide' again, so that they see each ten as a landmark in their adding.

Some teachers find it necessary, with less able children, to demonstrate the process of carrying by the use of an addition-board with bead-bars or number-strips. In the example given (Fig. 87) the child puts down a '6-bead-bar' in the units section and five '10-bead-bars' in the tens section. Then he also represents the eight units, which he is adding, by putting an '8-bead-bar' in the units section as shown. Now he has to find how many beads he has altogether. He begins with the units. The eight and the six bead-bars are changed for a '10-bar' and a '4-bar'. The '10-bar' is put with the tens in their section, and the four is left with the units. He now looks at each column. He finds four beads in the units and puts a '4' number-card in the answer. Then he sees that there are six '10-bead-bars' in the tens-column and puts a '6' number-card in the answer. His answer is then read as 'sixty-four'.

D—*Common errors made by children in the addition process*

We should always try to discover the nature of the errors made by children, so that we can give the most effective help to put matters right at once.

Written tests, *when the results are properly examined*, may show up some of the difficulties; but, whenever possible, the teacher should also listen to individual children working out the process aloud.

It is well to remember that 'prevention is better than cure'. Errors should be few if the original teaching has been satisfactory.

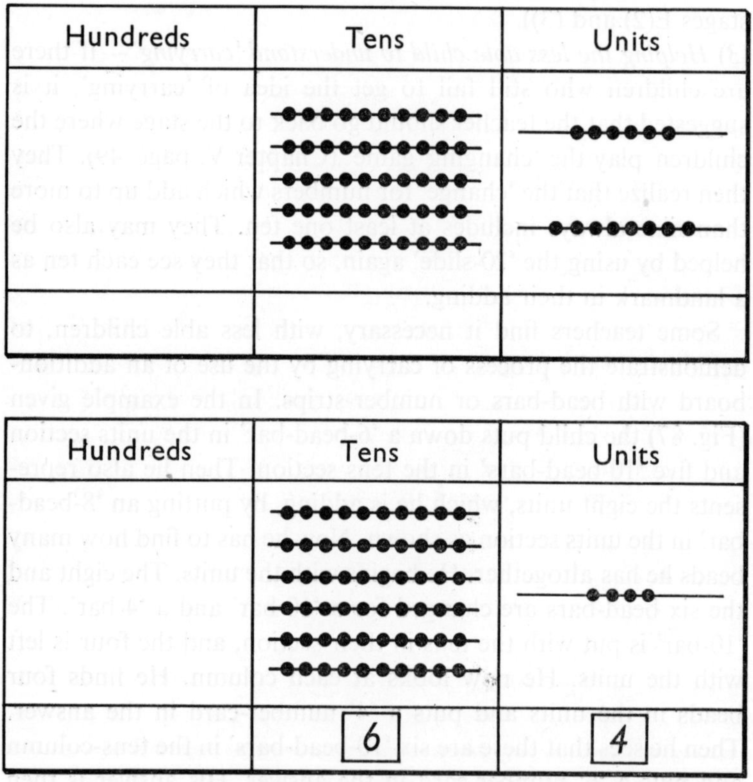

Hundreds	Tens	Units

Hundreds	Tens	Units
		6 4

FIGURE 87.—An 'addition-board' and 'bead-bars', to help children with 'carrying'

Common *errors*, with their probable *causes*, and suggested *ways of putting matters right*, are given here:—

(*a*) Not knowing the addition facts, for example $9 + 8 = 17$. Further work is needed on the facts not known. Practice-cards, flash-cards, and games involving repetition of the facts, should be included.

(b) Loss of place during the working process, due to fatigue and lack of concentration. This, again, is often associated with imperfect knowledge of the facts. The child has to 'count' his addition slowly, laboriously, and sometimes inaccurately, on his fingers. While doing so he loses his place. This is obviously an indication that the child is being pushed on to a stage for which he is not ready. The teacher should take him back to an earlier stage.

The child sometimes loses his place when adding more than two numbers (for example, $4 + 5 + 7$) because he fails to keep the unseen nine $(4 + 5)$ in his mind when he goes on to add the seven.

(c) Faulty setting down, particularly when the addition has been dictated by the teacher, or when the example is given in horizontal form. For instance, $504 + 26 + 169$ may be written down *incorrectly* instead of in the correct form as shown.

This may sometimes be due to carelessness, but more frequently to lack of understanding of place-value. The teacher should revise the idea of place-value and make sure that squared-paper is used.

5	0	4 +
2	6	
1	6	9

Incorrect

H.	T.	U.
5	0	4 +
	2	6
1	6	9

Correct

(d) Confusion and inaccuracy due to the *bad* habit (sometimes even encouraged by teachers) of searching up and down a column for pairs of numbers which make up ten. It is best to have a standard procedure, using standard phrases in working. This gives confidence and promotes accuracy. (Later, the standard procedure can be adjusted to give greater speed. In this example, for instance, children may reach the stage where they can add the units-column

T.	U.	
1	2	+
2	7	
1	3	
1	8	

The child should NOT search for pairs of numbers making up ten.

without having to say the 'steps': 'Eight, (and 3) eleven, (and 7) eighteen, (and 2) twenty.')

(*e*) Mistakes in 'carrying' are various.

(*i*) Forgetting to add the 'carrying' figure. This can be avoided if the child adopts the suggested procedure of starting his adding from the bottom, and of checking by adding downwards from the top.

(*ii*) Omitting to write down the 'carrying' figure.

(*iii*) Putting in the wrong 'carrying' figure. For example, when the total of the units-column is 21 a child puts the '2' in the units column and 'carries' the '1'. (Again this may be due to carelessness, but more likely shows lack of understanding of the process.) The teacher should go back to a practical demonstration of 'carrying'.

$$\begin{array}{cc} \text{T.U.} & \text{T.U.} \\ \frac{2}{1} & \text{instead of} \quad \frac{1}{2} \end{array}$$

(*iv*) Adding the 'carrying' figure twice in the same column.

(*v*) Adding the 'carrying' figure in the tens-column and using it again in the hundreds-column. (This is almost always due to imperfect setting down.) The use of squared-paper, to keep the separate columns clear, is recommended.

(*vi*) Putting in 'carrying' figures when there is nothing to carry. (This is sometimes due to lack of understanding, and sometimes to 'habits' because all the examples given over a long period of practice have happened to require 'carrying'.) Revision should always include examples of varying types. Some should require 'carrying', some should not, so that the children learn to deal with each example according to its particular needs.

E—*Summary of points to remember in teaching addition*

1. A suitably graded scheme of work, such as that described in this chapter, and analysed on pages 158–166, should be followed.
2. The early work should be based on actual addition experiences.
3. At every stage examples in 'problem' form should be included, so that children learn to understand statements and

situations which require them to add and to use the addition process.

4. A perfect knowledge of the primary addition 'facts' is essential.

5. A proper understanding of the addition process is impossible without a good knowledge of 'place-value'.

6. Squared-paper should be used, particularly in the early stages and when new steps are being learned.

7. The use of standard phrases in working helps the children's confidence and accuracy.

8. Careful records should be kept of each child's progress. Mistakes should be noted so that they can be put right before going on to new work.

ANALYSIS 1

Suggested stages and steps in the teaching of addition
(Chapters V and XI)

1. STAGE	2. STEPS	3. THE TEACHER'S PART	4. TYPE OF WORK TO BE DONE BY THE CHILDREN
A. The IDEA of addition—see Chapter V.	(1) Renewing and *enlarging early experiences* of addition.	(1) To arrange for the children many and various activities involving addition.	(1) (a) The use of objects and apparatus: e.g. 'Put those five red books on top of each other and these three green books on top of each other. Now put the green books on top of the red books. How many are there altogether?' (b) The playing of games such as 'skittles' in which addition occurs. (c) The saying of addition rhymes such as: 'Three little cowries and one more Put them together, that makes four.'
	(2) *Learning the language of addition.* (a) Words and phrases meaning 'add'. (b) The addition sign. (c) The equals sign. (d) The recording of addition activities.	(2) To make use of all the words and phrases meaning 'add'. To introduce the '+' sign. To introduce the '=' sign. To show how to record addition by means of number-cards and symbol-cards. To show the method of recording addition on paper; for ex-	(2) The repetition and extension of activities as in (1). The extension of these activities to include: (i) The use of number-cards to represent groups of objects. (ii) The use of number-cards and the '+' and '=' symbol-cards to make a full statement of an addition,

			⌐ ⌐ ┌─┐ + ┌─┐ + ┌─┐ = ┌─┐ /
	then as 2 + 3 ― 5		(iii) The recording of the addition in the form $3 + 4 = 7$ (iv) The recording of the addition in the form 3 + 4 ― 7
B. Introduction to the 'PRIMARY ADDITION FACTS'.	(1) Covering, through *activities*, the addition *facts where the total is not greater than 10. Recording* these facts. (2) Using *further activities, to cover and record all the primary addition facts.*	(1) and (2) To arrange activities in which the primary facts are used. To use all the phrases indicating addition. To make sure that the children record their activities correctly. To include activities to illustrate: 'twin facts', e.g. $2 + 5 = 7$, $5 + 2 = 7$; 'nought facts', e.g. $6 + 0 = 6$, $0 + 6 = 6$. To make use of addition rhymes.	(1) and (2) (a) The working of examples, given orally by the teacher, such as: (i) 'On Monday Peter caught two fish and John seven. How many in all? On Tuesday Peter caught seven fish and John two. How many altogether this time?' (ii) 'Play skittles. Write down how many you knock down with each of the two balls. Find the total.' (iii) 'Find the sum of your age and Tom's age (in years). How old will you each be next year? What will your ages add up to then?' (b) The saying of further addition rhymes.
	(3) *Working out examples, using apparatus if necessary, such as:* 3 + 4 + 9 + 2 7 9 ― ― ―	(3) To set suitable examples for the children to work out (using List A, page 53), to make sure that all the facts are covered.	(3) The working of examples, set by the teacher on the blackboard, such as: 4 + 7 + 8 + 3 8 0 ― ― ―

ANALYSIS 1 (cont.)

1. STAGE	2. STEPS	3. THE TEACHER'S PART	4. TYPE OF WORK TO BE DONE BY THE CHILDREN
C. LEARNING the 'primary addition FACTS'.	(I) *Learning the facts* in carefully selected sets.	(I) To arrange the facts in carefully selected sets. To provide suitable 'practice-cards' and 'flash-cards'. To arrange individual activities with 'practice-cards' and 'flash-cards'. To arrange activities for the whole class. To provide plenty of activities in 'problem' form. To keep a careful record of each child's progress.	(I) (a) The learning of the facts through (i) The use of addition 'practice-cards'. (ii) The use of 'flash-cards' in games. (iii) Helpful class activities. (b) The working of examples in a 'problem' form, such as: (i) "How many days are there in two weeks?" (ii) "John is eight years old. Jack is three years older than John. How old is Jack?"
D. The addition process using the idea of *PLACE-VALUE* (*no 'carrying'*—see Chapter XI.	(I) *Learning the vocabulary and understanding the structure of numbers* up to one hundred. (a) Counting to one hundred in ones and in tens. (b) The idea of 'tens' and 'units'. (c) The use of the 'T' and 'U' notation.	(I) To arrange varied counting activities. To introduce the idea of expressing numbers in 'tens' and 'units', and the use of the symbols 'T' and 'U'. To see that the children set down the numbers correctly, using squared-paper. To make sure that the children say the numbers correctly, e.g. 'fifty-four' *not* 'five four'. To give practice in writing numbers from dictation.	(I) The learning of the names and symbols of numbers up to one hundred and the understanding of the 'T.U.' notation through: (a) Oral counting in 'ones' and 'tens'. (b) The use of apparatus, e.g. $1\,0 + 4 = 1\,4$ $5\,7 = 5\,0 + 7$ (c) The saying and writing of the results of (b) in words, e.g. Fifty-four is five tens and seven units. (d) Writing numbers, from dictation, with the 'T.U.' notation, e.g. 'Fifty-seven' $\begin{array}{cc} T. & U. \\ 5 & 7 \end{array}$

(e) Oral and written work with sequences, e.g.

$10+4=14$
$20+4=24$
$30+4=34$

T.U.	T.U.	T.U.
1 0 +	2 0 +	3 0 +
4	4	4
1 4	2 4	3 4

T.U.	T.U.	T.U.
4 +	4 +	4 +
1 0	2 0	3 0
1 4	2 4	3 4

etc.

---

(2) The working of many examples such as those given in column 2 to illustrate this step.
The working of examples, given in problem form, such as:
'There are 3 cows in one field and 13 cows in another. How many cows are there altogether?'
The working of examples, given orally or in a written form, such as:
'Find the sum of 2, 14 and 3.'

(3) The working of many graded examples such as those given in column 2 to illustrate this step.
The working of examples, given in problem form, such as:
(i) 'There are 25 boys in a class. 4 new boys join them. How many are there in the class now?'

---

(2) and (3). To show the method of setting down and working the examples using the 'T.U.' notation.
To introduce and insist upon the use of standard phrases in working (see page 150 for an example).
To give the children practice in writing down examples from dictation.
To make full use of all the words and phrases which indicate that addition must take place.

---

(2) *Setting down and working out examples, using the 'T.U.' notation and the primary addition facts, where the total is not more than 20*, e.g.

T.U.	T.U.	T.U.
1 2 +	3 +	1 2 +
3	1 2	3
		4
—	—	—

T.U.	T.U.
3 +	2 +
1 2	1 0
4	5
—	—

(3) *Setting down and working out examples, using the T.U. notation and the primary addition facts, where the total is not more than 99.*

ANALYSIS 1 (cont.)

1. Stage	2. Steps	3. The Teacher's Part	4. Type of Work to be done by the Children

D. The addition process (*continued*)	(a) Tens and units in each number, e.g.
	
	T.U. T.U. T.U.
	1 2 + 2 3 + 4 1 +
	2 3 1 2 2 4
	                3 2
	—
	
	(b) Tens and units in one number; units only in the other(s), e.g.
	
	T.U. T.U. T.U. T.U.
	3 2 + 3 + 3 2 + 3 +
	  3 3 2 3 3 2
	               4
	—
	
	(c) Noughts in the units column, e.g.
	
	T.U. T.U. T.U. T.U.
	2 0 + 3 0 + 2 0 + 3 0 +
	1 3 5 0 1 5 4
	          1 4 1 0
	—
	
	(4) *Setting down and working out examples, using the 'H.T.U.' notation* and the primary addition facts, where the *total is not greater than 999*: e.g.
	
	H.T.U. H.T.U. H.T.U.
	1 4 2 + 1 4 2 + 1 4 2 +
	2 4 5 4 5 5
	—
		(4) To arrange counting activities for numbers beyond a hundred. To give practice in expressing numbers in hundreds, tens and units, and in the use of the 'H.T.U.' notation.
		To see that the children say the numbers correctly.
		To give practice in writing numbers from dictation.
			(ii) 'There are twenty blue pencils and thirty-five red pencils in the box. How many altogether?'
			The working of examples, given orally or in a written form, such as:
			(i) Twenty-one plus thirty-seven.
			(ii) $15 + 10 + 20 + 44$.
			
			(4) The learning of the names and symbols of numbers up to a thousand through:
			(a) Oral counting in tens and hundreds.
			(b) The use of apparatus, e.g.
			
			2 0 0 + 7 0 + 5
			= 2 7 5

tation, with the 'H.T.U.' notation,
e.g. 'two hundred and seventy-five':

```
H.T.U.
2 7 5
```

The working of many graded examples, such as those given in column 2 to illustrate this step.

The working of examples given in 'problem' form, e.g. 'John takes 142 steps to school; Tom takes 214; Jack takes 133. Find the total number of steps.'

The working of examples such as:

'Add together 140, 3, 35, 401.'

down and working addition examples using the 'H.T.U.' notation.

To insist upon the correct use of standard phrases in working.

```
1 0 0+     1 0 0+     1 4 0 0+
2 0 0      2 5 0          5 0
————       ————        ————


H.T.U.     H.T.U.     H.T.U.
1 4 2+     1 4 2+     1 4 2+
2 0 5      2 0 5          4 5
3 1 2        1 2           2
————       ————        ————


H.T.U.
1 4 2+
    5
    2
————
```

Note—It will be noticed that the same numbers are used in many of these examples. This has been done deliberately, in order to emphasize the difference between the steps. The teacher, of course, should give varied examples to make use of all the known facts.

ANALYSIS 1 *(cont.)*

1. STAGE	2. STEPS	3. THE TEACHER'S PART	4. TYPE OF WORK TO BE DONE BY THE CHILDREN

E. The IDEA and PROCESS of 'CARRYING' in addition.	(*1*) *Setting down and working out examples which require 'carrying'. Two-figure numbers (with 'carrying' to the 'tens' only)*
	
	(*a*) Two figures in one number; one figure in the other(s),
	
	T.U. T.U.
	1 5 + 8 +
	  6 2 7
	— —
	
	T.U. T.U. T.U.
	 8 + 1 6 +
	2 7 8
	       8
	
	T.U. T.U.
	1 5 + 2 0 +
	  6 7
	  4 5
	— —
	
	(*b*) Two figures in each number, e.g.
	
	T.U. T.U.
	1 5 + 2 7 +
	2 6 3 8
	— —
	
	T.U. T.U. T.U.
	1 5 + 1 4 + 2 8 +
	2 6 3 0 1 7
	3 5 2 8 3 6
	— — —
	
	(*c*) As for (*a*) and (*b*) but with noughts in the units column of the answer, e.g.
	
	T.U. T.U. T.U. T.U.
	2 5 + 1 6 + 3 3 + 1 9 +
	  5 2 4 2 4 2 7
	— 4 3 4 3 3 4
		(*1*) To revise the primary addition facts where the total is greater than ten and to give practice in giving the answer as separate 'tens' and 'units' (e.g. 16 . . . 1 ten and 6 units).
		
		To introduce the idea of 'carrying' in addition.
		To show the method of setting down and working.
		
		To make sure that the children use the standard phrases in working.
		To include examples where the 'carried' number is greater than one.
		To include examples which bring in noughts.
		To include some examples where *no* carrying is required.
			(*1*) The working of many graded examples, such as those given in column 2, to illustrate the step.
			
			The working of examples given in 'problem' form, e.g.
			(*i*) 'Twenty-seven children were each given a banana. Thirty-five were left. How many bananas were there at the start?'
			
			(*ii*) 'John had 14 marks out of 20 for Arithmetic, 26 out of 40 for Geography and 20 out of 30 for History. What were his total marks?'
			
			Examples, given orally or in a written form, such as:
			(*i*) 'Add together, five, thirty-seven and seven.'
			(*ii*) 'Sixty-five plus seventeen.'
			(*iii*) 'Find the sum of all the numbers from 8 to 12.'

examples, such as those given in column 2, to illustrate the step.

The working of examples given in 'problem' form, e.g.

(i) 'There are 156 pages in the first part of a book and 229 pages in the second part. How many pages in the whole book?'

(ii) 'A farmer planted 460 sweet potatoes in one strip of land and 375 in another. How many did he plant altogether?'

(iii) 'In a village there are 124 men, 136 women and 292 children. How many people are there altogether in the village?'

(iv) 'Count 1, 2, 3, . . . as far as you can in one minute. Do this three times. Add up the three numbers.'

Examples, given orally or in a written form, such as:

(i) '7 + 242 + 25 + 309.'

(ii) 'Write down and find the sum of two hundred and thirty-four, seventy-threeand two?'

(iii) 'Find the sum of 27, 209, 394, 402.'

...ens and units with no carrying.

To introduce, and give adequate practice in the steps (a), (b), (c) and (d).

To make sure that the work is set down correctly (squared-paper should be used where necessary).

To introduce new phrases in working as they become necessary.

To include some examples where *no* carrying is necessary.

'carrying'.

Three-figure numbers.

(a) 'Carrying' to the 'tens' only. (Examples included which give a nought in the units-column of the answer), e.g.

```
H.T.U.    H.T.U.    H.T.U.
1 5 2 +   1 5 2 +   1 5 2 +
2 2 9     2 2 9     2 0 8
```

```
H.T.U.    H.T.U.
1 4 6 +     7 +
2 0 9       4 9
1 3 8     1 2 6
```

(b) Carrying to the 'hundreds' only. (Examples included with a nought in the tens column of the answer), e.g.

```
H.T.U.    H.T.U.    H.T.U.
2 6 2 +   2 6 0 +   2 6 2 +
  5 4     3 5 4     3 4 4
```

```
H.T.U.    H.T.U.    H.T.U.
2 6 2 +   2 8 2 +     7 4 +
2 4 5     1 9 4       5 2
1 0 2     3 3 1
```

(c) Carrying to both 'tens' and 'hundreds'. (No noughts in the answer), e.g.

```
H.T.U.    H.T.U.
2 6 7 +   2 6 7 +
  7 7     3 7 4
```

ANALYSIS 1 (cont.)

1. STAGE	2. STEPS	3. THE TEACHER'S PART	4. TYPE OF WORK TO BE DONE BY THE CHILDREN

E. Carrying (continued)	H.T.U. H.T.U.
	2 6 7 + 7 +
	3 7 8 2 9
	1 8 6 2 0 4
	           9 7
	—————
	
	(d) Carrying to both 'tens' and 'hundreds'. (Noughts in the answer.)
	
	H.T.U. H.T.U. H.T.U.
	2 6 7 + 2 6 7 + 2 6 7 +
	7 3 1 3 4 1 3 3
	—————————————
	
	H.T.U. H.T.U.
	6 7 + 2 9 7 +
	1 0 3 1 0 4
	4 3 0 4 9 9
	—————————
	
	(3) Setting down and working out examples which require 'carrying'. Numbers of any size. e.g.
	
	Th.H.T.U. Th.H.T.U.
	2 3 4 5 + 2 4 5 9 +
	1 6 3 4 5 0 3 4
	—————————————
	
	Th.H.T.U.
	5 0 7 2 +
	8 6 8
	   6 0
	—————
		(3) To introduce the method of dealing with thousands. First with no 'carrying', then with 'carrying'.
		
		To extend the work to bigger numbers as the need arises.
		
		To give plenty of practice in setting down and working examples given in words, either orally or in written form.
			(3) The working of graded examples such as those given in column 2, to illustrate the step.
			
			The working of examples given in 'problem' form, e.g. 'After the floods in one area, 1,572 injections against malaria were given on the first day, 5,079 on the second, 12,203 on the third, and 9,000 on the fourth. How many was this altogether?'
			
			Examples, given orally, or in a written form, such as:
			(i) '4,059 + 27 + 309 + 6.'
			(ii) 'Find the sum of four thousand and seven, three hundred and ninety-five, twelve and fifty-seven.'

SOMETHING TO THINK ABOUT—3
(Subtraction)

In the section preceding Chapter XI it is stated that teachers do not find it easy to understand children's difficulties in arithmetic. We have to try to put ourselves, in imagination, in the position of a child. It is suggested that we may find it helpful to do some arithmetic in a different number system from that to which we are accustomed.

The system suggested for our experiment is based on eight fingers. We have new number-names but keep the same figures (Fig. 85, page 145).

In the section preceding Chapter XI you were asked to work out a few simple examples of addition using this new number system. It is suggested that you now try to do the same thing with simple subtraction examples:*

(a)	Units	(b)	Aitches	Units	(c)	Aitches	Units
	6 −		1	7 −		1	0 −
	3		1	2			5
	___		_____	___		_____	___

(d)	Aitches	Units	(e)	Aitches	Units
	1	2 −		3	4
		6		1	7
	_____	___		_____	___

Did you get them all right? You probably found that (a) and (b) were easy. In (c) and (d) you needed a knowledge of the subtraction facts in this particular system: $10 - 5 = 3$; $12 - 6 = 4$. But when you came to (e) you probably found yourself facing the difficulty met

* The *answers* are: (a) 3 (*See*); (b) 5 (*Ee*); (c) 3 (*See*); (d) 4 (*Dee*); (e) 15 (*Aitch-Ee*).

by many children in subtraction. You had to think very clearly about what you were doing, because you had to find a way of dealing with the situation arising *when the number of units in the top line is smaller than the number of units in the bottom line.*

You may find it interesting and instructive to consider in detail how you yourself dealt with this difficulty. What methods did you use? What methods would you use in teaching this step in subtraction to children to give them a full understanding?

The following chapter discusses in detail the ways of helping children to deal with the situation.

CHAPTER XII

LEARNING MORE ABOUT SUBTRACTION

The first approach to subtraction is discussed in Chapter VI. First, children have subtraction activities, using apparatus and games. They then learn how to write down these practical experiences of subtraction in figures. Later they learn the primary subtraction 'facts' so that they can state each one correctly and without hesitation.

During this early work children are continually meeting and using all the words and phrases which indicate that subtraction must take place. We must try to make sure that the children fully understand the meaning of words and phrases such as: 'take away', 'take from', 'subtract', 'how many more?', 'what is the difference?', 'what must I add to?', 'how many are left?'

These beginnings are a necessary basis for extending their knowledge of the subtraction process and dealing with larger numbers.

A—*The simple subtraction process*

After the children have learned the primary subtraction facts, they can proceed to examples like this, where they deal with bigger numbers. This type of example is not difficult because the children are already familiar, from their work in *addition*, with the idea of place-value, and know that they can deal with the units and tens in turn. If they can take the 2 from the 9 in the units-column and the 5 from the 6 in the tens-column they arrive at the correct answer.

T.	U.	
6	9	—
5	2	

Because this type of example is easy, this is the stage at which we should begin to insist upon a standard method of working. It helps the children to become more confident and more accurate, and, provided that the same methods are used throughout

G

the school, they find less difficulty when they are introduced to more complicated examples.

Before the children begin to work any example aloud, they should be encouraged to think of how it may be stated in words. For instance the example given here may be stated by the child in one of a variety of ways:

'Take fifty-two from sixty-nine.'
'How much bigger is sixty-nine than fifty-two?'
'What is the difference between fifty-two and sixty-nine?'

They then go on to work the example.

Here are two possible methods:

(a) (Using the method of 'subtracting upwards'.)

'First deal with the *units*.
Two from nine leaves seven.
Put the "7" in the units-column of the answer.
Now deal with the *tens*.
Five from six leaves one.
Put the "1" in the tens-column of the answer.
The answer is seventeen.'

(b) (Using the method of 'subtracting downwards'.)

'First deal with the *units*.
Nine, take away two leaves seven.
Put the "7" in the units-column of the answer.
Now deal with the *tens*.
Six, take away five leaves one.
Put the "1" in the tens-column of the answer.
The answer is seventeen.'

The children can easily go on to deal with hundreds, tens and units in subtraction examples of this nature. The detailed steps for teaching are given in Analysis 2 (page 182, stage D).

B—*The next stages in the subtraction process**

Now let us look at an example where, in the units-column, the figure (eight) in the bottom line is greater than the figure (four)

---

* *Note*—Some teachers will realize that this is the stage in subtraction where the words 'borrowing' and 'paying back' are commonly used. In this book these words are *not* used, because *they do not describe what happens* in subtraction. As will be seen, *neither* 'borrowing' *nor* 'paying back' occurs at any time.

in the top line. We immediately find that we are in difficulty because we cannot take eight from four. Some method of dealing with this situation must be found.

There are several different methods in use at the present time, but, after many years of argument and research by teachers, there is still lack of agreement as to the *best* method. It appears that all these methods, if taught properly, give good results. What is *most important* is: that the teachers within a school, or better still within a

	T.	U.	
	3	4	−
	1	8	

group of schools, should agree upon which method they are going to use. As a child moves from class to class within a school, or from school to school within an area, he should not be faced with the very great difficulty of having to change from one method of subtraction to another. This applies particularly to the less able child.

If, as sometimes happens, a child moves into an area where a different method of subtraction is used, *he should be allowed to keep to his own method*, provided that he can use it successfully.

This emphasizes the need for the teacher to know and understand all the more common methods. He is then able not only to teach the standard method for his school but also to help children who have already learned to use another method.

It is proposed here to discuss in detail the two methods most commonly in use.

(1) Subtraction by the method known as 'decomposition'

The method of 'decomposition'* appeals to many teachers because the idea is easy for children to understand. It follows very simply from the early work in subtraction and can be demonstrated easily.

(a) The idea explained—Let us consider the example already given. We cannot take the eight units from the four units. We can, however, make

T.	U.			T.	U.	
3	4	−		2	14	−
1	8			1	8	

use of one of the three tens and think of it as ten units, thus

* The children do not have to learn this word.

giving a total of fourteen units, as shown. The eight units can now be taken from the fourteen units to leave six units. The '6' is put down in the units-column of the answer. We now deal with the tens: one from two leaves one. The '1' is put down in the tens-column of the answer. The answer is sixteen. The completed example is as shown on the right.

T.	U.
2	14
3	4 —
1	8
1	6

Note—Some teachers prefer not to add the ten units to the four but to write it above the four. The eight is subtracted from the ten, leaving two. This is then added to the four to give six. The completed example is set down as shown here. It is claimed that this method helps the children because it uses fewer subtraction facts. It is also more natural when dealing with the subtraction of money and other measures.

T.	U.
2	10
3	4 —
1	8
1	6

The same idea is used when dealing with bigger numbers.

In this example we cannot take the seven from the two in the tens-column. We have to make use of one of the five hundreds and think of it as ten tens, making twelve tens in all. The completed example then looks as in (a) below.

H.	T.	U.
5	2	8 —
2	7	4

This breaking down (or 'decomposing') of the numbers in the hundreds- and tens-columns gives this method its name.

Here we must notice how the idea of 'decomposition' is applied to yet another example. See (b) below.

H.	T.	U.
4	12	
5	2	8 —
2	7	4
2	5	4

(a)

H.	T.	U.
5	0	2 —
3	5	7

(b)

We cannot take the seven units from the two units. We look
to the tens-column but find there are no tens
for us to use. In order to get some tens we
make use of one of the five hundreds and
think of it as ten tens. We can now start
again and make use of one of the ten tens.

The completed example looks as shown on
the right.

H.	T.	U.
4	9 ~~10~~	12
5	0	2 −
3	5	7
1	4	5

(*b*) *Teaching the idea of 'decomposition' to children*—We put the
example on the blackboard and ask a child to begin working
aloud. He begins with the units-column and
finds he cannot take eight from four. The working is stopped and we ask what the 3 and the 4
stand for in the number 34—'Three tens and
four units'. This can be made more vivid by
representing the 34 as 3 bundles of ten sticks
and 4 single sticks (Fig. 88). The teacher then
goes on: 'Here are thirty-four sticks. We have to

T.	U.
3	4 −
1	8

take eighteen away and find how many are left. Let us take
eight away to start with. There are not enough single sticks to
do this. We must use one of the bundles of
ten. Untie the bundle. We now have fourteen
single sticks. It is easy to take eight away
now. There are six left. Now let us deal
with the bundles of tens. We only have two
bundles of ten because we used one bundle.
Now we have to take one ten away, leaving
us with one ten. Altogether we have one ten
and six single sticks left, so that our answer
is sixteen.

'Now let us work out the example on the
blackboard without using apparatus.' (We are thus introducing
our 'standard phrasing'.)

'First deal with the *units*.
I cannot take eight from four:

3 bundles of ten sticks	4 single sticks
┼┼┼┼┼┼	‖‖
┼┼┼┼┼┼	
┼┼┼┼┼┼	

FIGURE   88. —
Teaching the idea
of 'decomposition'
in the subtraction
process

So I use one of the three tens (leaving two tens*), and think
of it as ten units.
Now I have fourteen units.
Eight from fourteen leave six.
Put the "6" in the units-column of the answer.
Now deal with the *tens*.
One from two leaves one.
Put the "1" in the tens-column of the answer.
The answer is sixteen.'

T.	U.
2	14
3	4 —
1	8
1	6

This type of demonstration and explanation
can be extended to deal with hundreds (ten
bundles of ten), and thousands *if necessary*. With most children, however, once the idea is understood with tens and units,
further practical demonstration may be unnecessary. It is essential, however, that the children should follow a carefully graded
scheme of work in dealing with bigger numbers.

These stages and steps in teaching are suggested in Analysis 2,
pages 180–5.

(2) *Subtraction by the method known as 'equal additions'*
This method does not follow as naturally from the earlier work
as does that of 'decomposition'. But it is found that, if the
method is explained carefully, children can understand it and
can use it accurately.

(*a*) *The idea explained*—The method is based on the idea that
the difference between two quantities is unchanged if equal
quantities are added to both. For example:

(*i*) Starting with $17 - 8 = 9$, it follows that $27 - 18 = 9$ and
$37 - 28 = 9$, etc.

---

* *Note*—It is good for a child, when learning a new process, to be
allowed to use 'helping' figures, and to change figures where necessary.
Though this sometimes leads to untidy work, it is valuable as an aid to
understanding of the process and so makes the child's work more accurate.

There is no particular method which is widely accepted for this 'crossing
out' and use of 'helping' figures. Teachers should use their own judgement
in the matter. The method chosen in this book is that which the authors
and editor consider to be as neat and clear as is possible in print.

We should encourage children to stop using 'helping figures' when the
process is well known and greater speed is required.

(*ii*) The difference between the heights of two children is unchanged if they both stand on boxes of the same height.
(*iii*) The difference between the ages of two children remains the same because their ages both increase equally.

The equal quantities added to the two original quantities need not both be in the same units. For example, it does not matter whether we add twelve months to one age and one year to the other, or whether we add ten units to one number and one ten to the other. In each case the difference remains the same.

To illustrate the use of this idea in subtraction let us look at the same example as before.

We cannot take eight units from four units. We therefore add ten units to the top line to make it three tens and fourteen units. This enables us to deal with the units. Eight from fourteen leaves six.

T.	U.
3	4 —
1	8

Now in order to keep the difference between the top and bottom lines the same, we must add ten to the bottom line. This ten must go to the tens-column (since we have finished dealing with the units) making two tens in the bottom line. Now we can deal with the tens. Two from three leaves one. The answer is sixteen.

The completed example* looks like (*a*) on the right.

T.	U.
	14
3	4 —
1²	8
1	6

(*a*)

Now let us look at another example, (*b*) on the right.

H.	T.	U.
5	0	1 —
3	5	7

(*b*)

---

* *Note*—Some teachers prefer not to add the ten to the four units but to write it above the '4'. The '8' is then subtracted from the '10' leaving two. This is then added to the '4' to give six.
The completed example is set down as shown on the right:
It is claimed that this method helps the children because it uses fewer subtraction facts. It is also more natural when dealing with the subtraction of money and other measures.

T.	U.
	10
3	4 —
1²	8
1	6

We cannot take seven units from one unit. Add ten units to the one unit to make eleven units and at the same time add one ten to the five tens to make six tens. Seven units from eleven units leaves four units. Now deal with the tens. We cannot take the six tens from the nought tens. Add ten tens to the nought tens to give ten tens and, at the same time, add one hundred to the three hundreds to give four hundreds. Six tens from ten tens leaves four tens. Finally, four hundreds from five hundreds leaves one hundred, giving an answer of one hundred and forty-four. The completed example is shown here.

	H.	T.	U.
		10	11
	5	0	1	—
	3⁴	5⁶	7
	1	4	4

(*b*) *Teaching the idea of 'equal additions' to children*—The children must first be introduced to the idea that if two quantities are increased by the same amount then the difference between them remains the same. This idea should be demonstrated in as many ways as possible. For example:

(*i*) How many cows (or pigs, hens, etc.) do the familes of two boys possess? How many has one more than the other? If three cows were given to each of the two families, how many would one family then have more than the other?

(*ii*) Examples like this are worked on the blackboard:

```
              T.U.                            T.U.
                5 —          add ten to       1 5
                3            both numbers      1 3 —
               ___                            ___
                2                               2

              T.U.                            T.U.
add ten to      2 5 —        add ten to       3 5 —
both numbers    2 3          both numbers     3 3
               ___                            ___
                2                               2     etc.
```

The difference is always the same.

Once this idea of 'equal additions' is understood, we can work an example like this with the children. They begin: 'Eight from four', and find that they cannot do it. We then refer to the idea discussed previously and say: 'If we add ten to the top line and ten to the bottom line we get the same answer. Let us first add ten units to the four units making fourteen units. We can now take the eight away, leaving six. But we must remember also to add ten to the bottom number. This ten must go to the tens-column (since we have finished with the units) making two tens in all. Now we deal with the tens. Two from three leaves one. The answer is sixteen.'

T.	U.
	14
3	4 —
1²	8
1	6

After working several similar examples with the children we should gradually get them to use standard phrases in working and a standard method of setting the subtraction down. So as to prevent them forgetting the addition of the ten to the bottom number, we should insist that it be done *at the same time* as the addition of the ten units in the top line.

The standard working may then be:

'First deal with the *units*.
I cannot take eight from four:
So I add ten to the four (making fourteen), and add one ten to the ten in the bottom line (making two tens).
Eight from fourteen leaves six.
Put the "6" in the units-column of the answer.
Now deal with the *tens*.
Two from three leaves one.
Put the "1" down in the tens-column of the answer.
The answer is sixteen.'

The work can then be extended gradually to examples which use the principle of 'equal additions' in the tens- and hundreds-columns.

Note—Analysis 2 of steps in teaching (page 180) is based (from stage D onwards) on the method of 'decomposition', but the graded examples quoted are also typical of those that may be used at each stage in teaching subtraction by the method of 'equal additions'.

C—*Common errors made by children in the subtraction process*
We should always try to discover the nature of the errors made by the children, so that we can give the most effective help to put matters right at once.

Written tests, when the results are properly examined, may show up some of the difficulties; but, whenever possible, the teacher should also listen to individual children working out the process aloud.

It is well to remember that 'prevention is better than cure'. Errors should be few if the original teaching has been satisfactory.

Common *errors*, with their probable *causes*, and suggested *ways of putting matters right*, are given here:—

(*a*) Failure to remember the subtraction facts, particularly those in which a nought appears. Further work is needed on the facts not known.

We should be aware that *some children understand the subtraction process perfectly, but sometimes get their work wrong because they do not know the subtraction facts.*

(*b*) Forgetting to make the necessary change in the tens-column after a ten has been added in the units-column. This may be due to:

(*i*) Carelessness.
(*ii*) Fatigue and lack of concentration arising from an imperfect knowledge of the subtraction 'facts'. So much effort has been used in working out the 'facts' that the child loses his place.
(*iii*) Lack of proper understanding of the process.

This may mean that the work is too difficult, and that the child is being pushed on to a stage for which he is not ready. We should take him back to an earlier stage.

(*c*) Faulty setting down of the example, particularly when it has been stated in problem form or when it has been dictated by the teacher.

(*d*) Taking the figures in the top line from those in the bottom line. This may be due to inaccurate teaching in the early stages, when the children have been told, *wrongly*, to take the smaller number from the larger number. The error should not arise if standard methods of working are insisted upon from the start.

(*e*) Discouraging the use of 'helping figures' too soon. It is wise to remember that accuracy in subtraction is more important than speed. Some children need any help they can get, particularly in the early stages.

D—*Summary of points to remember in teaching subtraction*

1. A suitable graded scheme of work (such as that given on pages 180–5) should be followed.
2. The early work should be based on actual subtraction experiences.
3. At every stage examples in 'problem' form should be included, so that children learn to understand statements which require them to subtract.
4. A perfect knowledge of the primary subtraction facts is essential.
5. Squared-paper should be used, particularly when new steps are being learned.
6. Careful records should be kept of each child's progress and mistakes.
7. The teachers in a school (or area) should get together and decide upon which method of subtraction and which standard phrases in working they are going to use. They should then keep strictly to them.

ANALYSIS 2

Suggested stages and steps in the teaching of subtraction
(see Chapters VI and XII)

1. STAGE	2. STEPS	3. THE TEACHER'S PART	4. TYPE OF WORK TO BE DONE BY THE CHILDREN
A. The IDEA of subtraction—see Chapter VI.	(1) Renewing and enlarging *early experiences*.	(1) To arrange for the children *many and various activities* involving subtraction.	(1) (a) The use of objects and apparatus, e.g. 'Count these coloured pencils. Pick out the red ones and put them in the box. Count how many pencils are left.' (b) The playing of games, such as 'skittles', in which subtraction occurs. (c) The saying of subtraction rhymes, such as 'Ten green bottles hanging on a wall'.
	(2) Learning *the language of subtraction*. (a) Words and phrases meaning 'subtract'. (b) The subtraction sign. (c) The recording of subtraction activities.	(2) To make use of all the words and phrases indicating subtraction. To introduce the '−' sign and show how to record subtraction by means of number-cards and symbol-cards. To show the method of recording subtraction on paper: first as $8 - 3 = 5$; then as $\begin{array}{r} 8 \\ -\ 3 \\ \hline 5 \end{array}$	(2) The repetition and extension of activities as in (1). The extension of these activities to include: (i) The use of number-cards and the '−', and '=' symbol-cards to make a full statement of a subtraction: e.g. $\boxed{9} - \boxed{5} = \boxed{4}$ (ii) The recording of the subtraction in the form of $9 - 5 = 4$. (iii) The recording of the subtraction in the form $\begin{array}{r} 9 \\ -\ 5 \\ \hline 4 \end{array}$

PRIMARY SUBTRACTION FACTS'.	subtraction facts, where the subtraction is *from ten or less*. *Recording* these facts. (2) Using further activities *to cover and record ALL the primary subtraction facts.*	which the primary facts are used. To use all the phrases indicating subtraction. To make sure that the children record their activities correctly. To include activities to illustrate: 'twin facts', e.g. $7 - 4 = 3$, $7 - 3 = 4$; 'nought facts', e.g. $9 - 0 = 9$, $9 - 9 = 0$. To make use of subtraction rhymes.	given orally by the teacher, such as: (i) 'Count the books in this pile. Put the top three on my desk and count how many are left. Write down what you have done in figures.' (ii) 'There are some brown beans and some yellow beans in this tin. Sort them, and count the number in each heap. How many more yellow beans are there than brown beans? Write down, in figures, what you have found out.'
	(3) *Working out examples*, using apparatus if necessary, such as: $$9 - \quad 11 - \quad 17 -$$ $$4 \qquad 6 \qquad 9$$ $$\overline{\quad} \qquad \overline{\quad} \qquad \overline{\quad}$$	(3) To set suitable examples for the children to work out (using List B, page 71) to make sure that *all* the facts are covered.	(3) The working of examples, set by the teacher on the blackboard, such as: $$8 - \quad 15 - \quad 10 -$$ $$3 \qquad 7 \qquad 0$$ $$\overline{\quad} \qquad \overline{\quad} \qquad \overline{\quad}$$
C. LEARNING the primary subtraction facts.	(1) *Learning the facts* in selected sets.	(1) To arrange the facts in carefully selected sets. To provide suitable 'practice-cards' and 'flash-cards'. To organize individual activities with practice-cards and flash-cards. To arrange activities for the whole class. To show how the subtraction facts are linked with the addition facts. To provide plenty of examples in problem form. To keep a careful record of each child's progress.	(1) (a) The learning of the facts through: (i) The use of subtraction 'practice-cards'. (ii) The use of 'flash-cards' in games. (iii) The use of 'subtraction-addition' practice-cards. (iv) Helpful class activities. (b) The working of subtraction examples set in a problem form, such as: (i) 'Find the difference between twelve and seven.' (ii) 'John is seven years old; his sister is thirteen. How much younger is John than his sister?'

ANALYSIS 2 (cont.)

1. STAGE	2. STEPS	3. THE TEACHER'S PART	4. TYPE OF WORK TO BE DONE BY THE CHILDREN
D. Introduction to the simple subtraction PROCESS. (Each figure in the top line not less than the corresponding figure in the bottom line.)	(1) Setting down and working out *examples in which only tens and units occur.* (a) Subtraction in both units- and tens-columns (no noughts) T.U. 4 6 — 3 2 (b) Subtraction in units-column only (no noughts) T.U. 4 6 — 2 (c) Noughts in the units-column T.U. T.U. 4 6 — 4 6 — 2 6 6 ⎯⎯ ⎯⎯ T.U. T.U. 4 6 — 4 0 — 3 0 3 0 ⎯⎯ ⎯⎯ (d) Gaps in the tens-column of the answer T.U. T.U. 4 6 — 4 6 — 4 2 4 6 ⎯⎯ ⎯⎯	(1) and (2) To show how the sub-traction is set down and worked out by dealing with the units and tens in turn (see pp. 169–170). To introduce and insist upon the use of a standard method of working and setting down (see page 170). To give some examples in prob-lem form. *N.B.* If children have not a suffi-cient reading ability to under-stand *written* problems, these should be given orally by the teacher. The problems should not be omitted merely because the children cannot read well enough. To continue to give regular prac-tice in the primary subtraction facts, particularly those not per-fectly known. To make sure that the children are confident in dealing with examples in which a nought appears.	(1) and (2) The working of many graded examples, such as those given in column 2, set by the teacher, to illustrate the various steps in this stage of the work. The working of examples, given in 'problem' form, such as: (1) (a) 'There are 46 children in one class and 32 in another. How many more children are there in the first class than the second?' (b) 'John has a heap of 46 stones. He threw 2 into the river. How many were left?' (c) 'A boy had 46 nuts in a bag. He gave some to his brother and found he had 30 left. How many did he give to his brother?' (d) 'A boy sowed 46 beans in his garden. Later he found he had 40 plants. How many beans did not grow?' (2) (a) 'There are 546 children in a school; 324 are boys. How many are girls?' (b) 'There are 546 letters on the first page of a book and 344 on the last page. How many more letters are there on the first page than the last?'

Note.—It will be noticed that the same numbers are used in many of these examples. This has been done deliberately in order to emphasize the difference between the steps. The teacher of course should

...examples in which *hundreds, tens and units occur*.

(a) Three figures in the top line. Three, two and one figure in the bottom line (no noughts).

H.T.U.	H.T.U.	H.T.U.
5 4 6 –	5 4 6 –	5 4 6 –
3 2 4	2 4	4

(b) Noughts or gaps in the working.

H.T.U.	H.T.U.	H.T.U.
5 4 6 –	5 4 6 –	5 4 6 –
6	3 4 4	5 2 4

H.T.U.	H.T.U.	H.T.U.
5 4 6 –	5 4 6 –	5 4 6 –
4 6	5 0 6	5 4 0

E. Subtraction by the METHOD of 'decomposition'.

[*Note* — Similarly, steps like those in column 2 should be followed if the method of 'equal additions', is used.]

(1) *Setting down* and *working out* (using the method of 'decomposition') examples in which *only tens and units occur*.

(a) Tens and units in both numbers. No noughts

T.U.
3 4 –
1 8

(1), (2) and (3) To give the children a clear understanding of the 'decomposition' method (see pp. 173–4).

To introduce and insist upon the use of a standard method of working and setting down (see pp. 173–7).

To give plenty of examples in 'problem' form (oral and written).

(1), (2) and (3) The working of many graded examples (set by the teacher), such as those given in column 2, to illustrate the steps in this stage of the work.

The working of examples, given in problem form, such as:

(1) (a) 'John and Mary found 34 different flowers by the lakeside. John found 18 of them. How many did Mary find?'

ANALYSIS 2 (cont.)

1. STAGE	2. STEPS	3. THE TEACHER'S PART	4. TYPE OF WORK TO BE DONE BY THE CHILDREN
	(b) Units only in the bottom line. No noughts T.U. 3 4 — 8 ————— (c) Nought in the units column in the top line T.U. 3 0 — 1 8 ————— (d) Gap in the tens column in the answer T.U. 3 4 — 2 8 ————— (2) *Setting down* and *working out examples in which hundreds, tens and units occur.* (a) Decomposition of the *tens* only: H.T.U. H.T.U. H.T.U. 5 3 4 — 5 3 4 — 5 3 4 — 2 1 8 1 1 8 2 8 ————— ————— ————— H.T.U. H.T.U. H.T.U. 5 3 0 — 5 3 4 — 5 3 4 — 2 1 8 2 0 8 5 2 8 ————— ————— —————	To take particular care that the children understand how to deal with examples in which a nought appears. To include from time to time examples in which no 'decomposition' is required. To continue to give regular practice in the primary subtraction facts.	(b) 'There were 34 eggs in a basket; 8 were found to be cracked. How many sound eggs were there?' (c) 'Jack shot 30 arrows at a target. He hit it 18 times. How many times did he miss?' (d) 'One boy took 34 minutes to get to school. Another boy took 28 minutes. How much longer did it take the first boy than the second?' (2) (a) 'There are 534 people in a village, 218 are children. How many grown-ups are there?' (b) 'John is reading a big book. It has 534 pages. He has read 272 of them. How many more has he to read?' (c) 'Two farmers are cleaning a ditch 320 yards long. On the first day they clean 135 yards. How much have they still to clean?' (3) 'In an election one candidate received 5,437 votes and the other received 2,519 votes. What was the winning candidate's majority?'

H.T.U.	H.T.U.	H.T.U.
5 3 4 −	5 3 4 −	5 0 4 −
2 7 2	7 2	2 7 2

H.T.U.	H.T.U.
5 3 4 −	5 0 2 −
4 7 2	3 7 2

(c) Decomposition of both tens and units:

H.T.U.	H.T.U.	H.T.U.
3 2 4 −	3 2 4 −	3 0 4 −
1 3 5	3 5	1 3 5

H.T.U.	H.T.U.
3 2 4 −	3 0 0 −
2 3 5	1 3 5

(3) *Setting down and working out examples which involve *bigger* numbers.

5,437 −	5,047 −
2,519	798

* *Note.*—Comparatively few people have to use the subtraction process when more than three figures are involved. Therefore we should not make children spend a lot of time on such examples. If children *understand* the meaning of subtraction, the various steps in the written process, and how to apply these to simple problems, most of them will find little difficulty in applying the principles to larger numbers *when the need arises.*

SOMETHING TO THINK ABOUT—4
(*Multiplication*)

Teachers often find that a child's main difficulties in the multiplication process arise from an imperfect knowledge of the primary multiplication facts. The children who do not know the facts also tend to make mistakes in the process, because their power of concentration has been wasted on trying to remember or work out the facts.

To show that this is so, it may be helpful for us to try to put ourselves in the position of the child and work out a few multiplication examples in which we ourselves have an imperfect knowledge of the facts.

As before (pages 144 and 167), it is suggested that we teachers use, in this multiplication, a different system of numbers: that is, with a base of eight instead of the usual base of ten. This will ensure that, like some children, we do not readily know the multiplication facts.

For example, the early facts in the table of '*3*'s ('*Sees*') in the 'new' system are, and look like, this:

$$1 \times 3 = 3 \quad (Aye \text{ times } See \text{ is } See)$$
$$2 \times 3 = 6 \quad (Bee \text{ times } See \text{ is } Eff)$$
$$3 \times 3 = 11 \quad (See \text{ times } See \text{ is } Aitch\text{-}Aye$$
$$4 \times 3 = 14 \quad (Dee \text{ times } See \text{ is } Aitch\text{-}Dee)$$
$$5 \times 3 = 17 \quad (Ee \text{ times } See \text{ is } Aitch\text{-}Gee)$$
$$6 \times 3 = 22 \quad (Eff \text{ times } See \text{ is } Bee\text{-}Aitch\text{-}Bee)$$
$$7 \times 3 = 25 \quad (Gee \text{ times } See \text{ is } Bee\text{-}Aitch\text{-}Ee)$$

Now, can you work out the following multiplication examples.* First try them by referring to the table and

---

* The answers in this system are: *74* (*Gee-Aitch-Dee*); *545* (*Ee-Aitch-Aitch and Dee-Aitch-Ee*) and *16,164*. (Try writing this in words!)

then try them again separately by remembering the facts without the table:

$$2\ 4\ \times \qquad 1\ 6\ 7\ \times \qquad 4\ 5\ 7\ 4\ \times$$
$$\underline{\ 3\ } \qquad\qquad \underline{\ 3\ } \qquad\qquad\quad \underline{\ 3\ }$$

Do you not find that it is quite easy to make mistakes, unless you are perfectly familiar with the 'facts'? You probably spent more time and concentration on the 'facts' than on the process itself.

CHAPTER XIII

LEARNING MORE ABOUT MULTIPLICATION

A—*Introduction*

In the work described in Chapter VII, children are introduced to the idea of multiplication as a special form of addition, which can be done quickly because the numbers to be added are all the same. The children are given practical experience, such as finding out how many objects there are altogether when they bring the same number of objects a given number of times. The teacher shows how these calculations may be recorded as facts, and the children have practice which enables them to learn these facts (up to a product of twenty-four). During this work the words 'multiply' and 'multiplication' are introduced. The children now go on to learn the multiplication process and the later multiplication facts, so that they can deal with bigger numbers. But, before this work is discussed in detail, it is well to consider again the meaning of an expression such as 5×4, and how it may be put into words. Is it expressed as:

(*i*) Five times four? (*iv*) Four times five?
(*ii*) Five fours? (*v*) Four fives?
(*iii*) Four multiplied by five? or (*vi*) Five multiplied by four?

Does it mean:

(*a*) Five groups of four?
(*b*) Four groups of five?

Children should not be worried by such questions. What they *must* learn is the *complete* expression, $5 \times 4 = 20$; and what they *must* understand is that it can be looked at in *two ways*—namely, five groups of four and four groups of five, each giving the same total of twenty. When this idea is fully understood, it helps children to learn the multiplication facts much more easily, since 'twin' facts can be learned together. The idea is also helpful when, later, the children come to the multiplication of money and measures. For example, when multiplying '9*d.*' by

'365' it is possible to multiply by the '9' much more easily than by the '365'.

The following method is useful in demonstrating the idea to children. We put dots or small circles on the blackboard, as in the pattern in Fig. 89(*a*). The children count them and agree that there are six. We then cover the pattern with a cardboard screen (Fig. 89(*b*)) and ask: 'How many twos?'—Three. (We write '3 × 2' on the blackboard.) 'And what do three twos make?'—Six. (We add '= 6' on the blackboard.) 'From this

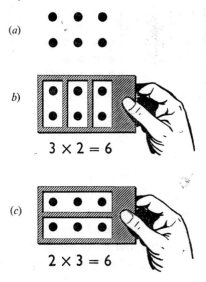

(*a*)

b)

$3 \times 2 = 6$

(*c*)

$2 \times 3 = 6$

FIGURE 89.—The use of 'screens' to show 'twin facts' in multiplication

we see that 3 × 2 = 6.' We then remove the screen and show the six dots as they were to begin with. We then cover the pattern with another screen (Fig. 89(*c*)), and ask: 'Now what do we see?—Yes, two threes.' (We write '2 × 3'.) 'So that two threes also make six.' (We add ' = 6'.) We now see that 2 × 3 = 6 and 3 × 2 = 6. If we know 'two threes' we also know 'three twos'. So we can learn both facts at the same time.

We also demonstrate, in the same way, the various multiplication facts which are involved in a number like twenty-four (see Fig. 90).

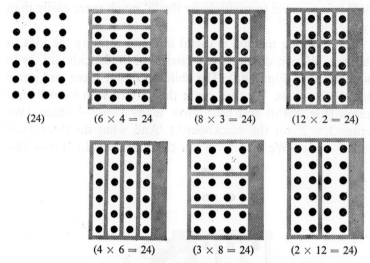

FIGURE 90.—Screens showing the 'multiplication facts' for the number
twenty-four

B—*Short multiplication*

(*1*) *Using early multiplication facts* (*as in List VI*)

When the children know the early facts they should be introduced gradually to the multiplication *process* itself. There is no
need to wait until the later facts are known, provided examples
are chosen which use only the early facts. The children are
familiar with the ideas of place-value and 'carrying', and so they
can give their main attention to the process. (If necessary,
squared-paper may still be used as an aid.)

Here are the first five steps which, it is suggested, may be
used in teaching the process.

(*a*) *No 'carrying'*—For example:

T.U.
$$2\ 4\ \times$$
$$2$$
$$\overline{4\ 8}$$

H.T.U.
$$1\ 2\ 2\ \times$$
$$4$$
$$\overline{4\ 8\ 8}$$

(*b*) *'Carrying' to the tens-column only*—
For example:

T.U.
$$3\ 6\ \times$$
$$2$$
$$\overline{7\ 2}$$
$$1$$

H.T.U.
$$2\ 1\ 7\ \times$$
$$3$$
$$\overline{6\ 5\ 1}$$
$$2$$

(c) *'Carrying' to the hundreds-column only*—For example:

H.T.U.		H.T.U.	
1 5 2 ×		1 6 2 ×	
3		4	
4 5 6		6 4 8	
1		2	

(d) *'Carrying' to both the tens- and hundreds-columns*—For example:

H.T.U.		H.T.U.	
1 5 8 ×		1 5 6 ×	
3		4	
4 7 4		6 2 4	
1 2		2 2	

(e) *Examples involving noughts*—For example:

H.T.U.	H.T.U.	H.T.U.	H.T.U.
1 2 0 ×	4 5 ×	1 0 4 ×	2 0 5 ×
4	2	3	4
4 8 0	9 0	3 1 2	8 2 0
	1	1	2

It will be seen that *all* these steps are worked through using no more than the sixty easy facts in List VI, page 83.

It is advisable to insist upon standard phrases in working and setting down, particularly in these early stages.

Here is a standard method of working the second example in step (b):

'First multiply the *units*.
Three sevens are twenty-one (2 tens and 1 unit).
Put the "1" in the units-column of the answer and "carry" the "2" to the tens-column.
Now multiply the *tens*.
Three ones are three, and the two being carried make five.
Put the five in the tens-column of the answer.
Now multiply the *hundreds*.
Three twos are six.
Put the "6" in the hundreds-column of the answer.
The answer is six hundred and fifty-one.'

H.	T.	U.	
2	1	7	×
		3	
6	5	1	
	2		

(2) *Learning and using further multiplication facts*

While the children are getting used to the multiplication process by using the 'facts' they already know, they should also be learning further multiplication 'facts'. Part of every lesson should be given to this work.

LIST VIII

MULTIPLICATION FACTS

Top section (0 × column at right):

1×12=12	2×12=24	3×12=36	4×12=48	5×12=60	6×12=72	7×12=84	8×12=96	9×12=108	10×12=120	11×12=132	0×12=0
1×11=11	2×11=22	3×11=33	4×11=44	5×11=55	6×11=66	7×11=77	8×11=88	9×11=99	10×11=110		0×11=0
1×10=10	2×10=20	3×10=30	4×10=40	5×10=50	6×10=60	7×10=70	8×10=80	9×10=90			0×10=0
1×9=9	2×9=18	3×9=27	4×9=36	5×9=45	6×9=54	7×9=63	8×9=72				0×9=0
1×8=8	2×8=16	3×8=24	4×8=32	5×8=40	6×8=48	7×8=56					0×8=0
1×7=7	2×7=14	3×7=21	4×7=28	5×7=35	6×7=42						0×7=0
1×6=6	2×6=12	3×6=18	4×6=24	5×6=30							0×6=0
1×5=5	2×5=10	3×5=15	4×5=20								0×5=0
1×4=4	2×4=8	3×4=12									0×4=0
1×3=3	2×3=6										0×3=0
1×2=2											0×2=0
1×1=1											0×1=0
											0×0=0

Bottom section (0 × column at right):

12×1=12	12×2=24	12×3=36	12×4=48	12×5=60	12×6=72	12×7=84	12×8=96	12×9=108	12×10=120	12×11=132	12×12=144	12×0=0
11×1=11	11×2=22	11×3=33	11×4=44	11×5=55	11×6=66	11×7=77	11×8=88	11×9=99	11×10=110	11×11=121		11×0=0
10×1=10	10×2=20	10×3=30	10×4=40	10×5=50	10×6=60	10×7=70	10×8=80	10×9=90	10×10=100			10×0=0
9×1=9	9×2=18	9×3=27	9×4=36	9×5=45	9×6=54	9×7=63	9×8=72	9×9=81				9×0=0
8×1=8	8×2=16	8×3=24	8×4=32	8×5=40	8×6=48	8×7=56	8×8=64					8×0=0
7×1=7	7×2=14	7×3=21	7×4=28	7×5=35	7×6=42	7×7=49						7×0=0
6×1=6	6×2=12	6×3=18	6×4=24	6×5=30	6×6=36							6×0=0
5×1=5	5×2=10	5×3=15	5×4=20	5×5=25								5×0=0
4×1=4	4×2=8	4×3=12	4×4=16									4×0=0
3×1=3	3×2=6	3×3=9										3×0=0
2×1=2	2×2=4											2×0=0
1×1=1												

List VIII shows 169 multiplication 'facts', which the children must learn eventually, in order to be able to multiply quickly and accurately. The many ways in which these facts can be learned are given in further detail in Chapter XV: the gradual building up of tables, the learning of the separate facts through practice-cards (compare Figs. 43, 51, and 53, and pages 84 and 102), flash-card games, and oral class-activities. The latter should take as many varied forms as possible. For instance, with the 'table of fours':

(i) Children say the table backwards, beginning 'twelve fours are forty-eight', 'eleven fours . . .', etc.

(ii) Children say the odd numbers only (*1* × 4, *3* × 4, *5* × 4, etc.), and then the even numbers only (*2* × 4, *4* × 4, *6* × 4, etc.).

(iii) Boys say the odd numbers, girls the even numbers, and vice versa.

(See page 249 for further examples.)

As each new set of facts (see Chapter XV, pages 256–60) is learned they should be used in actual multiplication examples. These examples should cover the same five steps with which the children are familiar, namely, *short multiplication*:—

(*a*) Without 'carrying'.
(*b*) 'Carrying' to the tens-column only.
(*c*) 'Carrying' to the hundreds-column only.
(*d*) 'Carrying' to both the tens- and hundreds-columns.
(*e*) Examples involving noughts.

In this way the children get further practice both in 'fixing the facts', and in using the multiplication process.

C—*Quick multiplication by 10, 20, 30 . . . 90*

(1) Multiplying by 10

When the children are building up the 'table of tens', they probably notice that each product has a nought at the end. When they come to short examples in which the larger numbers are multiplied by ten (for example, 26 × 10; 135 × 10), again they find that the last figure of the answer is always a nought.

Having drawn attention to this, some teachers UNWISELY go on to give a 'rule': 'to multiply by ten we just put a nought at the end of the number'. To do so is *unwise* because children may be led to apply the 'rule' without understanding, and thus to make mistakes later. Moreover, a good chance to help children's understanding is missed, for it is possible to point out the real principle. This important principle, which helps children's understanding of future work (particularly in decimals), may be stated thus: 'when a number is multiplied by ten, the answer has the same figures *but they are one place to the left and there is a nought in the units-column*'. There is no need for children to learn the *words* of this statement. They should understand and learn to use the principle (for a 'short method' of multiplication by ten) through examples.

Two useful methods for making the principle clear are:

(*a*) An example, such as that shown here, is first worked on squared-paper in the usual way (that is: 'Ten threes are thirty; put a nought in the units-column and carry the three tens . . .' etc.). We then say: 'Look at the number. Now look at the answer. A three is still there but it is one place to the left. A four is still there, but it is also one place to the left. There is a nought in the units-column.'

H.	T.	U.	
	4	3	×
	1	0	
4	3	0	
	3		

The multiplication is now done again, but this time we think of the ten as '1 ten'. In other words we multiply by the '1'. But since this is one ten, our answer must begin in the tens-column. We go on: 'Once three is three. Put the three in the tens-column. Once four is four. Put the four in the hundreds-column. There are no units so we must put a nought in the empty space in the units-column.* The answer, as before, is four hundred and thirty. What has happened? The three in the units-column was

---

* The symbol for nought is necessary in our number system to indicate the position, and therefore the value, of other figures. Before the use of place-value was introduced in about the ninth century A.D., a dot (·) was used to indicate an empty column. Later, a small ring was put round the dot (⊙) to make sure it was not overlooked. Then the dot came to be left out, and the ring became our present-day figure nought (0).

multiplied by ten, so there is now a three in the tens-column. The four in the tens-column was multiplied by ten, so there is now a four in the hundreds-column. A nought has been put in the units-column.'

(b) The second method also begins with the working of an example by the usual process. An apparatus (Fig. 91)* is then used to show how the same (correct) answer can be got quickly by moving the figures of the number one place to the left and putting a nought in the units-column. We say: 'We have multiplied forty-three by

H.	T.	U.	
	4	3	×
	1		
4	3	0	

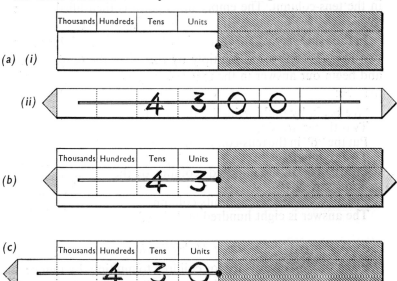

FIGURE 91.—The 'place-value' slide: (a) (i) the frame, (ii) the runner. (b) The runner in the slide, showing the number 43. (c) The runner moved along to show 430, i.e. 43 multiplied by 10, the 4 having moved from tens to hundreds, the 3 from units to tens, and a nought appearing in the units

(For construction of apparatus, see page 474)

ten and found that the answer is four hundred and thirty. Now look at this: it shows how we can get the answer very quickly.

* This apparatus may be used equally well to show division by ten of numbers which have a nought in the units-column. Details for the making of the apparatus are given on page 474, and its use in the teaching of decimals is described on pages 404–5.

Here we have forty-three. If we slide the strip along one place to the left, the three units become three tens, and the four tens become four hundreds. We write a nought under "units" and there is the answer, four hundred and thirty.' The figures are then rubbed out and several more examples are shown.

(2) Multiplying by 20, 30 . . . 90

Once the children have grasped how to multiply by ten, they should be able to go on to multiply by twenty, thirty, etc. They know that when we multiply by ten we multiply by the one (remembering that the '1' is one ten) and we begin the answer in the tens-column. The empty units-place is then filled with a '0'.

In the same way when we multiply by twenty we think of it as two tens. Therefore we multiply by the '2' in the tens-column and begin our answer in the tens-column. The working for this may be:

'We begin by multiplying by the two tens.
Two threes are six.
Put the "6" in the tens-column of the answer.
Two fours are eight.
Put the "8" in the hundreds-column of the answer.
Put a "0" in the empty units-column.
The answer is eight hundred and sixty.'

H.	T.	U.
	4	3 ×
	2	0
8	6	0

D—Long Multiplication

When it becomes necessary for children to multiply by numbers greater than twelve it is no longer possible to use short multiplication. They do not know the facts beyond those that occur in the 'table of twelves'. The idea of long multiplication must now be introduced.

(1) Multiplying by two-figure numbers (13–99)

The children are asked to do an example like this. They quickly realize that they cannot do it in the usual way because they do not know the 'table of thirteens'. So we then say: 'Let us leave this example alone for a

2 3 ×
1 3

while. We will come back to it presently. Let us look at an example you have done before, such as this. You can all multiply by twelve. Let us do it.'

$$\begin{array}{r} 2\ 3\ \times \\ 1\ 2 \\ \hline 2\ 7\ 6 \\ \hline {\scriptstyle 3} \end{array}$$

The example is worked with the class on the blackboard. We then go on: 'Let us see if we can do this example in a different way. What is another way of thinking of twelve? One ten and two units. Can we multiply the twenty-three by the two units and by the one ten separately?

'Let us do it. First by two. And now by ten. Now we have two times twenty-three and ten times twenty-three. If we add them together, we have twelve times twenty-three.

$$\begin{array}{rl} 2\ 3\ \times & \\ 2 & \\ \hline 4\ 6 & \text{2 times 23} \end{array}$$

$$\begin{array}{rl} 2\ 3\ \times & \\ 1\ 0 & \\ \hline 2\ 3\ 0 & \text{10 times 23} \end{array}$$

'Let us do it. We see that, using the new method, we get the same answer as when we multiplied by the twelve straight away.'

We now have to go through the same three steps with the example (namely, 23×13) which the children could not do at

$$\begin{array}{rl} 4\ 6 & \text{2 times 23} \\ 2\ 3\ 0 & \text{10 times 23} \\ \hline 2\ 7\ 6 & \text{12 times 23} \end{array}$$

first. The children see that the thirteen times may be thought of as three times and ten times. They work out the two multiplications and then add the results.

Now we have to set down these three steps in a shorter form as shown. It is important to make sure that the early examples at this stage do not contain 'carrying'

$$\begin{array}{rl} 2\ 3\ \times & \\ 1\ 3 & \\ \hline 6\ 9 & \text{3 times 23*} \\ 2\ 3\ 0 & \text{10 times 23} \\ \hline 2\ 9\ 9 & \text{13 times 23} \end{array}$$

difficulties. The children should be free to concentrate on the new process itself. We should choose examples where the actual calculations are as simple as possible.

The process of multiplying by two-figure numbers which

---

* *Note*—There is sometimes disagreement among teachers as to whether children should be taught to multiply first by the three units and then by the one ten or vice versa. There is little evidence to show which is preferable. It does not matter which comes first if the children understand what they are doing. The important thing is that the same method should be used throughout the school. *Children become confused and are led to make more mistakes if teachers in the same school demand different methods of procedure in different classes.*

contain more than one ten (for example, 27, 49, etc.) follows
the same pattern. (The children already know how to multiply
by 20, 30 . . . 90.) A typical example is shown here:
(It will be noted that this example again
does not require 'carrying'. When, later,
examples are used where 'carrying' becomes necessary, the children should be
encouraged to 'carry in their heads' to
avoid confusing the carrying figures with

H.T.U.
4 1 ×
2 3

1 2 3   3 times 41*
8 2 0   20 times 41
9 4 3   23 times 41

the figures of the example itself. The less able children, however,
may still need to use small neat 'carrying' figures to help them.)

(2) Multiplying by three-figure numbers

(a) Multiplying by 100, 200 . . . 900—We should repeat, briefly,
the work on multiplication by ten (page 193). Then, using the
same methods, we should show the children the quick and easy
way of getting the answer when multiplying by a hundred. The
'place-value slide' (Fig. 91, page 195) makes it
quite clear that the answer has the same figures
as the number we start with, but now they are *two*
places to the left, and with noughts in the tens-
and units-columns. In the example given here,

Th.H.T.U.
4 3 ×
1 0 0
4 3 0 0

43 × 100, the three units become three hundreds and the four
tens become four thousands.

To go on from multiplication by a hundred to multiplication
by two hundred, three hundred, etc., needs only the same steps
as in going from ten to twenty, thirty, etc. (page 196).

(b) Multiplying by numbers from 101 to 999†—The use of three
figures is merely an extension of the
work done previously. We should
remember that, as each new step is
begun, we must take care to avoid
the difficulties of 'carrying'. However,
'carrying' should be included *after* the
children have succeeded in mastering

3 2 1 ×
1 2 3

9 6 3   3 times 321
6 4 2 0   20 times 321
3 2 1 0 0   100 times 321
3 9 4 8 3   123 times 321

the new step. For instance, the first examples in working this
step are of this kind (where the children do not have to carry
while they are multiplying).

* The writing down of '3 times 41' etc. is omitted when the children are used
to the idea of long multiplication.
† The need for such multiplication is rarely met. We should not spend much
time on it.

Some children find difficulty with examples where a nought is contained in the tens-column of the multiplier. The trouble often arises when they have been working on examples in which it is necessary to make three multiplications. But, if they have understood the previous work, they realize that in such an example as this there are

$$
\begin{array}{r}
2\ 5\ 9 \\
1\ 0\ 7 \\
\hline
1\ 8\ 1\ 3 \\
2\ 5\ 9\ 0\ 0 \\
\hline
2\ 7\ 7\ 1\ 3 \\
\end{array}
\qquad
\begin{array}{l}
\text{7 times 259} \\
\text{100 times 259} \\
\hline
\text{107 times 259} \\
\end{array}
$$

only two multiplications: there is no need to multiply by the nought.

E—*Multiplication by factors**

It may be noticed, perhaps with surprise, that multiplication by factors† has not been discussed. This omission is deliberate. It is not absolutely necessary for the children to know the method, and it is *unwise* to introduce it, at this stage, since the use of two different methods of multiplication nearly always leads to confusion. Moreover, many numbers do not lend themselves easily to multiplication by the factor method.

The more able children may be introduced to the factor method as a convenient way of dealing with special examples which arise in oral and written problems. For example: 'How many hours are there in the month of August (31 days)?' The children can work this by multiplying thirty-one by twenty-four. They can also do it by thinking of the twelve-hour clock which goes round twice per day. In this case they multiply thirty-one by two, and then this result by twelve to find the number of hours.

The factor method of multiplication is useful in later arithmetic, particularly when dealing with problems of money and measures. Children must also understand the idea of factors if they are to go on to a study of algebra.

---

* One number is said to be a *factor* of another when there is no remainder after division. Thus 3 is a factor of 12. So are 2, 4 and 6, since each divides twelve exactly, i.e. without remainder.

† For example to multiply 692 × 132 by the factor method we multiply 692 by 11 and then multiply this result by 12, like this. (In any case, how often do we find this kind of example in everyday life? It is doubtful, to say the least, whether children in primary schools should ever be asked to work it out.)

$$
\begin{array}{r}
6\ 9\ 2 \\
1\ 1 \\
\hline
7\ 6\ 1\ 2 \\
1\ 2 \\
\hline
9\ 1\ 3\ 4\ 4 \\
\end{array}
$$

F—*Some common errors made by children in the multiplication process*

The diagnosis* of children's mistakes in multiplication will depend upon whether we have the time and the ability to deal with the individual. A great deal can be done by carefully analysing the children's test-papers, but a far more accurate diagnosis can be made if we are able to listen to the individual child working through his multiplication exercise—that is, if we know what to look for.

Here are the most common errors made by children, with possible causes and suggested remedies:—

(*a*) Mistakes arising from an imperfect knowledge of the multiplication facts. This requires very careful testing, followed by practice on the facts not known (see pages 191–3).

(*b*) Mistakes arising from 'carrying'. These often occur because of the necessity, in long multiplication, to do a great deal of calculation 'in the head'. If the teacher is sure that the child understands the principle of 'carrying' (see pages 152–3) then 'carrying' mistakes are most frequently due to lack of concentration. The child finds the calculation too difficult and loses his place. It is probable that this is an indication that the child is being given work for which he is not ready. He should be put back to an easier level.

A particular case of difficulty in 'carrying' arises when children have to multiply by eleven or twelve and, for the first time, they meet examples (if such are really necessary!) in which they have to 'carry' numbers greater than nine, as in the one shown here. This should be treated as a separate step and the children should be given ample practice in dealing with this kind of example.† (See Analysis 3, page 203.)

$$
\begin{array}{r}
3\ 9\ 9\ \times \\
1\ 2 \\
\hline
4\ 7\ 8\ 8 \\
\text{11 10}
\end{array}
$$

(*c*) Mistakes due to carelessness in simple addition. For

---

* A doctor makes a 'diagnosis' of a patient's illness (that is, tries to find out what is causing the illness) by examining the patient's body and listening to what he has to say. In the same way a teacher can make a 'diagnosis' of a child's mistakes in arithmetic by examining his written work and listening to him working examples aloud.

† Some children, of course, see that this particular example can be done by a much quicker method.

example, a child says: 'Four nines are thirty-six, and five make forty-two' (instead of forty-one). Quick oral practice should be given in answering questions such as 'five nines and eight?' The 'clock-game' (Chapter XV, page 249) can be used for this kind of practice.

(*d*) Mistakes with noughts. These include multiplication facts which are confused with addition facts. (For example, a child, thinking of $7 + 0 = 7$, says or writes *incorrectly* $7 \times 0 = 7$.) Further practice should be given to help the children to understand and remember the various nought facts.

(*e*) Mistakes caused by the incorrect setting down of the example. For instance, 464×37 may be set down *incorrectly*. Sometimes this leads to the mistake of multiplying by a seven and a three instead of by a seven and a thirty. This is often due to a lack of understanding of place-value. The child should return to the use of squared-paper and H.T.U. notation until he no longer makes the error.

```
4 6 4    Incorrect
  3 7    setting
           down
```

G—*Summary of points to remember in teaching multiplication*
1. A suitably graded scheme, such as that described in this chapter and analysed on pages 203–11, should be followed.
2. The multiplication 'facts' should be learned so that children can use them quickly and accurately.
3. At every stage examples in 'problem' form should be given, so that the children become familiar with the words and phrases which show that multiplication must take place.
4. Practical examples and everyday situations should be used whenever possible to illustrate the use of multiplication. This is particularly important in the early stages.
5. Squared-paper may be used in the early stages, and when new steps are being taught, to help the children set down their work correctly.
6. Standard phrases in working, and standard methods of setting down, should be insisted upon, particularly in the early stages. (When the children have learned to work

H

accurately they should gradually be allowed to work in their own way, so as to increase their speed.)

7. Careful records should be kept of each child's progress. Errors should be carefully examined so that help can be given in order to put matters right as quickly as possible.

ANALYSIS 3

Suggested stages and steps in the teaching of multiplication
(see Chapters VII and XIII)

1. STAGE	2. STEPS	3. THE TEACHER'S PART	4. TYPE OF WORK TO BE DONE BY THE CHILDREN
A. The IDEA of multiplication.	(1) Renewing and enlarging early grouping activities.	(1) To arrange for the children many and various activities involving equal grouping of objects.	(1) (a) The use of objects and apparatus. For example: (i) 'Put four beans into each section of a matching tray.' 'Here are fifteen beads. Thread three beads on each of these pieces of wire. How many threes have you?' (b) The telling of number 'tales' in which groupings are involved (see page 79).
	(2) Learning to count in equal groups.	(2) To introduce the idea of finding the total of a number of objects by counting them in equal groups.	(2) (a) The repetition of grouping activities, as in (1) (a). The extension of the activities to finding the total number of objects by counting them in equal groups. The recording of these activities. (b) The saying of suitable number rhymes.
	(3) Learning the language of multiplication. (a) The word 'times'.	(3) To introduce the word 'times'. To introduce the '×' sign. To show how to record multi-	(3) (a) The use of activities in which equal groups of objects have to be fetched, brought, put

ANALYSIS 3 (cont.)

1. STAGE	2. STEPS	3. THE TEACHER'S PART	4. TYPE OF WORK TO BE DONE BY THE CHILDREN
	(b) The multiplication sign. (c) The recording of multiplication activities.	plication activities, using the '×' and '=' signs: first as, for example, $$4 \times 3 = 12$$ then as $\begin{array}{r} 3 \times \\ 4 \\ \hline 12 \end{array}$	out, etc., a number of times. The recording of the activities, using the word 'times', e.g. '4 times 3 makes 12'. (b) *and* (c) The recording of activities, using the '×' and '=' in place of 'times' and 'make', e.g. $4 \times 3 = 12$ The recording of the same activities in another form, e.g. $\begin{array}{r} 3 \times \\ 4 \\ \hline 12 \end{array}$
B. Introduction to the EARLY multiplication FACTS.	(I) Covering, through activities, *the multiplication facts* where the *product is not more than twenty-four.* *Recording* these activities.	(I) To arrange activities in which the early multiplication facts are used. To make sure that the children record the results correctly. To include activities to illustrate: (a) 'twin' facts, e.g. $4 \times 3 = 12$ and $3 \times 4 = 12$ (pp. 84, 188). (b) 'nought' facts, e.g. $5 \times 0 = 0$ (page 81). To make use of everyday happenings which involve multiplication.	(I) The working of examples, given orally by the teacher, such as: (i) 'Count the number of pencils in each of these three boxes. Find how many pencils there are altogether. Write down, in figures, what you find out.' (ii) 'How many days are there in three weeks? Write down, in words, what you find out. Then write it down in figures.'

are covered.

C. LEARNING the early multiplication FACTS and USING them in the multiplication PROCESS.	(1) *Arranging the early multiplication facts in tables. Learning these tables as they are built up. Learning the separate facts.* $\dfrac{5}{\underline{}}\quad\dfrac{3}{\underline{}}\quad\dfrac{8}{\underline{}}$	(1) To set down, with the children, the early multiplication facts in table form. To arrange various activities to help the children to learn the tables (see pp. 84-8 etc.). To arrange the facts in sets for learning. To provide practice-cards, flash-cards and other apparatus to help in the learning of the separate facts. To organize many and various individual and class-activities to help the children to memorize the separate facts (see p. 84). To make use of everyday happenings, which help to 'fix' the facts. To give practice in using the facts to work examples given in a 'problem' form.	(1) The setting down of the facts in table form. The learning of these tables through many and varied activities (see pp. 84-8 and Chap. XV). The memorizing of the separate facts through: (i) The use of multiplication practice-cards. (ii) The use of flash-cards in games. (iii) Class-activities. The working of examples, given in a problem form, such as: (i) 'Some children are playing a game in teams. There are four teams with six children in each. How many children are there altogether?' (ii) 'How many children can sit in eleven desks if two children sit at each desk?' $\dfrac{5\times}{2}\quad\dfrac{7\times}{3}\quad\dfrac{2\times}{8}\quad\dfrac{6\times}{4}$

	(2) Using the early multiplication facts *to work multiplication examples involving bigger numbers.*
	(*a*) No carrying.
	e.g. T.U. H.T.U.
	    2 4 × 1 2 2 ×
	      2 4
	   — ——
		(2) To show the children how to use their knowledge of 'place-value' to deal with the units, tens and hundreds in turn when multiplying bigger numbers.
		To make sure that the children set down their work correctly and use the standard phrases in working.
			(2) The working of many graded examples, such as those given to illustrate the steps in column 2.
			The working of examples, given in problem form, such as:
			(i) 'A farmer packs 122 oranges in a box. How many will he pack in four boxes?'
			(ii) 'How many days are there in twenty-three weeks?'

ANALYSIS 3 (cont.)

1. STAGE	2. STEPS	3. THE TEACHER'S PART	4. TYPE OF WORK TO BE DONE BY THE CHILDREN

	(b) Carrying to the tens-column only.
	
	T.U. H.T.U.
	e.g. 3 6 × 2 1 7 ×
	     2 3
	
	(c) Carrying to the hundreds-column only.
	
	H.T.U. H.T.U.
	e.g. 1 5 2 × 1 6 2 ×
	      3 4
	
	(d) Carrying to both the tens-column and hundreds-column.
	
	H.T.U. H.T.U.
	e.g. 1 5 8 × 1 5 6 ×
	      3 4
	
	(e) Examples involving noughts.
	
	H.T.U. H.T.U.
	e.g. 1 2 0 × 4 5 ×
	      4 2
	
	H.T.U. H.T.U.
	1 0 4 × 2 0 4 ×
	   3 5
		To grade the examples carefully, as in the examples given in column 2.
		To continue to give regular practice in the learning of tables and the memorizing of the early multiplication facts.
		To give plenty of examples in problem form at each step.
		To give examples set out in words.
			(iii) 'A school served 152 dinners on each of 3 days. How many dinners was this in all?'
			(iv) 'How many beads will be needed to make four necklaces if there are 162 on each?'
			(v) 'A man is nailing some lids on to boxes. He uses four nails for each box. How many nails will he need for 156 boxes?'
			The working of examples set out in words such as:
			(i) 'Multiply two hundred and thirteen by four.'
			(ii) 'What are three times one hundred and fifty-eight?'
			The practising of the facts not well known, through the use of practice-cards, flash-cards and class activities.

FACTS up to 12 × 12, and using them in the multiplication process.

...ally all the tables are completed.
Learning the tables as they are built up.
Learning the separate *facts*.
Using all the *facts* as they are learned to work multiplication examples. Arranging this work in the same five steps as in Stage C, Steps 2 (a), (b), (c), (d) and (e).

given on pp. 256–60) for the building up, in easy stages, of the other multiplication facts into tables.
To repeat the work set down in this column at Stage C, Steps 1 and 2, each time the table chart is extended and the new facts are learned.

set down in this column at Stage C, Steps 1 and 2, each time the table chart is extended and the new facts are learned. All the facts so far covered are used in the multiplication examples.

E. Multiplying by 10 (a QUICK METHOD). Multiplying by 20, 30, 40, . . . 90.

(1) (a) *Understanding and using the quick method* of multiplying by 10.
(b) Multiplying by 10 by thinking of it as '1 ten'.

(1) (a) and (b) To give further examples of multiplying by 10 by using the known facts.
To use these examples to show how the answer can be written down quickly.
To use apparatus to illustrate the method.
To be very careful to see that the children use the right phrases when they describe what they are doing.
To insist upon careful setting down of written work.
To give plenty of oral and written examples.
To give the written examples in varied forms.

e.g.
```
   H.T.U.
   3 5 ×
     1 0
   ------
```
ten times thirty-five.

(1) The working of examples, using known facts to multiply by 10, e.g.

```
H.T.U.    H.T.U.    Th.H.T.U.
3 7 ×     3 0 ×     2 3 5 ×
  1 0       1 0         1 0
-----     -----     ---------
```

The writing down of the answers to similar examples without doing any working.
The working of examples, set down in words, e.g.
(i) 'Multiply three hundred and fifteen by ten.'
(ii) 'What is ten times one hundred and nine?'

The working of examples, given in problem form, such as:
(i) 'Each of ten bags contain 240 coins. How many coins are there in all?'

ANALYSIS 3 (cont.)

1. STAGE	2. STEPS	3. THE TEACHER'S PART	4. TYPE OF WORK TO BE DONE BY THE CHILDREN
		To give some examples in problem form. To show how these examples can be worked by thinking of the 10 as '1 ten' (see pp. 194–5).	(ii) 'A farmer planted 84 rows of seedlings, with ten in each row. How many did he plant altogether?' The working of examples by multiplying by '1 ten'.
	(2) Multiplying by 20 by thinking of it as '2 tens'. Likewise for 30, 40, . . . 90.	(2) To show how to multiply by 20 by thinking of it as '2 tens'. To make sure that the children use correct phrases when they work examples aloud. To insist upon careful setting down of written work. To avoid 'carrying' in the early examples. To give some examples in 'problem' form. To extend the use of the method to multiplying by 30, 40, . . . 90.	(2) The working of many examples, such as:

H.T.U.   Th.H.T.U.   H.T.U.
3 4 ×   2 3 4 ×   3 9 ×
  2 0   2 0   2 0
─────   ───────   ─────

H.T.U.   H.T.U.   Th.H.T.U.
4 0 ×   5 0 ×   5 0 5 ×
  2 0   2 0   2 0
─────   ─────   ───────

The working of examples, set down in words, such as: (i) 'Multiply three hundred and five by twenty.' (ii) 'What do twenty times fifty-nine make?' The working of examples, given in 'problem' form, such as: (i) 'There are 48 matches in a box. How many are there in 20 boxes?' (ii) 'Work out how many fingers |

CATION' to multiply BY TWO-FIGURE NUMBERS.	*and tens in turn.*			

and tens in turn.

(a) Setting down the two multiplications separately.

e.g.   23 × 13

$$
\begin{array}{ll}
23 \times & 23 \times \\
\;\,3 & 10 \\
\hline
69 & 230 \\
\text{3 times 23} & \text{10 times 23}
\end{array}
$$

$$
\begin{array}{ll}
69 & \text{3 times 23} \\
230 & \text{10 times 23} \\
\hline
299 & \text{13 times 23}
\end{array}
$$

(*Note*—The examples chosen should not involve 'carrying' in the multiplication.)

(b) Setting down the working in a shorter form.

e.g. (i)
$$
\begin{array}{ll}
23 \times & \\
13 & \\
\hline
69 & \text{3 times 23} \\
230 & \text{10 times 23} \\
\hline
299 & \text{13 times 23}
\end{array}
$$

(ii)
$$
\begin{array}{ll}
41 \times & \\
23 & \\
\hline
123 & \text{3 times 41} \\
820 & \text{20 times 41} \\
\hline
943 & \text{23 times 41}
\end{array}
$$

(iii)
$$
\begin{array}{ll}
123 \times & \\
32 & \\
\hline
246 & \text{2 times 123} \\
3690 & \text{30 times 123} \\
\hline
3936 & \text{32 times 123}
\end{array}
$$

To show how to use the same method to multiply by two-figure numbers greater than twelve.

To set down the working in full with the early examples to help the children to understand what they are doing.

To choose, in the early stages, examples which do not involve 'carrying'.

To show how to set down the working in a shorter form.

To extend the work to cover examples which involve 'carrying', and examples in which noughts occur in the numbers to be multiplied.

To examine children's incorrect work, to find out whether the mistakes arise from a lack of understanding of the process or from an incomplete knowledge of the facts used.

To give plenty of examples in 'problem' form.

To give examples with the numbers expressed in words.

To give practice in 'facts' not well known.

illustrate Step (a) in column 2.

The setting down and working of many graded examples, such as those given to illustrate Steps (b) and (c) in column 2.

The working of examples, set down in words, such as:

(i) 'Multiply forty-one by twenty-three.'

(ii) 'Multiply fifty-eight by ninety-seven and write down your answer in words.'

The working of examples, given in a 'problem', form such as:

(i) 'A bus holds 32 people. How many people can travel on 14 buses?'

(ii) 'The Forestry Department planted a small clearing with seedlings. There were twenty-three rows with forty-six seedlings in each. How many seedlings were planted in all?'

(iii) 'A lorry made twenty-one journeys from the store to the river steamer. It carried forty-five bags of cocoa beans on each journey. How many bags were moved altogether?'

The learning of facts still not well known by the use of practice-cards, flash-cards and oral activities.

(*Note*—The examples chosen should not involve 'carrying' in the multiplication.)

ANALYSIS 3 (cont.)

1. STAGE	2. STEPS	3. THE TEACHER'S PART	4. TYPE OF WORK TO BE DONE BY THE CHILDREN

	(c) Dealing with examples in which 'carrying' occurs in the multiplication, e.g.
	
	(i) 23 ×
	     46
	   ---- 	
	    138
	    920
	   ---- 	
	   1058
	
	(ii) 58 ×
	      97
	    ---- 	
	     406
	    5220
	    ---- 	
	    5626
	
	(iii) 847 ×
	       76
	     ---- 	
	     5082
	    59290
	    ----- 	
	    64372
	
	(iv) 807 ×
	      76
	    ---- 	
	    4842
	   56490
	   ----- 	
	   61332
	
	(v) 850 ×
	     76
	   ---- 	
	   5100
	  59500
	  ----- 	
	  64600		

G. Using the method of 'LONG MULTIPLICATION' to multiply BY THREE-FIGURE NUMBERS.	(1) *Multiplying by 100, 200, 300, ...900*, e.g.
	Th.H.T.U.
	    4 3 ×
	    1 0 0
	  -------- 	
	  4 3 0 0
	
	Th.H.T.U.
	     4 3 ×
	     2 0 0
	   -------- 	
	   8 6 0 0
	
	(2) *Setting down and working out*
		(1) To show how to multiply by 100 by thinking of it as '1 hundred'. To show how to use the same method to multiply by 200, 300, ...900.
		(2) To introduce the method of multiplying by a three-figure number
			(1) The setting down and working of examples, such as those given to illustrate Step 1 in column 2.
			(2) The setting down and working of many graded examples, such as those given to illustrate Steps 2 (a), (b) and (c).
			The working of examples given

(a) No 'carrying' in the multiplication, e.g.

$$\begin{array}{r} 321\ \times \\ 232 \\ \hline 642 \\ 9630 \\ 64200 \\ \hline 74472 \end{array} \qquad \begin{array}{r} 301\ \times \\ 232 \\ \hline 602 \\ 9030 \\ 60200 \\ \hline 69832 \end{array}$$

(b) 'Carrying' in the multiplications, e.g.

$$\begin{array}{r} 454\ \times \\ 376 \\ \hline 2724 \\ 31780 \\ 136200 \\ \hline 170704 \end{array} \qquad \begin{array}{r} 709\ \times \\ 376 \\ \hline 4254 \\ 49630 \\ 212700 \\ \hline 266584 \end{array}$$

(c) Examples with a nought in the multiplier, e.g.

$$\begin{array}{r} 321\ \times \\ 203 \\ \hline 963 \\ 64200 \\ \hline 65163 \end{array} \qquad \begin{array}{r} 457\ \times \\ 306 \\ \hline 2742 \\ 137100 \\ \hline 139842 \end{array} \qquad \begin{array}{r} 709\ \times \\ 306 \\ \hline 4254 \\ 212700 \\ \hline 216954 \end{array}$$

'carrying' in the multiplication.

To make sure that the children set down their work correctly.

To extend the work to cover examples in which 'carrying' occurs.

To give plenty of examples in 'problem' form.

To give examples of multiplication by 4-figure, and longer numbers, as the need arises.

sent 800 books to each of 135 schools. How many books were sent altogether?'

(ii) 'When checking his stock a merchant found that he had 237 boxes of pencils each containing 144. How many pencils had he in all?'

(iii) 'An aeroplane flies between two towns which are 175 miles apart. In one year it flew from one town to the other and back again 219 times. What total distance did it cover on these journeys?'

* *Note.*—Multiplication by numbers with three figures or more is seldom necessary. Hence we should not spend much time on such examples. In any case, many children are not 'ready', in the primary school, to deal with big numbers of which they have no experience. Moreover, if children have a thorough understanding of multiplication, and a firm grasp of the process for smaller numbers, they can usually deal with larger numbers *when the need arises.*

SOMETHING TO THINK ABOUT—5

(*Division*)

When children know the processes of addition, sub-traction and multiplication, it is easy to teach them how to work out examples of *division* by following a set method of working. But this does not mean that they are certain to understand the *nature* of the division process. Many children fail as soon as they are faced with an example which does not follow the usual pat-tern, or is not stated in the usual way.

Let us consider the following examples:

(*a*) Fifty-six bananas are *shared* between eight boys. How many will each boy receive?

(*b*) How many boys can be *given* eight bananas from a basket containing fifty-six?

(*c*) How many eights must I *add together* to make fifty-six?

(*d*) How many times can I *take away* eight from fifty-six?

(*e*) By what must I *multiply* eight to make fifty-six?

(*f*) How many pieces, each eight inches long, can be *cut off* a length of rope fifty-six inches long?

Each of these examples can lead to the expression $56 \div 8 = 7$, though the words used to indicate that division takes place are: 'shared', 'given', 'add together', 'take away', 'multiply', and 'cut off'. Indeed some of these words appear to indicate the other processes. Let us see how some of these examples may be worked out practically:

(*a*) A banana may be given to each boy in turn until all the bananas are given out. Each boy receives *seven bananas*. This is a method of continuous subtraction by ones.

(*b*) Eight bananas may be taken from the box and given to a boy. Then, another eight are given to another boy until all the bananas are given out. *Seven boys* receive bananas. This is a method of continuous subtraction in groups.

(*c*) and (*e*) A series of '8's' may be added together until the total becomes fifty-six. Seven eights are needed. This is a method of continuous addition in groups.

(*d*) and (*f*) Eight may be taken from fifty-six. Then eight is taken from the answer, and so on until nothing is left. Eight is taken away seven times. This is a method of continuous subtraction in groups as in example (*b*).

If we look closely at the methods used, we see that either:

(*i*) The '56' is split up into '8' equal *parts*, and the *number in each part* is found.

or (*ii*) The '56' is arranged in *groups* of eight and the *number of groups* is found.

We can express what has been done in the division form $56 \div 8 = 7$.

This two-fold aspect of division may be made clearer by a diagram:

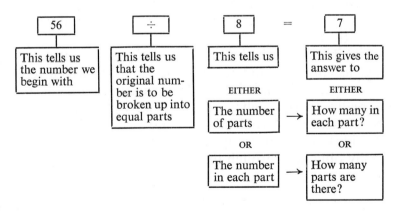

You, as a teacher, were able to give the answers

quickly to the six questions at the beginning of this section because:

(*a*) You understood what the question said.

(*b*) You knew and understood all the forms of the fact $7 \times 8 = 56$ (that is, $7 \times 8 = 56$, $8 \times 7 = 56$, $56 = 8 \times 7$, $56 = 7 \times 8$, $56 \div 7 = 8$, $56 \div 8 = 7$).

(*c*) You could see that there was a relationship between the information given in the question (that is, what the question asked) and the fact $7 \times 8 = 56$.

(*d*) You could select the form of the fact most appropriate to the question (that is, $56 \div 8 = 7$).

But it is not so easy for children to get this understanding of division until they also have been given the right kind of experiences and teaching. They will not fully understand until:

(*i*) They have learned, through their knowledge of the multiplication 'facts', how a number can be split up into various equal groups. (For example, twenty-four may be grouped as three eights, eight threes, four sixes, six fours, two twelves, and twelve twos.) They are then able to see that if they know the fact $3 \times 8 = 24$ they also know the facts $24 \div 8 = 3$ and $24 \div 3 = 8$.

(*ii*) They have dealt with many practical situations which lead to division, such as sharing, grouping, measuring off, etc. (see Chapter VIII for division activities).

(*iii*) They have had a great deal of practice in speaking, listening to, and reading the language which tells them that division is involved. For instance, they begin to realize that though words like 'add' or 'subtract' may be used in the 'problem', they are really dealing with the idea of equal groups and that the answer is most easily obtained through division.

CHAPTER XIV

LEARNING MORE ABOUT DIVISION

In Chapter VIII methods of introducing children to the idea of division are discussed, together with activities which lead to a knowledge of the early division facts. It is suggested that the teacher refreshes his memory of Chapter VIII before going on with this chapter, since the children's further progress depends upon how well they understand the early work.

Of the four basic processes in arithmetic, division may be regarded as the least important from the point of view of everyday use. It is less often needed in daily life, being mainly concerned with the sharing of money and calculating the cost of one article when the price of several is given. It is also used occasionally in measuring. For example, a man may use it in finding the number of posts needed to make a long fence.

It is necessary, nevertheless, for children to be able to divide quickly and accurately if they are hoping to go on to a further study of mathematics and science.

A—*Setting down the division process* (*long or short form?*)

It is suggested in Chapter VIII that, from the start, children should be shown the long form of setting down the division process.

The thinking and the steps involved, in an example of division, are the same, whether the division is recorded in a long or a short form. In short division, however, some of the steps are not written down: children do the working 'in their heads'. For some children, this increases the possibility of error. It is also more difficult for the teacher to decide why a child has obtained a wrong answer. Again, the child who starts by using the short division method of setting down no sooner gets used to the method than he has to change to the long division form, in order to deal with larger numbers.

It seems more sensible for children to learn long division

from the beginning, rather than to come to it later as a new process—just at a time when other new difficulties arise. The abler children may use short and less laborious ways of dividing, but we can help the majority by using long division from the start. This method has been shown to give more accurate results. It enables the teacher to find out more easily where the child goes wrong, if mistakes are made in the calculation. As the need arises at later stages, short methods of division can be introduced (for example, in changing pence to shillings, etc.).

B—*Learning the division facts and using them in the simple process*

In the work described in Chapter VIII children are helped to learn the 'facts', up to the division of twenty-four, by linking them with their knowledge of the multiplication facts. They also learn to use these facts in division examples which show a remainder. Similarly, while learning further multiplication facts the children also build up a knowledge of the corresponding division facts. For example, as they learn $7 \times 8 = 56$ they should also see that $56 \div 8 = 7$ and that $56 \div 7 = 8$. In this way they should eventually build up a complete knowledge of the division facts shown in List IX, page 217.

We should make sure that *all* these facts are known, so that the children are not hindered when dealing with the division *process*. A useful way of doing this is to arrange the facts into selected sets (as for the learning of previous facts) and to test the children on them. In this way we make sure that all the facts are covered and that mistakes can be corrected. (See also Chapter XV for ways of helping children to remember arithmetical facts.)

The children should be given practice in *using* the facts they are learning, through simple examples of division where a remainder occurs. This not only strengthens their knowledge of the facts but also forms a basis for the working of further and more difficult examples. In examples where a remainder occurs the children begin to see the reason for the written working: it helps them to find the remainder.

LIST IX

DIVISION FACTS

$\frac{1}{1)1}$	$\frac{2}{1)2}$	$\frac{3}{1)3}$	$\frac{4}{1)4}$	$\frac{5}{1)5}$	$\frac{6}{1)6}$	$\frac{7}{1)7}$	$\frac{8}{1)8}$	$\frac{9}{1)9}$	$\frac{10}{1)10}$	$\frac{11}{1)11}$	$\frac{12}{1)12}$
$\frac{1}{2)2}$	$\frac{2}{2)4}$	$\frac{3}{2)6}$	$\frac{4}{2)8}$	$\frac{5}{2)10}$	$\frac{6}{2)12}$	$\frac{7}{2)14}$	$\frac{8}{2)16}$	$\frac{9}{2)18}$	$\frac{10}{2)20}$	$\frac{11}{2)22}$	$\frac{12}{2)24}$
$\frac{1}{3)3}$	$\frac{2}{3)6}$	$\frac{3}{3)9}$	$\frac{4}{3)12}$	$\frac{5}{3)15}$	$\frac{6}{3)18}$	$\frac{7}{3)21}$	$\frac{8}{3)24}$	$\frac{9}{3)27}$	$\frac{10}{3)30}$	$\frac{11}{3)33}$	$\frac{12}{3)36}$
$\frac{1}{4)4}$	$\frac{2}{4)8}$	$\frac{3}{4)12}$	$\frac{4}{4)16}$	$\frac{5}{4)20}$	$\frac{6}{4)24}$	$\frac{7}{4)28}$	$\frac{8}{4)32}$	$\frac{9}{4)36}$	$\frac{10}{4)40}$	$\frac{11}{4)44}$	$\frac{12}{4)48}$
$\frac{1}{5)5}$	$\frac{2}{5)10}$	$\frac{3}{5)15}$	$\frac{4}{5)20}$	$\frac{5}{5)25}$	$\frac{6}{5)30}$	$\frac{7}{5)35}$	$\frac{8}{5)40}$	$\frac{9}{5)45}$	$\frac{10}{5)50}$	$\frac{11}{5)55}$	$\frac{12}{5)60}$
$\frac{1}{6)6}$	$\frac{2}{6)12}$	$\frac{3}{6)18}$	$\frac{4}{6)24}$	$\frac{5}{6)30}$	$\frac{6}{6)36}$	$\frac{7}{6)42}$	$\frac{8}{6)48}$	$\frac{9}{6)54}$	$\frac{10}{6)60}$	$\frac{11}{6)66}$	$\frac{12}{6)72}$
$\frac{1}{7)7}$	$\frac{2}{7)14}$	$\frac{3}{7)21}$	$\frac{4}{7)28}$	$\frac{5}{7)35}$	$\frac{6}{7)42}$	$\frac{7}{7)49}$	$\frac{8}{7)56}$	$\frac{9}{7)63}$	$\frac{10}{7)70}$	$\frac{11}{7)77}$	$\frac{12}{7)84}$
$\frac{1}{8)8}$	$\frac{2}{8)16}$	$\frac{3}{8)24}$	$\frac{4}{8)32}$	$\frac{5}{8)40}$	$\frac{6}{8)48}$	$\frac{7}{8)56}$	$\frac{8}{8)64}$	$\frac{9}{8)72}$	$\frac{10}{8)80}$	$\frac{11}{8)88}$	$\frac{12}{8)96}$
$\frac{1}{9)9}$	$\frac{2}{9)18}$	$\frac{3}{9)27}$	$\frac{4}{9)36}$	$\frac{5}{9)45}$	$\frac{6}{9)54}$	$\frac{7}{9)63}$	$\frac{8}{9)72}$	$\frac{9}{9)81}$	$\frac{10}{9)90}$	$\frac{11}{9)99}$	$\frac{12}{9)108}$
$\frac{1}{10)10}$	$\frac{2}{10)20}$	$\frac{3}{10)30}$	$\frac{4}{10)40}$	$\frac{5}{10)50}$	$\frac{6}{10)60}$	$\frac{7}{10)70}$	$\frac{8}{10)80}$	$\frac{9}{10)90}$	$\frac{10}{10)100}$	$\frac{11}{10)110}$	$\frac{12}{10)120}$
$\frac{1}{11)11}$	$\frac{2}{11)22}$	$\frac{3}{11)33}$	$\frac{4}{11)44}$	$\frac{5}{11)55}$	$\frac{6}{11)66}$	$\frac{7}{11)77}$	$\frac{8}{11)88}$	$\frac{9}{11)99}$	$\frac{10}{11)110}$	$\frac{11}{11)121}$	$\frac{12}{11)132}$
$\frac{1}{12)12}$	$\frac{2}{12)24}$	$\frac{3}{12)36}$	$\frac{4}{12)48}$	$\frac{5}{12)60}$	$\frac{6}{12)72}$	$\frac{7}{12)84}$	$\frac{8}{12)96}$	$\frac{9}{12)108}$	$\frac{10}{12)120}$	$\frac{11}{12)132}$	$\frac{12}{12)144}$
$\frac{0}{1)0}$	$\frac{0}{2)0}$	$\frac{0}{3)0}$	$\frac{0}{4)0}$	$\frac{0}{5)0}$	$\frac{0}{6)0}$	$\frac{0}{7)0}$	$\frac{0}{8)0}$	$\frac{0}{9)0}$	$\frac{0}{10)0}$	$\frac{0}{11)0}$	$\frac{0}{12)0}$

Here is an example of how the working, at this stage, is set down.

It is a good thing if, from the beginning, children learn to use standard phrases and standard methods of working. These make it easier to understand and follow the steps in the process. In the example shown, a suggested standard working is:

$$\begin{array}{r} 6 \\ 9\overline{)57} \\ 54 \\ \hline 3 \end{array}$$

$57 \div 9 = 6$, and 3 over

'How many nines in fifty-seven?—Six.
Put the "6" in the units-column of the answer.
Six nines are fifty-four.
Put the "54" under the "57" and take away to find what is left over.

Four from seven leaves three.
Put down the "3".
Five from five leaves nothing.
The remainder is three.
The answer is: six, and there are three over.'

It cannot be over-emphasized that the basic 'fact' *must* be known if accuracy and speed are to be achieved in later work. We are well advised *not to hurry* over this stage, but to make sure, by adequate oral and written testing, that these facts are known and can be used in the simple process. Suitable oral and written work should be devised to ensure that children know when to divide and why they are dividing: for instance, examples are regularly given where they can see clearly that the required answer can be arrived at by dividing. Here are two examples of the kind suggested:

(*i*) Suppose we are going to have some new tables for the class room. Eight children can sit at a table. There are forty children in the class. How many tables shall we need?

(*ii*) There are fifty-nine days till the end of the year. How many weeks and days is this?

C—*Using known facts to divide larger numbers*

The stage is now reached when children are going to divide bigger numbers (that is, numbers outside the tables) by using the division facts which they already know: for example, 79 ÷ 2 and 357 ÷ 2. They do not know the 'table of twos' beyond 12 × 2 = 24, so they will have to deal with the '79' as separate tens and units and the '357' as separate hundreds, tens and units.

(*1*) *Dividing tens and units only* (*by numbers up to 12*)

(*a*) *Remainders in both tens and units** —It is suggested that this

---

* *Note*—It will be noticed that the steps in teaching are given in the following order:

(*a*) Remainders in both tens and units; for example, 79 ÷ 2.
(*b*) Remainder in the tens only; for example, 72 ÷ 3.
(*c*) Remainder in the units only; for example, 87 ÷ 4.
(*d*) No remainder in either the tens or units; for example, 69 ÷ 3.

Some teachers reverse this order. It is chosen here, however, because experience has shown that:

(*i*) It enables the children to get used to the method of setting work should be introduced orally, with many examples worked out on the blackboard. For 79 ÷ 2, for instance, we say: 'Seventy-nine is seven tens and nine units. We have to divide by two. So we begin by dividing the seven tens by two and then go on to divide the units. Let us put it down.' We then work the example aloud with the class.

'First deal with the seven *tens*.
How many twos are there in seven?—Three
   (three twos are six).
Put the "3" in the tens-column of the answer,
   and put the "6" down under the "7".
Take away to find how many tens are over.
Six from seven leaves one.
Put down the "1".
Now deal with the *units*.
Bring down the nine units to the side of the
   one ten, making "19" (that is, nineteen units).
How many twos in nineteen?—Nine (nine twos are eighteen).
Put the "9" in the units-column of the answer, and the "18"
   under the "19".
Take away to find what is left over.
There is one left over.
Put down the "1".
The answer is: thirty-nine and there is one over.'

	T.	U.
	3	9
2)	7	9
	6	
	1	9
	1	8
		1

It is important to encourage correct habits from the start. So this kind of standard working should be insisted upon and many similar examples should be given before going on to the next step.

(*b*) *Remainders in the tens only*—In examples of this type (72 ÷ 3) the suggested working is:

'First deal with the seven *tens*.
How many threes are there in seven?—Two (two threes are six).
Put the "2" in the tens-column of the answer, and put the "6" under the "7".

down the working when the tens and units are being divided separately.

(*ii*) It postpones the examples which cause difficulty to some children, namely those in which empty spaces appear because there are no remainders.

Take away to find how many tens are over.
Six from seven leaves one.
Put down the "1".
Now deal with the *units*.
Bring down the two units by the side of the one ten, making "12" (that is, twelve units).
How many threes in twelve?—Four (four threes are twelve).
Put the "4" in the units-column of the answer, and the "12" under the "12".
Take away to find what is left over.
There is nothing left over.
The answer is: twenty-four.'

	T.	U.
	2	4
3)	7	2
	6	
	1	2
	1	2

(*c*) *Remainders in the units only*—In examples of this type (87 ÷ 4) the suggested working is:

'First deal with the eight *tens*.
How many fours in eight?—Two (two fours are eight).
Put the "2" in the tens-column of the answer, and put the "8" under the "8".
Take away to find how many tens are over.
Eight from eight leaves nothing.
There is nothing left over in the tens.
Now deal with the *units*.
Bring down the seven units.
How many fours in seven?—one (one four is four).
Put the "1" in the units-column of the answer, and the "4" under the "7".
Take away to find what is left over.
There are three left over.
Put down the "3".
The answer is: twenty-one and there are three over.'

	T.	U.
	2	1
4)	8	7
	8	
		7
		4
		3

(*d*) *No remainder in either tens or units**—In this type of example (69 ÷ 3) the suggested working is:

'First deal with the six *tens*.
How many threes in six?—Two (two threes are six).

* This step may appear to be easier than the previous steps because there are no remainders. But if children begin with this type of example they often see no reason for having to put in all the working. As they find later, the working is really necessary: for instance in an example like 4864 ÷ 16. See also the footnote on pages 218–19.

Put the "2" in the tens-column of the answer, and put the
"6" under the "6".
Take away to find how many tens are over.
Six from six leaves nothing.
There is nothing left over in the tens.
Now deal with the *units*.
Bring down the nine units.
How many threes in nine?—Three (three
threes are nine).
Put the "3" in the units-column of the answer
and the "9" under the "9".
Take away to find what is left over.
There is nothing left over.
The answer is: twenty-three.'

T.	U.
2	3
3) 6	9
6	
	9
	9

(*e*) *Examples when a nought occurs in the units-column of the
answer*—This step introduces the children to the method of
dealing with the working when a nought appears in the answer—
that is, when subtraction is unnecessary (e.g. $62 \div 3$):

'First deal with the six *tens*.
How many threes in six?—Two (two threes
are six).
Put the "2" in the tens-column of the answer,
and put the "6" under the "6".
Take away to find how many there are over.
Six from six leaves nothing.
There is nothing left over in the tens.
Now deal with the units.
Bring down the two units.
How many threes in two?—None.
Put a "0" in the units-column of the answer.
The "2" is left over.
The answer is: twenty and there are two over.'

T.	U.
2	0
3) 6	2
6	
	2

(2) *Dividing hundreds, tens and units*

The children are dividing by numbers up to twelve and are now
extending the work to hundreds, tens and units.

*It is strongly advised that squared-paper and the H.T.U. nota-
tion are used in all this work. This helps the children to keep their
working in the correct columns and to understand the steps in the
process.*

The first four steps are in the same order as was followed with tens and units, and are dealt with in the same way:

(*a*) Remainders in hundreds, tens and units; for example, 716 ÷ 3.

(*b*) Remainders in two columns only; for example, 976 ÷ 8, 849 ÷ 7, 697 ÷ 6.

(*c*) Remainders in one column only; for example, 955 ÷ 5, 798 ÷ 7, 847 ÷ 4.

(*d*) No remainder in any column; for example, 696 ÷ 3.

There is then a fifth case to consider:

(*e*) *Examples where a nought occurs in the answer.*

(*i*) A nought occurs in the tens-column of the answer in an example like 617 ÷ 3. The suggested method of working is:

'First deal with the six *hundreds*.
How many threes in six?—Two (two threes are six).
Put the "2" in the hundreds-column of the answer, and the "6" under the "6".
Take away to find how many hundreds are over.
Six from six leaves nothing.
There is nothing left over in the hundreds.
Now deal with the *tens*.
Bring down the "1".
How many threes in one?—None.
Put a "0" in the tens-column of the answer.
There is one ten left over.
Now deal with the *units*.
Bring down the "7" to the side of the one ten (making "17" units).
How many threes in seventeen?—Five (five threes are fifteen).
Put the "5" in the units-column of the answer and the "15" under the "17".
Take away to find what is left over.
There are two left over.
The answer is two hundred and five, and there are two over.'

```
H.T.U.
 2 0 5
3)6 1 7
  6
  1 7
  1 5
    2
```

(*ii*) In the example shown (347 ÷ 5) on page 223 the nought occurs in the hundreds-column of the answer.

Looking first at the hundreds figure (the '3') the children see that there are no fives in three. They therefore put a '0' in the hundreds-column of the answer.* They now consider the first two figures—the '34' (that is, thirty-four tens). Now they begin again: 'How many fives in thirty-four?' and go on as before.

```
        H.T.U.
        0 6 9
     5) 3 4 7
        3 0
        ─────
          4 7
          4 5
        ─────
            2
```

It will be seen that when children can do this type of example, they may begin to get their first practice in dividing by two-figure numbers (that is, by ten, eleven, and twelve).

(*iii*) An example of the kind shown here (605 ÷ 3) sometimes causes trouble, but there should be little difficulty if the child understands what he has been doing in each step of the process. However, we should arrange for adequate practice.

In this example '0' occurs in the tens-column of the answer, and another '0' in the tens-column of the number to be divided. The suggested method of working is:

'First deal with the *hundreds*.
How many threes in six?—Two (two threes are six).
Put the "2" in the hundreds-column of the answer, and "6" under the "6".
Take away to find what is over.
Six from six leaves nothing.
Now deal with the *tens*.
Bring down the "0" in the tens-column. How many threes in nought?—None.
Put a "0" in the tens-column of the answer. There *cannot be any remainder* in the tens.
Now deal with the *units*.
Bring down the "5" units.
How many threes in five?—One (one three is three).
Put the "1" in the units-column of the answer, and the "3" under the "5".
Take away to find what is over.
There are two left over.
The answer is: two hundred and one, and there are two left over.'

```
       H.T.U.
       2 0 1
    3) 6 0 5
       6
       ─────
         0 5
           3
       ─────
           2
```

---

* Putting the '0' in the hundreds-column of the answer ensures that the '6' goes into its right place. When the children are used to this kind of example they can stop putting in the '0'. The final answer should be expressed as 'sixty-nine, and two over' and written as '69, and 2 over' (*not* 069).

(3) Quick division by ten

In division by ten the place-value slide (Fig. 91, page 195) is a useful means of showing how to find the answer quickly. For instance, 'What is 368 divided by 10?' We write 368 in the correct position on the slide. We move it one place to the right: the '3' is now in the tens-column, the '6' in the units-column, and the '8' is 'left over'. Thus the answer is '36 and 8 over'. This follows easily from the earlier work on place-value. At a later stage the idea is readily extended to division by a hundred, etc. (In due course we may go on to decimals, when the example mentioned here gives the answer 36·8.)

D—*Dividing by the easier two-figure numbers* (20, 21, 22; 30, 31, 32; . . . 90, 91, 92)

By this time children should be used to the steps in the method of working long division, and should understand what they are doing at each step. The stage is now reached when the teacher can gradually introduce division by numbers greater than twelve. This is an important stage because, for the first time, the children have to work examples where their knowledge of the primary division facts is not enough to enable them to get the answer. They must be introduced to the idea of 'trying out' the division at each step.

(1) Introducing the idea of 'trying out'

The teacher should return for a while to examples of division by ten, and should point out that *counting in tens* can be helpful in dividing by ten. In other words, counting in tens is a short way of saying the 'table of tens', and this is helpful in dividing by ten.

The children should then be given practice in *counting in twenties*, that is: 'Twenty, forty, sixty, eighty', etc.

This counting ability may now be used to divide by twenty.

$$
\begin{array}{r}
7 \\
2\,)\,\overline{1\ 4\ 6} \\
1\ 4\ 0 \\
\hline
6
\end{array}
$$

In the example shown the children see that they can get the answer by counting in twenties. They say: 'Twenty, forty, sixty, eighty, a hundred, a hundred and twenty, a hundred and forty. There are seven twenties in a hundred and forty. Put the "7" in the answer and the "140" under "146". Take away, etc.'

The children should be given plenty of examples of this kind, and then the work should be extended to examples of division where counting in thirties and forties is necessary.

The *same* examples should then be used to show the children how to divide by twenty *without* counting. They are introduced to the idea of letting the first figure of the twenty (that is the '2') act as a guide in deciding how many times the '20' *will go*.

In the example shown the '2' and the '6' may be written on the blackboard in coloured chalks.

$$\begin{array}{r} 3 \\ 2\,0)\overline{6\ 5} \\ 6\ 0 \\ \hline 5 \end{array} \qquad \begin{array}{r} 20 \\ 3 \\ \hline 60 \end{array}$$

It is pointed out the '2' is two tens and the '6' is six tens. So that we can think: 'How many two tens are there in six tens?' or shortly: 'How many twos in six?' This gives us a guide to how many twenties there *may* be in sixty-five. That is *three*. So we try three (working it out at the side). Three twenties are sixty. We decide therefore that '20' will go into '65' three times. We put the '3' in the answer and take the '60' from the '65', etc.

Further examples should be given in which the division is by 21, 22, up to 91, 92. Each time the 'trial' answer is the correct one.

The important thing for the children to remember in all the work where they are dividing by two-figure numbers is that they must *try out* the answer at each step. That is, having decided how many times one number '*might* go' into another, they must try it out by multiplication at the side of the example before making the decision that it '*will* go' that number of times. *Teachers should see that this procedure becomes a habit with the children.*

The detailed steps and types of example for this stage of division are given in Analysis 4 on pages 236–9.

(2) 'Trying out' where the first 'try' is not correct

Now the children are shown an example where the first trial answer is eventually found to be incorrect. The example is

worked on the blackboard. The children first look at the '2' and
the '6' to find a trial answer. They say: 'It
might go three times because there are three
twos in six. Let us try it. Three times twenty-
one make sixty-three. This is too many because
we only have sixty-one. Let us try two. Two
times twenty-one make forty-two. This *"will*
go". We put a "2" in the answer, etc.'

```
        2                   21
2 1) 6 1                      3
     4 2                     ――
     1 9                     63

                            21
                             2
                            ――
                            42
```

The necessity to 'try out' becomes clearer to the children
when they come to examples such as the one
here. The first figure in the answer might
appear to be '7' (since there are seven twos in
fourteen), but when tried out this is found
to be too big. On a further trial '6' is found
to be the correct figure.

```
             6 7
2 1) 1 4 1 2
     1 2 6
     ――――――
       1 5 2
       1 4 7
       ――――
             5
```

E—*Dividing by the more difficult two-figure numbers*

Children can now be introduced to the idea of arriving at a
suitable trial answer by increasing or decreasing the number
they arc dividing by until it reaches a 'round figure', that is,
the nearest number of tens. For example, for the purpose of
finding a trial answer:

nineteen is thought of as twenty;
twenty-one, twenty-two, twenty-three, twenty-four are thought
of as twenty;
twenty-five, twenty-six, twenty-seven, twenty-eight, twenty-
nine are thought of as thirty.

Thus, in the example shown (657 ÷ 28) the '28' is thought of
as '30' to find the first trial answer. It is easy to see that '30'
goes into '65' twice. Twenty-eight is less than thirty.
Therefore twenty-eight will also go into sixty-five
at least twice. This is now 'tried out' and found to
be correct. Similarly when dividing the '28' into the
'97' it is seen that the trial answer is probably '3'
since '30' goes into '97' three times. This again
has to be 'tried out'.

```
             2 3
2 8) 6 5 7
     5 6
     ――――
       9 7
       8 4
       ――――
       1 3
```

The early examples should be chosen so that the method of

increasing or decreasing *does* give a trial answer which is found
to be correct. But later examples should be given
where the first trial answer leads to a remainder
which is 'too big'. For instance, in the example
shown here the suggested working (thinking of
the '19' as '20') is:

$$\begin{array}{r} 8 \\ \hline 1\,9\,)\,\overline{1\ 5\ 4} \\ 1\ 5\ 2 \\ \hline 2 \end{array}$$

'How many "2"s in "15"?—Seven. So we try seven.
Seven nineteens make one hundred and thirty-three.
If we take this away we find that there is a remainder of
   twenty-one.
This is "too big" since we are only dividing by nineteen.
We must try "8".
Eight nineteens make one hundred and fifty-two.
If we take this away we find that there is a remainder of two.
So we are sure that "19" goes into "154" eight times.'

It is essential to emphasize, in the division process, that *we
must never have a remainder which is greater than the number we
are dividing by. If this happens the trial answer is not the true
answer and we must look for another.*

It should be noted that some children have more difficulty
with division by numbers '13' to '18' than with numbers such as
'43' to '48'. This is because the trial answer, when dividing by
'16' for example, is less likely to be the true answer than when
dividing by '46'. It is probably wise to give extra help to the
children when they have examples of division by numbers '13'
to '18'.

Some teachers find it helpful to allow children to build up
into a chart the tables of thirteens to nineteens for reference at
this stage (see Chart II).

Other teachers, at this stage, prefer to build up *with the children*
a chart which helps them to find a trial answer quickly, but
still requires them to do their own calculation and 'trying out'
(see Chart III). For example: (*i*) How many '16's' in '126'?—
'126' lies between '120' and '130'. By reference to the chart it
can be seen that '16' goes into '120' seven times and into '130'
eight times. Therefore '16' goes into '126' either seven or eight
times. If eight times is tried out it is found to be 'too big'. Seven

CHART II

THE TABLES OF 13's, 14's, 15's, 16's, 17's, 18's AND 19's

Times	1	2	3	4	5	6	7	8	9
13	13	26	39	52	65	78	91	104	117
14	14	28	42	56	70	84	98	112	126
15	15	30	45	60	75	90	105	120	135
16	16	32	48	64	80	96	112	128	144
17	17	34	51	68	85	102	119	136	153
18	18	36	54	72	90	108	126	144	162
19	19	38	57	76	95	114	133	152	171

CHART III

A 'TRYING OUT' (*trial answer*) CHART FOR DIVISIONS
BY THE NUMBERS 13 TO 19

	20	30	40	50	60	70	80	90	100	110	120	130	140	150	160	170	180
13	1	2	3	3	4	5	6	6	7	8	9						
14	1	2	2	3	4	5	5	6	7	7	8	9					
15	1	2	2	3	4	4	5	6	6	7	8	8	9				
16	1	1	2	3	3	4	5	5	6	6	7	8	8	9			
17	1	1	2	2	3	4	4	5	6	6	7	7	8	8	9		
18	1	1	2	2	3	3	4	5	5	6	6	7	7	8	8	9	
19	1	1	2	2	3	3	4	4	5	5	6	6	7	7	8	8	9

times is found to give the correct trial answer. (*ii*) How many
'17's in '145'?—'145' lies between '140' and '150'. By reference
to the chart it can be seen that '17' goes into '140' and '150'
eight times. Therefore '17' must go into '145' eight times.

These charts need only be used while the children are getting
accustomed to the idea of 'trying out'. When they become
confident they should be encouraged as often as possible to look
at the figures before them and use their own judgement.

F—*Dividing by numbers of more than two figures*

Dividing by larger numbers should begin with simple examples of division by one hundred, two hundred, three hundred, up to nine hundred. The working of examples such as 695 ÷ 200 gives children confidence for dealing later with examples such as 695 ÷ 178. Here a trial answer must be found by thinking of the '178' as '200'. (In everyday life examples of this kind are seldom met. Children should not spend much time on them.)

The children do not have to learn any new ideas at this stage of division but the teacher should be careful in the selection and grading of the examples for the children to do. A suggested grading is given in the Analysis, stage H, page 239.

G—*Common errors in division*

When a child gets an answer wrong, some teachers immediately assume either that the child does not know how to divide or that he does not understand the example. But this may not be so. It may be that the mistakes made are connected with the child's lack of accuracy in using the basic facts. It may be that the child has some difficulty in addition, subtraction and multiplication which are all involved in the division process.

An analysis of the mistakes made in the division process by a large number of children has shown that:—

(*a*) Almost half the mistakes are connected with the basic facts of addition, subtraction, multiplication and division. For example, a child may wrongly say: ' "8" from "13" is "6".' Again, he may say: 'How many "8"s" in "54"?' and give the answer as '7' instead of '6'. He says wrongly: 'Seven eights are forty-eight.'

```
       1
8)1 3 4 3    Incorrect
    8        subtraction
  ───
    6
  ───
```

(Errors of this nature show that the child needs more practice in learning the basic facts.)

```
     1 7
8)1 3 4 3    Incorrect
    8        multiplication
  ───
    5 4
    4 8
  ─────
```

(*b*) Almost a quarter of the mistakes are connected with remainders at various stages of the process. For example, failure to 'bring down' a figure in order to complete the division, as shown here. The answer is given as twelve with a remainder of six. It should be one hundred and twenty-three with a remainder of ten. (The use of squared-paper, and insistence upon the use of the symbols H.T.U. to indicate place-value, help children who tend to make this kind of mistake: they can then see more easily that the division is not finished.)

```
        1 2
1 9)2 3 4 7   Incorrect
    1 9        because the
    ———        '7' has not
    4 4        been dealt
    3 8        with.
    ———
      6
```

(c) Many errors arise when a nought occurs in any part of the process. For instance, in the examples shown the nought is left out of the tens-column in the answer. (When this kind of mistake is made the child should return for a while to the use of squared paper and H.T.U. symbols. This helps him to see that he has left a gap in the answer.)

```
             Incorrect                        Incorrect
      1 8    because the        2 5           because the
1 7)1 8 3 6  nought has been   7)1 8 0 1      '0' has not
    1 7      left out of the     1 4          been brought
    ———      tens-column of      ———          down, so that
    1 3 6    the answer, and     4 1          the answer is
    1 3 6    the answer is       3 5          given as '25'
    ———————  stated as '18'      ———          instead of '257'.
    · · · ·  instead of '108'.     6
```

(d) In other cases the mistakes do arise from a lack of understanding of what division means, and of the process by which it is brought about. In these cases the teacher is recommended to return to the practical approach suggested in Chapter VIII, and to consider whether previous teaching of the process has been sufficiently carefully graded. (See Analysis 4, pages 232–239.) Children may become confused if some steps are missed out or are too quickly passed over.

H—Summary of points to remember in teaching division

1. A suitably graded scheme (such as that given on pages 232–239) should be followed.
2. The early work should be based on actual experience of division.
3. At every stage examples in 'problem' form should be included so that children learn to understand statements which require them to divide.
4. A perfect knowledge of the primary division facts is essential. They should be learned in association with the corresponding multiplication facts.

5. Squared-paper should be used at the beginning and when new steps are being learned. It helps the children to set down their work correctly.
6. Careful records should be kept of each child's progress. Errors should be carefully examined so that help may be given in order to put matters right as quickly as possible.
7. Standard phrases in working and standard methods of setting down should be insisted upon, particularly in the early stages. (When the children have learned to work accurately they should gradually be allowed to work in their own way so as to increase their speed.)

ANALYSIS 4

Suggested stages and steps in the teaching of division
(see Chapters VIII and XIV)

1. STAGE	2. STEPS	3. THE TEACHER'S PART	4. TYPE OF WORK TO BE DONE BY THE CHILDREN
A. The IDEA of division.	(1) Renewing and *enlarging early experiences* of division.	(1) To arrange for the children many and various activities involving division. To include activities in which a remainder occurs after division.	(1) (a) The use of objects and apparatus: For example: (i) The use of the number tray to share a number of shells equally between the sections. (ii) The cutting of strips of paper, marked at intervals with dots, into pieces containing the same number of dots. (b) The playing of games, such as: (i) Paying workmen. (ii) Putting flags into sand-castles. (c) The saying of division rhymes, such as: 'Six ripe mangoes hanging on a tree, If two of us share them, we each have three.'
	(2) Learning *the language of division*. (a) Words and phrases meaning 'divide'. (b) The division sign. (c) The recording of division activities.	(2) To make use of all the words and phrases indicating division. To introduce the '÷' sign and to show how to record division activities: e.g. $24 \div 3 = 8$ and $19 \div 3 = 6$ and 1 over.	(2) The repetition and extension of activities as in (1). The recording of the results of these activities: First by drawings, words and figures. Later by using the '÷' and '=' signs.

ing the division.

e.g.
$$3\overline{)24} \quad \text{(8)} \quad \text{and} \quad 3\overline{)19} \quad \text{(6)} \quad 18 \quad \overline{1}$$

activities in the other form.

e.g.
$$3\overline{)15} \quad \text{(5)} \quad \text{and} \quad 3\overline{)17} \quad \text{(5)} \quad 15 \quad \overline{2}$$

| **B** Introduction to the EARLY DIVISION FACTS (for numbers up to 24). | (*1*) Covering, through *activities*, the division facts for *numbers up to* 24. *Recording* these facts. (*2*) Using further activities to cover and record all these early division facts. | (*1*) and (*2*) To arrange activities in which the early division facts are used. To use all the phrases indicating division. To make sure that the children record their division correctly. To include activities in which remainders occur. To direct the children's attention to the relationship between the division facts and the multiplication facts. To continue to make use of division rhymes. | (*1*) and (*2*) The working of examples, given orally by the teacher, such as:
(*i*) 'Count these pencils; then put them into these boxes, six to each box. Count the number of full boxes. How many pencils are left over? Write down what you have done in figures.'
(*ii*) 'Count these shells; then share them between John, Peter and Paul, making sure that they each have the same number. How many do they each have? How many are left over? Write down in figures what you have done?' |
| | (*3*) *Working out examples given by the teacher.* (Apparatus to be used, if necessary.) e.g. $5\overline{)20}$ $5\overline{)21}$ $4\overline{)16}$ $4\overline{)19}$ | (*3*) To set suitable examples for the children to work (using List D, page 101) to make sure that *all* the facts are covered. | (*3*) The working of examples, set by the teacher on the blackboard, such as those given in column 2. |

I

ANALYSIS 4 (cont.)

1. STAGE	2. STEPS	3. THE TEACHER'S PART	4. TYPE OF WORK TO BE DONE BY THE CHILDREN
C. LEARNING the early division FACTS.	*Learning the facts* in selected 'sets'.	To arrange the facts in carefully selected 'sets'. To provide suitable 'practice-cards' and 'flash-cards'. To organize individual activities with 'practice-cards' and 'flash-cards'. To arrange activities for the whole class. To show how the division facts are linked with the multiplication facts. To give plenty of examples in 'problem' form. To keep a careful record of each child's progress.	(a) The learning of the facts through: (i) The use of division practice-cards. (ii) The use of flash-cards in games. (iii) The use of 'division-multiplication' practice-cards. (iv) Class-activities. (b) The working of division examples, set in a problem form, such as: (i) 'How many children could be given two oranges each from a basket containing twenty-two?' (ii) 'If twenty-two oranges are shared between eleven children how many will they each receive?' (iii) 'If twenty-two oranges are shared equally between two baskets how many will there be in each?'
D. LEARNING the other division FACTS (for numbers up to 144) and USING them in the division PROCESS (where the answer is not greater than twelve).	*Learning the facts* in selected 'sets'. *Using the facts* in the simple division process. e.g. $2\overline{)17}$, $2\overline{)21}$, $7\overline{)44}$, $12\overline{)38}$, $12\overline{)155}$	To arrange the facts in carefully selected 'sets'. To emphasize the close link between the division facts and the multiplication facts. To provide suitable 'practice-cards' and 'flash-cards'. To arrange suitable individual and	(a) The learning of the facts through: (i) The use of 'practice-cards' and flash-cards. (ii) The use of 'division-multiplication 'practice-cards'. (iii) Class-activities. (b) The setting down and working out of examples, such as:

		without remainders). To make sure that the children set down their work correctly and use standard phrases in working. To give plenty of examples in 'problem' form.	(*i*) 'John went fishing with his father and five other men. They caught 70 fish which were then shared between the six men so that they each had the same number. John had the fish left over. How many did John have? How many did his father have? (*ii*) 'How many weeks are there in 60 days?' (*iii*) 'Seventy-eight children were arranged into six teams with equal numbers in each. How many were in each team?'

E. Using known facts to DIVIDE LARGER NUMBERS (when the answer is greater than twelve).	(*1*) Dividing *two-figure numbers*.
	  (*a*) Remainder in both tens and units, e.g. 2)79.
	  (*b*) Remainder in tens only, e.g. 3)72.
	  (*c*) Remainder in the units only, e.g. 4)87.
	  (*d*) No remainders in either the tens or units, e.g. 3)69.
	  (*e*) Examples where a nought occurs in the units-column of the answer.
	
	(*2*) Dividing *three-figure numbers*.
	  (*a*) Remainders in hundreds, tens and units, e.g. 3)716.
	  (*b*) Remainders in two columns only: e.g. 8)976, 7)849, 6)697.
		(*1*) and (*2*) To introduce the idea of dealing with the tens and units in turn.
		To introduce and insist upon the use of a standard method of working and setting down.
		To make sure that the children are confident in dealing with one step before going on to the next.
		To examine children's mistakes to find whether the errors arise from a lack of understanding of the process or from an incomplete knowledge of the division facts.
		To introduce the idea of dealing with the hundreds, tens and units in turn when dividing three-figure numbers.
			(*1*) and (*2*) The working of many graded examples, such as those given to illustrate the steps in column 2.
			The working of examples, given in 'problem' form, such as:
			  (*i*) 'How many canoes will be needed to cary 100 men if each holds 6 men?'
			(*ii*) 'How many pieces of rope, each 8 yards long, can be cut from a coil 200 yards in length?'
			(*iii*) 'A planter has 500 rubber trees. He must tap them all during the next six days. How many must be tapped each day?'

ANALYSIS 4 (cont.)

1. STAGE	2. STEPS	3. THE TEACHER'S PART	4. TYPE OF WORK TO BE DONE BY THE CHILDREN
	(c) Remainders in one column only, e.g. 5)955, 7)798, 4)847. (d) No remainders in any column, e.g. 3)696. (e) Examples where a nought occurs in the answer, e.g. 205 069 201 3)617 5)347 3)605 6 30 6 — — — 17 47 05 15 45 3 — — — 2 2 2 — — —	To explain carefully and exactly what to do when noughts appear in the working. To give plenty of examples in problem form. To give further practice in facts which are not well known.	The working of examples in which the numbers are given in words, such as: (i) 'How many twos are there in seventy-nine?' (ii) 'Divide eight hundred and forty-seven by four. What is the remainder?' (iii) 'When a certain number is multiplied by five the answer is one hundred and ninety-one? What is the number?'
F. Dividing by the easier TWO-FIGURE NUMBERS, (i.e. 20, 30, . . . 90 21, 31, . . . 91 22, 32, . . . 92).	(1) Dividing by the easier two-figure numbers where the 'trial' answer is the correct answer. (a) Dividing by 20, 21; 30, 31; 40, 41; . . . 90, 91. (i) Where a single-figure answer is obtained by counting (but the working is set down in full). e.g. 20)60, 20)65, 30)127, 21)63, 31)127, 51)160. (ii) Where the answer (single-figure) is obtained by using the first figure of the dividing number to give a 'trial' answer, e.g.	(1) (a) and (b) To revise counting in tens and to give practice in counting in twenties. To show how counting in tens and twenties can be used to divide by ten and twenty. To extend the use of this method to division by thirty, forty, etc. To work the same, and similar, examples by using the first figure of the dividing number as a guide to the answer. To see that the children make sure that the trial answer is the correct answer, by 'trying it out'. To insist upon the use of a stan-	(1) and (2) The working of many graded examples, such as those given to illustrate the steps in column 2. The working of examples, given in problem form, such as: (i) 'A man buys cigarettes in packets of 20. During one month he smoked 180 cigarettes. How many packets did he buy?' (ii) 'How many hours are there in 370 minutes?' (iii) 'How many class rooms will be needed for a school of 375 children if there are not

figure] must be obtained in two steps, e.g.

20)369, 21)369, 21)434
90996,) 91)996, 91)1924.
92.

The repetition of steps (i), (ii) and (iii) in (a) above.

(c) Dividing by 20, 21, 22; 30, 31, 32; . . .90, 91, 92, where a three-figure answer is obtained, e.g.

20)4654, 31)6612, 72)9461.

(d) Dealing with examples where a nought appears in the tens-column of the answer, e.g.

```
     107          108
21)2247       52)5642
   21            52
   147           442
   147           416
   ───            26
```

method for dividing by 21, 31, etc., and, later, by 22, 32, etc.

To show how to work examples with bigger numbers, where the division is done in two (and later, three) steps, each of which requires a trial answer.

To explain carefully and exactly how to work and set down examples in which a nought appears in the answers.

To give plenty of practice examples throughout all this work.

To give some examples in problem form.

To give further practice in facts not well known.

mark twenty examination papers in one hour. How long will he take to mark 420 papers?'

The working of examples in which the numbers are given in words, such as:

(i) 'How many times do eighty-two go into five hundred and seventy? How many remain?'

(ii) 'How many years are there in four hundred and seventy-six weeks?'

(iii) 'What number, when multiplied by forty-one, gives an answer of one thousand, five hundred and seventeen?'

(2) Dividing by the easier two-figure numbers when the 'trial' answer is not the correct answer.

(a) Examples which give a single-figure answer.

e.g. 21)61, 31)92, 22)64.

(b) Examples which give a two-figure answer.

(i) 21)415, 32)618, 32)731.
(Note— 'Trial' answer 'incorrect' in one step of the working only.)

(2) To repeat the work of (1) (a) and (b) with examples in which the 'trial' answer is not the correct answer.

To emphasize the need for careful 'trying out' before the answer is written down.

To grade the work carefully when giving examples which have two-figure answers.

ANALYSIS 4 (cont.)

1. STAGE	2. STEPS	3. THE TEACHER'S PART	4. TYPE OF WORK TO BE DONE BY THE CHILDREN
	(ii) 21)1405, 32)602. (*Note*—'Trial' answer 'incorrect' in *both* steps of the working.)		
G. Dividing by the more DIFFICULT TWO-FIGURE NUMBERS.	(1) Dividing by more difficult two-figure numbers. Dividing by 19. (*a*) Where the 'trial' answer is easily seen (because there is only one 'possibility'). e.g. 19)84, 19)165, 19)291. (*b*) Where the 'trial' answer is not easily seen (because there are two 'possibilities'). e.g. 19)78, 19)154, 19)324. (2) Dividing by 29, 39, . . . 99, e.g. 29)93, 29)73, 29)146, 29)564, 99)224, 99)298, 99)534, 99)2955. (3) Dividing by 13, 14, 15. e.g. 13)68, 14)79, 15)94, 13)224, 14)512, 15)424. (4) Dividing by 16, 17, 18. e.g. 16)91, 17)82, 18)91, 16)424, 17)731, 18)597. (5) Dividing by 23, 24, 25, 26, 27, 28; 33, 34, . . . etc. to 98, e.g. 23)425, 34)829, 45)1463, 66)2843.	(1) and (2) To introduce the idea of getting a 'trial' answer, when dividing by 19, by thinking of 19 as 20. To grade the examples carefully so that, to begin with, the 'trial' answer is the correct answer. To extend the method to division by 29, 39, etc. To emphasize the need to make sure that the remainder at any step must be less than the dividing number. To give examples in 'problem' form. (3) and (4) To build up, with the children, charts which help them in finding trial answers when dividing by 13, 14, 15, 16, 17, 18 (see pp. 227–8). (5) To show how to find a trial answer by increasing or decreasing the dividing numbers to the nearest ten, for two-figure num-	(1) and (5) The working of many graded examples, such as those given to illustrate the steps in column 2. The working of examples, given in a 'problem' form, such as: (*i*) 'A farmer has a thousand plants to put out in rows each containing forty-five plants. How many rows will there be?' (*ii*) 'A school has 154 books in its library. How many shelves will be needed for the books if each shelf takes eighteen books?' (*iii*) 'A school bus carries thirty-two children. How many buses will be needed to take all the 224 children in a school on a journey?'

bers of MORE THAN TWO FIGURES.*

bers.

(a) Where the 'trial' answers are the correct answers.

e.g. $124)\overline{297}$, $124)\overline{2977}$

(b) Where the 'trial' answers are not the correct answers.

e.g. $124)\overline{369}$, $124)\overline{2449}$

(c) Where a nought occurs in the dividing number or in the answer, e.g.

$207)\overline{435}$, $207)\overline{4205}$, $207)\overline{21740}$

(2) Dividing by four-figure numbers.

e.g. $2141)\overline{45671}$, $1007)\overline{69273}$

(j) To give practice in dividing by 100, 200, etc.

To show how to obtain a trial answer by considering the first two figures of the dividing number.

To make sure that the children set down their work correctly, particularly when noughts occur either in the dividing number or in the answer.

(1) The working of graded examples such as those given in column 2. The working of examples, given in a 'problem' form, such as:

'Ten thousand pencils are to be packed in boxes, each containing one hundred and forty-four. How many boxes will be needed?'

* *Note*—Most primary-school children are not 'ready' for this kind of example, which is rarely needed. Understanding of division, and a good grasp of the process, with smaller numbers, are sufficient: these enable children to learn quickly to deal with larger numbers if it becomes necessary to do so.

CHAPTER XV

TABLES—HOW TO ENSURE THAT THE 'NUMBER FACTS' ARE KNOWN

Teachers are often heard to say that they are worried because their pupils 'do not know their tables'. They usually mean that they think the children should already have 'learned their tables' in earlier classes; and that, until they have learned them, further work in arithmetic is impossible. Hence, many teachers begin a big scheme of 'table learning' in a way which often frustrates both children and teacher, and may even end in thorough dislike of all arithmetic. Is this necessary?

There are some famous men, able mathematicians and scientists, who found difficulty in 'learning tables' during early childhood. Without doubt, much of the trouble lay in the way the tables were presented. They were regarded as a necessary evil, and children were made to go through them again and again in the hope that, eventually, they would be able to repeat them perfectly.

The modern teacher agrees that tables are necessary, but *no* that they are an evil: they *can* be learned without drudgery and unhappiness. Hard work and repetition by both teacher and child are needed, but hard work can be pleasurable. In fact, the modern teacher is well aware that learning is more effective and lasting when it is accompanied by pleasurable feelings, and that repetition is not dull if it is done through a variety of suitable activities.

THE MEANING OF 'TABLES'

What do we mean by a 'table'? We mean simply a list of *separate but related* arithmetical *facts* arranged in a definite order. And it is the separate facts which are important and must be learned. The table is merely a convenient and systematic way of presenting the facts in related form.

When learned, the facts themselves make arithmetical calculation quicker and easier. They provide both the tools and the material of arithmetic. Just as a builder may use a trowel, bricks and mortar, in building a house, so we use number facts to build up our arithmetical processes. When the facts are not known thoroughly, the tools are broken or missing and the bricks badly made. Then the house of arithmetic is likely to fall down, or, more probably, it will never be built at all.

When we speak of 'tables' we often refer only to the multiplication tables, but we must not forget the others. All the 'primary facts',* in addition, subtraction, multiplication and division, are equally important as the tools and materials needed in our arithmetical processes. The better we know the facts and the more familiar they become, the more easily are we able to use them.

So we expect most children at school to learn the facts listed (see footnote*). They do not learn all the facts at once, of course, nor do all children learn at the same rate. There is a gradual and sound building-up of knowledge throughout the course.

HELPING CHILDREN TO LEARN THE FACTS

In this chapter the multiplication facts and tables are used to illustrate the various principles and methods suggested. But the same points apply with equal force to the facts of addition, subtraction and division.

A—*Understanding comes first*

The first and most important point is that a child should understand, at his own particular level, what he is doing. The facts, as he is learning them, should mean something to him and should not be mere sounds or symbols. It has been proved that learning and remembering become easier when there is understanding of what is to be learnt. Therefore we teachers must be very patient, especially in the early stages, taking time to ensure that meaning is given to the work.

* See: Addition facts: List III, page 51
   Subtraction facts: Lists IV, V, pages 67, 68
   Multiplication facts: List VIII, page 192
   Division facts: List IX, page 217.

Thus, children learning the multiplication facts should previously have understood *the nature* of multiplication, that it is a quick method of adding several numbers of equal size. This is explained in Chapter VII, where suitable activities and methods of approach are described. Related facts are then built up, using counters, or squared-paper, in table form as shown here.

One group of three   = 1 × 3 = 3

Two groups of three = 2 × 3 = 6

Three groups of three = 3 × 3 = 9

etc.

The facts have more meaning for children if we take every opportunity of pointing out everyday examples:—

(*i*) 'Here in our little garden we have three rows of tomato plants, with five in each row. How many plants altogether?'

(*ii*) A box of stores arrives and must be checked. It may contain pencils, chalks, ink-wells, exercise books—anything packed in rows, groups or packets. The children find that there are, for instance, twelve pencils in a packet. 'How many packets have we?' There are six. 'Now, how many pencils have we? —Yes, seventy-two. We found that out at once by knowing that 6 × 12 = 72.' Similarly, for things packed in rows the children count the number of rows and the number in each row, and find out how many objects there are by making use of a multiplication fact.

Such illustrations are easy to find. They are important not merely as examples but because they have local and up-to-date interest for the children.

B—*Memorizing follows understanding* ('*fixing the facts*')

The ability to memorize varies from child to child. We must always remember this when dealing with the facts and tables. It is found, in general terms, that children may be considered in three main groups:—(*a*) The comparatively few who very quickly learn the number facts. (It is waste of time to give them more apparatus and games when they already know the facts.) (b) The majority, those who learn the number facts quite well provided they have plenty of practice in games and other activities. (These, too, reach a stage where they can use the facts quickly and accurately without help.) (c) Some children who may never remember *all* the number facts. (For these we must provide something to which they can refer when in doubt.)

We must also realize that a child's ability to remember the facts depends partly on his use of them in actual examples. For instance, when a child has been introduced to the number facts in the 'table of twos', he should be given plenty of simple oral and written examples of multiplying by two. These should be carefully graded so that the child can easily get them right.

Besides this use of the facts there are many other ways by which children can be helped to learn and remember. We must have a variety of methods of approach, so that children can use as many of their senses as possible. Here are some suggestions.

(1) Learning through hearing and speaking

This has often been the main method of getting children to learn tables. They heard the sounds so many times (for example: 'four fives are twenty' over and over again) that they could repeat them at will, like nursery or nonsense rhymes, jingles, etc. *Some* children understood what they were saying and could use their knowledge, but many did not and, for them, it was 'mumbo jumbo' and quite useless for arithmetic.

Senseless repetition is to be deplored, but we must not make the mistake of neglecting oral learning. It is still an excellent way of 'fixing the facts' *after the child knows what the facts mean.* Up to a certain age children enjoy rhythmic repetition. In the saying of tables, however, such repetition should be in a 'natural' voice and not a 'sing-song'. Each fact should be spoken in the natural way in which any ordinary statement is made. When a child repeats that 'four fives are twenty', it should be clear to him and any listener that he means 'four groups of five make twenty'. Nothing is worse than the unpleasant and senseless drawl which has often been permitted in the 'saying of tables'.

The importance of tables lies in the facts. We want each child to know each fact by itself, and to be able to use it quickly and accurately. The essential speed is lost when a child has to chant through part of a table in order to find a particular fact. Therefore we must arrange practice in such a way that any single item of a table can be recognized and stated without hesitation.

Let us take the 'table of fours' as an example. We are repeating as a class or in groups, that is, using speech and hearing. Three suggestions are given on page 193; here are three more:

(*i*) Children play the 'game of echoes'. Half of them 'echo' (i.e. repeat) the facts said by the others. (The teacher makes sure that *this is a game*, the children thinking of echoes in mountains, from a building or the edge of the dense forest, etc.)

(*ii*) The teacher links the work with speech-training exercises by making use of lip-reading. A child stands in front of the class and 'says' a fact by exaggerating the movement of his lips, but without making a sound. The rest 'guess' what has been 'said'.

(*iii*) A leader of the group or class says a fact: 'Seven fours are twenty-eight'. The other children have to say the 'twin' fact (see page 188): 'Four sevens are twenty-eight.'

Many activities of this kind should be invented to provide variety and thus give pleasure and prevent boredom.

(2) *Learning through seeing*

This is clearly linked with oral learning of tables, since the children often have the written 'facts' in front of them. But we should help by using as many other 'visual aids' as possible. For instance:—

(*a*) *Charts*—The tables should be built up gradually (see Chart I, page 85), with the children, as more facts are learned (see pages 256–60), until the chart is complete. There are, of course, several possible forms of a chart of this kind. Such charts must be large enough to be seen from any part of the class room. Whatever kind of chart we make, we must show the children how it is built up and how it may be used. (Charts or tables should *not* be on view, of course, when knowledge of the number facts is being *tested*.)

Some teachers disagree with leaving a table chart in sight. They fear that children may come to rely on it, and therefore never learn to use the facts 'automatically'. But it must be remembered that *some* children will always need to refer to tables when making calculations. Such children can make little progress with new work if, at the same time, they have to struggle with the number facts.

(*b*) '*Number patterns*' *on cards*—Patterns of marks or objects often provide a practical demonstration of facts in the tables. Some may be found in real life: for example, the marks on a clock-face, a card of buttons, or lace-holes in a shoe. Others may

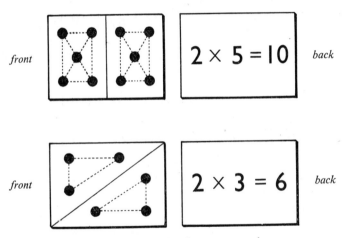

FIGURE 92.—Number-pattern cards

be invented by the teacher: for example, beads, shells, fruit-stones or other small objects are fastened to cards to illustrate various groupings (Fig. 92). The teacher shows a card and the children say what facts they can find from the pattern; the card is then turned over to see whether the answer is right. (Pairs of children may play this as a game.) Children may also make patterns to represent various groupings.

(*c*) *Patterns in a number-square*—The children make a number-square (Fig. 93). They go through the numbers from 1 to 100 and show the 'answers' in the facts of a particular table, either by drawing rings or crosses, or by shading. They note the

1	2	3	4	5	6	7	8	9	10
11	12	13	14	15	16	17	18	19	20
21	22	23	24	25	26	27	28	29	30
31	32	33	34	35	36	37	38	39	40
41	42	43	44	45	46	47	48	49	50
51	52	53	54	55	56	57	58	59	60
61	62	63	64	65	66	67	68	69	70
71	72	73	74	75	76	77	78	79	80
81	82	83	84	85	86	87	88	89	90
91	92	93	94	95	96	97	98	99	100

FIGURE 93.—Patterns in a 'number-square' (straight lines from the 'table of fives'; diagonal lines from the 'table of nines'). Children should make several of these number-squares if they want to show patterns from all the multiplication tables

pattern: for example, the diagonal for the 'table of nines' and the two straight lines for the 'table of fives'.

(*d*) *Table 'oddities'*—These often help in memorization and add to the fun and interest which children should find in numbers. For instance, in the 'table of nines' the figures in the 'answer' part of each fact add up to nine. (When we reach 99 the figures add up to 18, but adding the two figures of this number, 1 + 8, again gives 9.) There are several other interesting points about the 'table of nines' —to be found out, perhaps, by the children. They may also like to be told how, several centuries ago, this table was learned in a different way:

$$\begin{array}{ll} \mathbf{9} & 0 + 9 = 9 \\ \mathbf{18} & 1 + 8 = 9 \\ \mathbf{27} & 2 + 7 = 9 \\ \mathbf{36} & 3 + 6 = 9 \\ & \text{etc.} \end{array}$$

How many nines in ten	(10)?	1 and 1 over
How many nines in twenty	(20)?	2 and 2 over
How many nines in thirty	(30)?	3 and 3 over
How many nines in forty	(40)?	4 and 4 over
	etc.	

This story may also help children in division by nine.

Children sometimes find it easier to remember a particular fact after it has been shown in a special way. For instance, the teacher writes down: 1 2 3 4, and then puts in the signs to make up the fact $12 = 3 \times 4$; or 5 6 7 8 and inserts signs to get $56 = 7 \times 8$.

(*e*) *Flash-cards*—Self-corrective flash-cards (see pages 58, 73, 88 and 107) form one of the best aids to learning, through both seeing and hearing. Moreover they are simple to make (see page 472) and easy to use. The children may make them, provided the teacher ensures clarity and accuracy. These cards may be used in many games, of which the following are examples:

(*i*) '*Patience*' is a game which a child plays alone. In front of him he has a pile of eight or ten flash-cards, among which are six with multiplication facts he does not know. The 'question' sides of the cards are uppermost. He works through the cards, each time looking at the back of the card to see if his 'answer' is correct. When he is right he puts the card on his right-hand side; when wrong he puts the card to his left. He must then start again, using the left-hand pile of cards, and continue like this until all the cards are on the right, that is, until he knows all the facts on his set of cards. (If the child tries to 'cheat' himself by looking at the 'answers', it does not matter much! He is still making himself familiar with the facts.)

(*ii*) '*Snap*' (*or* '*Bingo*') may be played by pairs of children. Each child has a set of flash-cards, equal in number and with the same facts. One child has the 'question' sides on top, the other the 'answer' sides. The first puts a card on the table, and the second puts one over it. When a 'question' card (say '4 × 3 =') is followed by an 'answer' card with the right result (say '4 × 3 = 12', '3 × 4 = 12', '2 × 6 = 12' or '6 × 2 = 12'), the first child to say 'Snap' wins all the cards so far 'played' (put down). If a child says 'Snap' and is wrong, the other takes the pile of cards played. The child with most cards at the end of a given time is the winner.

This game gives enjoyable practice in finding and noticing that:

(I) Most facts have a 'twin', e.g. 6 × 4 = 24 and 4 × 6 = 24.

(II) In some cases different facts have the same 'answer', e.g. 6 × 4 = 8 × 3 = 12 × 2 = 24.

(*iii*) *The* '*Spinning Arrow*' (*or* '*Roulette*') is a game for a small group. The flash-cards with the facts which the teacher wants the group to learn are placed, 'question' side up, in a circle on a table. In the middle is a pointed stick or piece of stout cardboard which can spin on a nail or screw in a wooden base (Fig. 94). The children take it in turn to spin the arrow and answer the 'question' to which it points when it stops. The card is turned over to check the answer and is then put back in its place. A child who answers wrongly must quickly write down the 'fact' correctly. The child who has to write out the least number of facts (that is, who gets most right) is the winner.

The teacher may invent or adapt many other suitable games.

(3) Learning through touching and moving

Some children remember the facts more easily when allowed to use their sense of touch and movement. Let us suppose a child has difficulty in memorizing the fact 9 × 6 = 54. Here are two of the possible ways of helping:

(*i*) The teacher says: 'Look at it. Now say it to yourself—nine sixes make fifty-four. Now pretend to draw it on your desk with your finger, saying the numbers aloud. Now do it again without looking.'

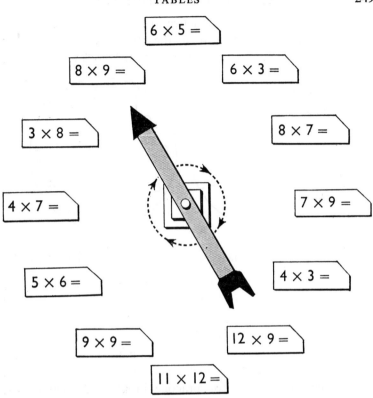

FIGURE 94.—The 'spinning arrow', a game for practice with flash-cards

(*ii*) The teacher says: 'Look at it. Now say it to yourself. Now pretend to "draw" it in the air.' (This is sometimes called 'sky-writing'.) The child shuts his eyes and imagines he has a huge pencil. He uses his whole arm to 'draw' the fact 'in the sky' while he repeats it aloud.

Such methods have sometimes proved effective when others have failed.

(*4*) *Learning through class-activities*

It is sometimes necessary (even desirable) to take all the children together as a class. Here are some suitable activities:

(*a*) *The clock-face*—This may be drawn quickly on the black-board, or a more permanent one can be made of cardboard or wood. If we want to give practice in the separate facts of the 'table of fours', we put a '4' in the middle of the clock-face (Fig. 95(*a*)). We point to any number on the clock and the child

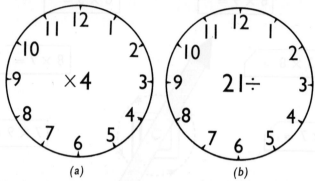

(a)   (b)

FIGURE 95.—A clock-face, used for practice in the arithmetical 'facts'

has to multiply it by four. The class may be divided into two or more teams, with one child appointed as scorer. Individual children in each team take their turns to answer. When an answer is wrong the question is passed to the next team, who, if correct, get an extra point. (*Note*—A nought should sometimes be put in the centre of the clock-face.) Several variations of this game may be devised for practice in all four arithmetical processes, as, for example, in Fig. 95(*b*).

(*b*) '*Find your partner*'—This game is best played out of doors, as it involves much movement. (Indoors it must therefore be played very quietly.) Half the class are given 'question cards', the other half 'answer cards', as shown here. At a given signal each child tries to find his 'partner'. When a pair are 'matched' they write down their 'fact', for example 18 ÷ 3 = 6. Then they go to the teacher and, if correct, continue the game with new cards.

$$18 \div 3 =$$

$$6$$

(*c*) *The 'tables relay race'*—The class is divided into teams and each is given a table to complete. For example, the teacher writes on the blackboard:

Team A	Team B	Team C
$1 \times 6 = 6$	$1 \times 9 = 9$	$1 \times 8 = 8$

On the word 'Go' the children in each team take it in turn to write the next fact in their table, as quickly as possible, and return to their seats. The team first completing its table correctly wins. A 'relay' of this kind may be made more difficult (e.g. writing the tables in reverse), and may be used in various other ways.

The teacher should devise many such games, using charts, cards, outline drawings, and so on.

(5) *Other varied activities*

As teachers we should always adapt apparatus and games to suit the particular children in our classes. We must also try to invent new activities, in order to keep our children alert and lively and prevent our methods becoming stale. The following suggestions for ways of helping children to remember the number facts may also prove useful in leading to further ideas.

(*i*) '*Snakes and ladders*' may be played with flash-cards by two, three or four children. The cards should be mixed (i.e. the facts should cover addition, subtraction, multiplication and division) and none of the 'answers' should exceed 20. The piece of cardboard, marked out in the manner shown in Fig. 96,

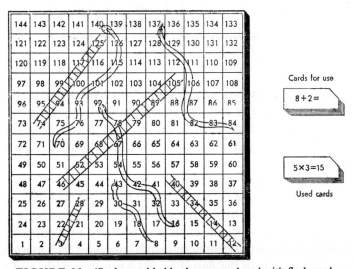

FIGURE 96.—'Snakes and ladders', a game played with flash-cards

should be about twelve inches square. The first child looks at the 'question' on the top flash-card, and gives his answer. He turns the card over to check. If correct (having given, for example, the answer 'ten' to '8 + 2 = '), he moves his counter forward (in this case, by ten places). If wrong he is not allowed to move his counter. The next child then takes his turn with the next card. When a move ends on a square at the *bottom* of a ladder the counter moves *up* the ladder. When a move ends on a square at the *head* of a snake the counter moves *down* the snake. The winner is the player who first reaches the last square (number 144).

(*ii*) *A 'four-way' flash-card* is useful when the teacher has shown that, by knowing one fact, it is possible to remember three related facts. Children may test each other, or the teacher may test a small group, by holding up the front of a card

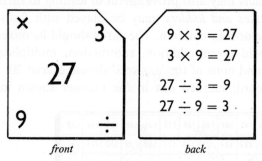

front   back

FIGURE 97.—A four-way flash-card, for learning related 'facts'

(e.g. Fig. 97(*a*)) and asking: 'What facts can you make up from these numbers?' The children should be able to give the four related facts (e.g. Fig. 97(*b*)). If the facts are given wrongly, the children are shown the back of the card, and should then repeat the facts correctly.

(*iii*) *'The elephant' never forgets!* So a model is used to help children to memorize facts with which they have had difficulty. The shape of an elephant is cut out of cardboard and hung in a convenient place. A saddle cloth is represented by a paper flap. Underneath this a different flash-card is concealed each morning. The children lift up the flap (Fig. 98) when they wish, and try

FIGURE 98.—'The elephant never forgets': another aid to memory

to memorize the fact. Towards the end of the school day the teacher asks every child to write down that day's fact.

FIGURE 99.—The 'tear-off' calendar, used as a reminder of multiplication 'facts'

(*iv*) *Calendar dates* give an opportunity to remind children of multiplication facts. When there is a movable or 'tear-off' calendar, the children usually take it in turn to change the date. Each child may write out the multiplication facts of which 'his' date reminds him, hanging his card on the calendar (Fig. 99). Children may notice that on certain dates, for example the 5th, 11th, etc., there are no facts except $5 \times 1 = 5$, $11 \times 1 = 11$, etc. (With children who are 'ready', this may be a good time to introduce *the idea* of prime numbers* and factors.†)

---

* If a number has no factors (other than 1 and itself) it is called a *prime number*, e.g. 3, 5, 7, 11, 13, 17, 19, 23, etc.
† See the footnote on page 199.

(*v*) *Practice sheets for revision* are useful. The arithmetical facts must be kept fresh in children's minds. For example, when a class is learning about measurement of length (British system), there is plenty of practice in the use of the tables of threes and twelves, but little in the others. It is important that *all* the facts should receive regular attention. A revision practice sheet (e.g. Fig. 100) ensures this. Each child has a copy of the same sheet.

A	1	5	3	8	0	6	4	2	7	9
B	5	9	7	2	4	0	8	6	1	3
C	9	3	1	6	8	4	2	0	5	7
D	3	7	5	0	2	8	6	4	9	1
E	6	0	8	3	5	1	9	7	2	4
F	0	4	2	7	9	5	3	1	6	8
G	4	8	6	1	3	9	7	5	0	2
H	8	2	0	5	7	3	1	9	4	6
J	2	6	4	9	1	7	5	3	8	0
K	7	1	9	4	6	2	0	8	3	5

FIGURE 100.—A revision practice sheet

(A sheet of numbers like this may be pasted in the back of a child's exercise book, as an aid to quick revision of the arithmetical facts)

The teacher writes his instructions on the blackboard; for example:

Multiply each number in line J by 4.
Multiply each number in line B by 7.
Add 5 to each number in line F.
Subtract each number in line D from 20.

Each child, having his sheet in front of him, writes the answers in his book as quickly as possible, like this:

J	8	24	16	36	4	28	20	12	32	0
B	35	63	49	14	28	0	56	42	7	21
F	5	9	7	12	14	10	8	6	11	13
D	17	13	15	20	18	12	14	16	11	19

It is sometimes useful to let children keep records of their speed and accuracy by writing down the number of facts they get right in a given time.

C—*The importance of using the facts*

(*1*) *Everyday examples*

To show how arithmetical facts are used in everyday life is one of the best ways of helping children to understand them. It is also a good way of helping to fix the facts in their minds. Here are a few examples to illustrate this.

(*i*) Except in leap years the month of February has 28 days. This may be linked with the fact that $4 \times 7 = 28$, since there are four weeks, each of seven days, in the month.

(*ii*) The table of fives may be linked with the minutes shown on a clock-face. (For instance, if the big hand moves round from twelve to four, it passes four groups, each of five minutes: $4 \times 5 = 20$.)

(*iii*) The table of twelves may be linked with feet and inches, or with shillings and pence.

(*iv*) The table of threes may be linked with feet and yards. (A line, measured by a yard-stick, is found to be 8 yards long. Its length in feet is then found from the fact: $8 \times 3 = 24$.)

(*2*) *Written exercises*

In this chapter we are concerned with understanding and memorizing the facts. But, as teachers, we must always remember that our main purpose is to help children to *use* the facts, quickly and correctly, in actual problems. So we must include written examples throughout the work. (An example such as 23×4 is easy to the child who knows that $4 \times 3 = 12$ and $4 \times 2 = 8$.)

We must remember, too, that the very act of working out examples, particularly when they are 'real', is itself an aid to memorizing the facts. It is advisable, therefore, to give ample practice in the use of the facts at every stage of the children's learning.

Before going on to consider the organization of this work, let us summarize our main points:

(a) Children should understand what the facts mean and how they are built up.
(b) Children should be helped to memorize the facts through enjoyable activities.
(c) Children should apply the facts to actual problems and written examples.
(d) The various methods of learning should go on together, side by side and linked together.

LEARNING THE FACTS—THE NEED FOR A SCHOOL PLAN

Children usually spend a great deal of time in learning the number facts. To avoid wasting this time and in order to reduce the risk of causing confusion and lack of confidence, we must plan and organize our work. This needs much careful thought and effort, as the plan should cover all the years of the course, so that a child may move from stage to stage, class to class and teacher to teacher without difficulty or delay.

Methods of learning the facts are discussed in previous chapters. The children gain understanding through many varied activities. Memorization is then aided by arrangement of the facts in 'sets', which are worked through in turn in various ways, including the use of practice-cards. Lastly, the facts are 'fixed' by flash-cards and other games, etc.

What about the 'tables'? Repetition of these used to be the common method of learning the facts. In itself it is not a bad method, for the tables show how the facts are related and they give children confidence. But it does become bad when it is the *only* method adopted. Children then tend to learn whole tables instead of the separate facts contained in them. So it is suggested that a better plan is to combine the gradual building-up and learning of tables with the use and learning of the separate facts suitably mixed in sets.

Chart I, page 85, shows the first stage in the building-up of the tables, and List C, page 87, is an example of the arrangement

CHART IV

EARLY MULTIPLICATION FACTS (88): THE BUILDING-UP OF TABLES (continued)

(The facts with a product not greater than twenty-four—from Chart I—and twenty-eight 'new' ones)

	0×1=0	0×2=0	0×3=0	0×4=0	1×5=5	1×6=6	1×7=7	1×8=8	1×9=9	1×10=10	1×11=11	1×12=12
1×0=0	1×1=1	1×2=2	1×3=3	1×4=4								
2×0=0	2×1=2	2×2=4	2×3=6	2×4=8	2×5=10	2×6=12	2×7=14	2×8=16	2×9=18	2×10=20	2×11=22	2×12=24
3×0=0	3×1=3	3×2=6	3×3=9	3×4=12	3×5=15	3×6=18	3×7=21	3×8=24	3×9=27	3×10=30	3×11=33	3×12=36
4×0=0	4×1=4	4×2=8	4×3=12	4×4=16	4×5=20	4×6=24	4×7=28	4×8=32	4×9=36	4×10=40	4×11=44	4×12=48
	5×1=5	5×2=10	5×3=15	5×4=20				1×0=0			0×1=0	
	6×1=6	6×2=12	6×3=18	6×4=24				2×0=0			0×2=0	
	7×1=7	7×2=14	7×3=21	7×4=28				3×0=0			0×3=0	
	8×1=8	8×2=16	8×3=24	8×4=32				4×0=0			0×4=0	
	9×1=9	9×2=18	9×3=27	9×4=36								
	10×1=10	10×2=20	10×3=30	10×4=40								
	11×1=11	11×2=22	11×3=33	11×4=44								
	12×1=12	12×2=24	12×3=36	12×4=48								

The 'new' facts:

9 × 3 = 27	7 × 4 = 28	3 × 9 = 27	4 × 7 = 28
10 × 3 = 30	8 × 4 = 32	3 × 10 = 30	4 × 8 = 32
11 × 3 = 33	9 × 4 = 36	3 × 11 = 33	4 × 9 = 36
12 × 3 = 36	10 × 4 = 40	3 × 12 = 36	4 × 10 = 40
	11 × 4 = 44		4 × 11 = 44
	12 × 4 = 48		4 × 12 = 48

in sets.* (The building-up of tables in horizontal and vertical form *at the same time* is chosen because it helps to show the relationship between a fact and its 'twin'.) Various forms of chart are possible, of course, but the following suggestions may be applied to any of them.

Having dealt with Chart I (the first sixty multiplication facts) and the eight practice sets of facts in List C, we go on to build up the tables in (say) six or seven stages. At each stage the facts are arranged in selected sets. From Chart I, for instance, we may go on to our second chart by adding (say) twenty-eight 'new' facts to the first sixty (as in Chart IV, page 257).

Thus our extension of the chart completes the tables of threes and fours (including the 'nought' facts), adds four facts to the 'table of noughts', two each to the tables of nine, ten, eleven and twelve, and one each to the tables of seven and eight. The children first build up the tables of threes and fours, and then learn them by the various methods described in this chapter. Then, knowing for example that $9 \times 3 = 27$, the children realize that they also know the 'twin' fact, $3 \times 9 = 27$, so they put this in the table of nines. They learn this table as far as this fact. Similarly, they add the new facts to, and learn, each of the other tables.

The next step is for the children to memorize each fact separately. List E, page 259, consists of nine selected sets of facts from Chart IV. Each of the twenty-eight 'new' facts is included twice, the others once each (with the exception of eight easy ones, which are left out). We take (say) the first set from the List:

Set 1 (from List E)

$1 \times$	$3 \times$	$11 \times$	$6 \times$	$0 \times$	$3 \times$	$4 \times$	$7 \times$	$12 \times$	$9 \times$	$1 \times$	$2 \times$
6	7	4	1	1	9	11	3	2	3	0	12
—	—	—	—	—	—	—	—	—	—	—	—
—	—	—	—	—	—	—	—	—	—	—	—

---

* Sets are made up on the following basis:
  (*i*) A List of sets contains *all* the facts in the tables so far built up at least once. (In the later Lists some of the very easy facts from Chart I may be omitted in order to limit the number of sets.) This ensures that *all* the facts at any particular stage are constantly practised and 'fixed'.
  (*ii*) In the first stage (List C, i.e. the facts from Chart I), each fact is included *once*. In the later lists of sets, each *new* fact should be included *twice*, in order to give more practice with it.
  (*iii*) Each set includes some 'easy' and some more difficult facts.
  (*iv*) A fact and its 'twin' are always included in the same set.

and the children learn these facts, using practice-cards, flash-card games, etc. We note, and help with, any difficulties. These same facts are then used in the multiplication process which

LIST E

EARLY MULTIPLICATION FACTS (from Chart IV)
ARRANGED IN SELECTED SETS*

Set 1	1 × 6	3 × 7	11 × 4	6 × 1	0 × 1	3 × 9	4 × 11	7 × 3	12 × 2	9 × 3	1 × 0	2 × 12
Set 2	2 × 11	1 × 9	3 × 8	2 × 0	10 × 3	9 × 4	9 × 1	11 × 2	8 × 3	0 × 2	3 × 10	4 × 9
Set 3	4 × 12	3 × 9	1 × 7	2 × 10	4 × 8	3 × 0	12 × 4	9 × 3	7 × 1	10 × 2	8 × 4	0 × 3
Set 4	0 × 4	4 × 9	3 × 11	1 × 8	2 × 9	4 × 7	4 × 0	9 × 4	11 × 3	8 × 1	9 × 2	7 × 4
Set 5	6 × 3	3 × 3	11 × 4	3 × 12	4 × 0	2 × 8	3 × 6	2 × 2	4 × 11	12 × 3	0 × 4	8 × 2
Set 6	7 × 2	5 × 3	4 × 4	3 × 10	4 × 7	2 × 0	2 × 7	3 × 5	1 × 1	10 × 3	7 × 4	0 × 2
Set 7	0 × 1	6 × 2	5 × 4	4 × 3	4 × 12	4 × 8	1 × 0	2 × 6	4 × 5	3 × 4	12 × 4	8 × 4
Set 8	10 × 4	3 × 0	5 × 2	6 × 4	1 × 11	12 × 3	4 × 10	0 × 3	2 × 5	4 × 6	11 × 1	3 × 12
Set 9	3 × 11	10 × 4	10 × 1	4 × 2	3 × 2	12 × 1	11 × 3	4 × 10	1 × 10	2 × 4	2 × 3	1 × 12

* The vertical columns may also be used as practice sets, though these tend to be 'random' rather than selected.

the child is learning or practising, and in suitable problems. Another set from the List is then treated in the same way, and so on until the children know *all* the facts in *all* the sets.

We then proceed to the building-up of the tables to the next stage (i.e. adding another group of 'new' facts). So we continue, in stages, until all the tables are complete and the children have learned them and the separate facts of which they consist.

All through this work the teacher must be prepared to adapt his plan to deal with any special difficulties. We may find, for example, that some children fail to learn '$6 \times 7 = 7 \times 6 = 42$'. Then we must not only make use of suitable apparatus and games again, but we must add these two facts to later sets in order to give further practice.

Time allocation

In general it is better to devote a short time *each* day, rather than a whole lesson once or twice a week, to the learning of arithmetical facts. Five to ten minutes per day, with a little longer on one day of the week, is probably enough. For example, at the start of a new stage, the building-up of a chart with the new facts may require twenty minutes or more of a lesson. But the learning or testing of a set, which may perhaps contain four of the new facts, is best done during the daily five-minute practice.

Children may be given the practice-cards for a particular set of facts, for instance, for five minutes at the beginning or end of a lesson; or while the teacher marks the register, attends to a visitor, or helps a small group with individual difficulties.

Extra time must be given to those children who cannot go on to new work because they do not know the facts well enough. They may be put into a small group, to have more practice with apparatus and games, while the rest of the class continues with normal work.

Tables of money and measures

The learning of the many tables concerned with money, length, weight, capacity, time, etc., is discussed, as the need arises, in later chapters of this book.

(The 'history' of money)

Most young children are interested in everything that goes on around them. They ask many questions: they want to know 'How?' and 'Why?' Sometimes they ask questions which their parents find it difficult to answer. Often these questions are about simple things to which grown-ups have become accustomed over the years and which they have accepted without thinking.

At school some children are too timid to ask questions even though they are still very curious about everything that goes on. Sometimes this is because the teacher is not approachable, but usually it is because it takes time for the children to get used to their new surroundings, and to find out that the teacher is very willing to listen to them.

A good teacher takes every opportunity of encouraging the children to ask questions. These help to keep the lessons 'alive'; they show that the children are taking an intelligent interest in what is being done; and they help the teacher to see whether the children really understand the work they are doing.

Like parents, teachers sometimes find it difficult to answer questions about simple things which they have themselves taken for granted. For example, a child may, with good reason, ask: 'Why do we put a "*d.*" at the side of the 6 when we write sixpence as 6*d.*? Why do we not put a "*p.*" for pence?' Other children may then follow this by asking why we use the '*s.*' and the '£' signs (in the British system of money). Many similar examples arise as the children are introduced to the various measures about which they have to learn.

The teacher should not discourage these questions, but should use them as a starting point for telling the children something about the history of the units they are considering. The five or ten minutes spent on such a discussion not only adds to the children's knowledge but also helps them to see that arithmetic grew out of, and is still concerned with, man's everyday needs.

Not all teachers know much about the history of money and measures. In some countries it may not be easy to find the information. Where it is possible, however, it is suggested that teachers should, at least, know something about the origin of the units of money and the common measures with which their teaching is concerned.

£ s. d.

Men's earliest kind of trading was the exchanging (or bartering) of goods for other goods. For example, if a farmer wanted to buy sheep from another farmer he might pay for them with sacks of grain. If he wanted someone to help him build a house he might pay for this help with food and wine. Difficulties used to occur, of course, when one of the traders refused to make an exchange because he did not want what the other trader had to offer. It became necessary for men to agree on standard objects for which anything else could be exchanged. In early days this standard of exchange consisted of common animals (for example, goats and sheep), which could easily be moved from place to place. Later, men began to find that pieces of metal (iron, copper, silver) were much more convenient as a standard means of exchange. They could be carried more easily; they could be kept to a standard size and quality; they could be split up into smaller units; and they lasted longer than other standards.

The value of these pieces of metal (or coins) was agreed upon by weighing them. A piece of a certain metal having a certain weight was given a particular value and was marked accordingly.

There have been many changes in the coinage of most countries since the early days. But in some countries the old *names* of the coins are still used, though their value, quality of metal, size and shape, may have changed a great deal.

For example, it is possible to see how the symbols £ *s.* *d.* for pounds, shillings and pence came into being in British money as a result of the Roman occupation of Britain, two thousand years ago.

The sign '£' is from the letter 'L' which is the first letter of the Latin word *libra* in the phrase *libra pondo*, which means 'a pound by weight'. This is clearly a reference to the days when the value of money was reckoned by weighing the metal of which it was made.

The '*s.*' for 'shillings' comes, perhaps, from a Roman coin called the *solidus*, but it is also probably linked with the Saxon word *scyllan* which means 'to cut' (that is, because a larger piece of metal was 'cut up').

The '*d.*' which in British coinage stands for 'pence' probably comes from another Roman coin, the *denarius* (though that was a silver coin, and not made of the same metal as the present-day penny).

Almost every coin in every country has an interesting history. Children often like to know about this. Teachers who find out a little about the history of their own coins have a good means of arousing children's interest. Moreover, if the 'history' is put simply, briefly, and in a lively manner, it helps the children to realize that to learn about money is not merely to 'do' another school subject. They begin to see how money developed from man's needs until it has come to play an important part in everyday life.

CHAPTER XVI

FURTHER STEPS IN MONEY

In the work described in Chapter IX the children are introduced to coins and their values through varied 'shopping' activities. This should now be extended, so that the children can deal with larger amounts of money. Written calculation now enters more and more into the work, but it is important to remember the principle that the work should be 'real' to the children. Wherever possible, we should bring into the lesson discussions which are related to money transactions in the children's everyday lives. Children may be old enough now to understand the talk they hear at home about wages. They themselves may even do some work for which they are paid. They now listen more intelligently to conversations among grown-ups about the buying and selling of animals, produce and other goods. In some areas they become interested in the payment and collection of taxes. Most children at this stage have begun to do real shopping, and so they take a much more active interest in coins.

Therefore, when dealing with money in both oral and written work, we should make use of these everyday situations.

It should be remembered that the main aim in teaching children about money is to enable them, as they grow up, to buy and sell, to trade, and to reckon their wages, salaries, savings, household expenses, etc. (Some children may have to pass examinations in arithmetic, for example, in order to go on to further schooling, or to enter or prepare for certain trades or professions. For some examinations, teachers may have to teach these children how to work out examples which are rarely found in real life. Such cases are discussed later in this chapter.

A—*The changing of money*

(1) *Learning the money facts**

So that 'shopping' activities can go on easily and with little

---

* In any currency, the money facts are made up by considering the ways in which each coin (or currency note) can be changed for a number of other coins

delay, the children have to learn how to change coins quickly. Coins of higher value are changed for a greater number of coins of lower value, and vice versa. This is done mainly in the 'shopping' itself, but extra practice in learning the important money 'facts' is worth while. Here are five ways in which this may be given:—

(*a*) *The 'bank'*—A number (say, two to four) of the more able children are the 'bankers'. They stand behind the 'cash-desk', on which piles of cardboard money, and paper 'notes', are placed. The other children in the class each have a 'coin' (or a number of 'coins'). They come in turn to the 'bank' and ask for their money to be changed. Having had it changed, they go back to their desks and write down what has been done. For example, if a child goes to the 'bank' with a florin (two-shilling piece) he may change it for four sixpenny-pieces. He then writes down in his book: 4 sixpences = 1 florin. This statement he takes to the teacher, who marks it, and if it is correct, supplies a new 'coin' for changing.

(*b*) *Practice-cards*—These should be made up by the teacher so as to ensure that the children get adequate practice in the money facts (Fig. 101) as well as in quick adding, subtracting, multiplying and dividing (Figs. 102* and 103).

Cards of the kind shown in Fig. 102 may be considered and used in two ways (see footnote*). It is advisable, therefore, to let children work through them twice. First they use them for counting out the coins required as 'change'. Then they use them for examples of subtraction to be worked out on paper.

(or notes). For example, in British currency a shilling can be changed for twelve pennies, twenty-four half-pennies, forty-eight farthings, four threepenny-pieces, or two sixpenny-pieces.

* *Note*—The 'making-up' asked for in the cards shown in Fig. 102 may be considered as a process of subtraction, if the calculation is worked out on paper. But many shop-keepers give 'change' by a method of adding, known as 'complementary addition'. They 'make up' the lower amount until it is the same as the higher amount. For example, the shop-keeper receives a ten-shilling note for something which costs three shillings and ninepence-halfpenny. He decides the amount of change by thinking first of the 3*s*. 9½*d*. He takes out enough coins (that is, 2½*d*.) to make up the amount to four shillings. Then he takes out six shillings to make up the amount to ten shillings. Then he hands over the 6*s*. 2½*d*. as 'change'.

K

Change	to shillings
£1 =	
£1 15s. =	
£1 18s. =	
48d. =	
96d. =	

Change	to pennies
3s. 6d. =	
5s. 0d. =	
1s. 10d. =	
2s. 11d. =	
6s. 1d. =	

Change	to s. d.
18 pennies =	
4 half-crowns =	
10 sixpences =	
8 3-halfpences =	
24 halfpennies =	

FIGURE 101.—Practice-cards for the 'changing' of money

How much to make up these amounts to 2s.?	
1s. 6d.	
1s. 2d.	
$10\frac{1}{2}$d.	
1s. $4\frac{1}{2}$d.	

How much to make up these amounts to 10s.?	
2s. 6d.	
7s. 3d.	
3s. $9\frac{1}{2}$d.	
6s. 8d.	

How much to make up these amounts to £1?	
15s. 6d.	
10s. 9d.	
2s. $8\frac{1}{2}$d.	
5s. 10d.	

FIGURE 102.*—Practice-cards for the giving of 'change' (by 'complementary addition') and the subtraction process with money

Addition of Money	7
8d. + 9d. =	
1s. 6d.+2s. 6d.=	
3s. 5d.+8s. 9d.=	
£1 12s.+£1 10s.=	
£6 5s.+£3 15s.=	

Multiplication of Money	4
8 × $1\frac{1}{2}$d. =	
4 × 6d. =	
4 × 2s. 6d. =	
6 × 1s. 8d. =	
8 × 2s. 6d. =	

Division of Money	2
£1 ÷ 2 =	
£1 ÷ 8 =	
2s. 6d. ÷ 5 =	
1s. ÷ 3 =	
2s. ÷ 8 =	

FIGURE 103.—Practice-cards for the addition, multiplication and division of money

(c) *Flash-cards*—These can be used in games to enable the children to learn to change money quickly. One side of the card (Fig. 104(*a*)) has a cardboard coin, or the name of a coin (or currency note), on it; the other side (Fig. 104(*b*)) tells how this coin (or note) may be changed for other coins. The children play in pairs, each pair having a small pile of cards. One child holds up a card, for example, the 'two-shilling piece', and shows it to the other child, who has to think of how to change it. If he

* See note on page 265.

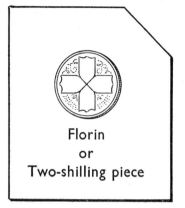

A **two-shilling** piece may be changed for:

2 shillings

or 4 sixpences

or 8 threepences

or 24 pence

Florin
or
Two-shilling piece

A **pound** may be changed for:

2 ten-shilling notes
or 8 half-crowns
or 10 two-shilling pieces
or 20 shillings
or 40 sixpences
or 240 pence

£1

(a) *fronts*   (b) *backs*

FIGURE 104.—Flash-cards for money 'changing': (a) fronts, (b) backs, of cards for the florin and the pound. (Teachers prepare similar cards for the coins and currency notes used in their own areas. The children may play various games with such cards)

Suitable size: about 5″ × 5″

gets any of the ways of doing this right, he can claim the card. He then holds up a card for the first child, and so on. At the end, the child with the most cards is the winner. (See Chapter XV for many other similar games.)

(d) *The 'money-fraction' board*—This piece of apparatus is also very useful at a later stage, when children have to learn the money facts expressed as fractions of a pound (see page 384). Strips of three-ply wood or stout cardboard, with models or drawings of coins on them, slide along ledges on a wooden board (see Fig. 133, page 384). The children come in turn to the front of the class to put a strip in its proper place. They then see, for example, how many five-shillings (or florins, shillings, etc.) there are in a pound note.

(*e*) *Money 'tables'*—These should be learned in the same way as other tables by the various detailed methods described in Chapter XV. For example, by:

(*i*) Short periods of oral repetition.
(*ii*) Games in groups (using flash-cards).
(*iii*) Class-activities.

The teacher should make sure that the children understand how the money is made up. It is not enough merely to be able to repeat the table. It is important therefore to *build up* the table (Chart V), *with the children*, making use of real or imitation coins to illustrate what is happening.

CHART V

A MONEY CHART—*The pence table*

Parts of a penny

2 farthings	=	1 half-penny
2 half-pennies	=	1 penny
4 farthings	=	1 penny

The pence table

12 pence	=	1 shilling
18 pence	=	1 shilling and sixpence
20 pence	=	1 shilling and eightpence
24 pence	=	2 shillings
30 pence	=	2 shillings and sixpence
36 pence	=	3 shillings
40 pence	=	3 shillings and fourpence
48 pence	=	4 shillings
50 pence	=	4 shillings and two pence
60 pence	=	5 shillings
70 pence	=	5 shillings and tenpence
72 pence	=	6 shillings
80 pence	=	6 shillings and eightpence
84 pence	=	7 shillings
90 pence	=	7 shillings and sixpence
96 pence	=	8 shillings
100 pence	=	8 shillings and fourpence
108 pence	=	9 shillings
110 pence	=	9 shillings and twopence
120 pence	=	10 shillings
130 pence	=	10 shillings and tenpence
132 pence	=	11 shillings
140 pence	=	11 shillings and eightpence
144 pence	=	12 shillings

The table of pence—The children should be shown that the table they are building up (Chart V) makes use of the 'table of twelves', but also includes the intermediate tens. This enables them to make calculations more quickly and accurately, since they have less difficulty with adding or subtracting. For example, if they want to change forty-one pence to shillings, they know that forty pence make three shillings and fourpence. So forty-one pence may be seen at once as three shillings and fivepence. *

The table of shillings—Some teachers like their children to learn a shillings table, but there is no need for this if the children know how to count in tens and twenties. For example, if they want to change seventy-three shillings to pounds and shillings, they count: 'Twenty, forty, sixty—that is, three pounds. Thirteen shillings more make three pounds, thirteen shillings. Other teachers prefer their children to think of each ten shillings as a ten-shilling note. So that seventy-three shillings are considered as seven ten-shilling notes and three shillings more. This then becomes three pounds, one ten-shilling note, and three shillings.

(2) *Changing money by written calculation*

When children know the important money 'facts', and can use their knowledge easily in shopping and everyday transactions, it may seem unnecessary for them to learn to change money by written calculation. For some children it is a waste of time, and the teacher must decide. It may sometimes be necessary, however (particularly for children who are going on to a further study of arithmetic), to work out problems in which sums of money must be changed from certain units into others. For example, it is necessary to change £5. 13*s*. 6*d*. into sixpences

---

* Some teachers prefer to make up the pence table by using the table of twelves only. That is:

$$12 \text{ pence} = 1 \text{ shilling}$$
$$24 \text{ pence} = 2 \text{ shillings}$$
$$36 \text{ pence} = 3 \text{ shillings, etc.}$$

With this method, if the children want to change forty-one pence to shillings, they say: 'Three shillings are thirty-six pence; fivepence more to make forty-one pence. So forty-one pence is three shillings and fivepence.'

in a problem such as 'How many children can each be given sixpence from a fund which amounts to £5. 13s. 6d.?'

Here is the method suggested for this example:—

The five pounds are changed to one hundred shillings by multiplying by twenty. The hundred shillings are added to the thirteen shillings making one hundred and thirteen shillings. These are changed to sixpences by multiplying by two, and the one sixpence is added to give the answer.

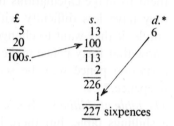

Again, this kind of written changing becomes necessary when considering certain types of division examples. For instance: 'How many books each costing 2s. 1d. can be bought for £3. 8s. 9d.?' In this it is necessary to change both amounts to pence.

The 2s. 1d. can easily be changed to twenty-five pence, but the £3. 8s. 9d. must be changed by written calculation as shown.

The children are helped in this work if they keep the columns widely spaced so that the working does not become confused.

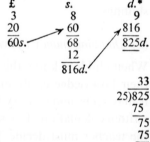

At times it may be necessary to change numbers of small units of money into larger units. For example, to find the total amount of money spent on one thousand three-penny stamps it becomes necessary to change the thousand three-pences into pounds, shillings and pence. This can be done either (*i*) by long division, dividing 1,000 by 80 (since there are eighty threepences in one pound); or (*ii*) by two division processes, dividing by 4 to bring the threepences to shillings and then dividing the shillings by 20 to bring them to pounds.

In this kind of changing, particularly when it is necessary for

* The 'arrows' do not, of course, appear in the children's working.

'carrying' in the multiplication process, it is often convenient to use a short form of division, in which the working is done 'in the head'. For example, to change 1,840 pence to shillings, the short form of dividing by 12 is as shown, and the answer is put underneath. To change 153 shillings to pounds the 15 tens are regarded as fifteen ten-shilling notes and divided by 2. (Because we are dealing with the tens only, the 0 and the 3 are crossed out.) This gives £7 and one ten-shilling note and 3 shillings, that is £7. 13s.

12)1840
153 shillings and
4 pence

2̶0̶)15̶3̶ shillings
£7 13 shillings

These two examples may be put together if we have to change 1,840 pence into pounds, shillings and pence.

In the past some teachers have made the mistake of wasting children's time and energies by giving too much work in the written changing of money. The children formed the impression that this changing is an end in itself, whereas it is only necessary for particular purposes. The method to be used for changing money has to be clearly taught in its various stages, but the importance of the work should not be over-emphasized.

12)1840*d.*
2̶0̶)15̶3̶ shillings and 4 pence
£7 and 1 ten-shilling
and 3 shillings

£7   13   4

B—*Addition of money*

The first activities which cause the children to add sums of money together are concerned with 'shopping'. For example, a child 'buys' one article for threepence and one for fourpence. He records this activity in his book as a simple addition showing that he has spent a total of sevenpence.

(*1*) *Further activities*

(*a*) *Making bills*—'Shopping' is also the best approach to the addition of larger sums of money. *Before* they 'buy' anything at the 'shop' the children make out a simple shopping list. They note down the price of each article, return to their seats and find the total money needed to pay for their purchases. Then they go back to the shop with the required money. The bill is written down as in Fig. 105.

Bought from Mr. Bolu		
	s.	d.
I toy	2	4
I plate	I	3
I book	I	3
Total	4	10

FIGURE 105.—Making out a simple shopping bill

We should always regulate the items carefully, so that the bills do not bring in difficulties for which the children are not ready. For example, in the bill shown in Fig. 105, the total of pence is less than twelve. This prevents any difficulty with 'carrying' at the early stages. After the 'carrying' stage is reached (see Analysis 5, page 284), there is no need to limit the prices.*

(b) *Using shopping boxes*—These are a means whereby the teacher can control the children's work in easy stages. There should be a box between each pair of children. Inside the box are a number of small articles (or pictures) with a price tag tied on each. The two children share the articles between them and then make out a bill for 'buying' them.

(c) *Collecting 'everyday' prices*—The children should be encouraged to look around the market and the shops, to read newspapers, magazines, advertisements, etc., for detailed information on the prices of all kinds of goods for sale in their area. They should also find out the rates of wages being paid, the selling price of farm produce, the cost of travelling, and any other money information which may help to give meaning and interest to their work in school.

We should use this collected information in making up the examples given to the children.

(2) The written work in addition of money

The detailed steps in teaching addition of money are outlined on pages 284–7. But there are also a few points which we should keep in mind, so that we can help the children to understand, and be more accurate in their working.

(a) *'Carrying' from pence to shillings*—In dealing with British

---

* Prices should also correspond with those found in local markets and shops (see paragraph (c)).

money children are faced with a new situation when they come to the 'carrying' step. They are previously used to the idea of 'carrying' (to the tens-column) if the units total is ten or more. They now have to learn the idea of 'carrying' only when the total of pence is twelve or more, and then only *after* they have 'changed' the pence into shillings. The idea is not difficult for children to grasp, if they have had plenty of practice in changing pence to shillings in shopping activities and at the 'bank'.

The children are already used to the idea of standard methods in ordinary addition. So it comes naturally to them to use standard phrases in dealing with money. In the example shown here, the standard working may be in one of two forms.

In the first method the pence are changed into shillings while the addition is being done:—

```
 s.  d.
 2   7 +
 8   6
 3   4
 4   8
────────
19   1
 2
```

(*i*) 'First add the *pence*.
    Eightpence and fourpence make a shilling.
        And sixpence makes one and sixpence.
        And sevenpence makes two shillings and a penny.
    Put the 1 penny in the pence-column of the answer, and 'carry' the 2 shillings to the shillings-column.
    Now add the *shillings*.
    Two shillings I am carrying, and four make six; and three make nine; and eight make seventeen; and two make nineteen.
    Put the nineteen in the shillings-column of the answer.
    The answer is: nineteen shillings and one penny.'

In the second method the pence are added together and changed into shillings *after* the total is reached, like this:

(*ii*) 'First add the *pence*.
    Eight and four make twelve.
        And six make eighteen.
        And seven make twenty-five.
    Twenty-five pence make two shillings and a penny.'

We then continue as in the first method.

(*b*) *Carrying from the shillings to the pounds*—When children reach the stage of working examples where the total of shillings is twenty or more, we must decide upon the method to be

K*

adopted and the standard phrases to be used. There are many variations in these and two of them are mentioned here:

(*i*) Dealing with the shillings-column in the example shown, the shillings are added as ordinary numbers and the *total* changed into pounds like this:—

£	s.	d.
2	14	2 +
1	8	0
2	16	3
1	15	4

'Five and six make eleven.
    And eight make nineteen.
    And four make twenty-three.
Now add the tens.
Twenty-three and ten make thirty-three, and ten   2
    make forty-three, and ten make fifty-three.
Fifty-three shillings are changed to two pounds, thirteen shillings.
Put the "13" in the shillings-column of the answer, and carry the "2" to the pounds-column,' etc.

(*ii*) In the shillings-column the units are added first, and the tens are then regarded as ten-shilling notes and added separately, like this:—

£	s.	d.
2	14	2 +
1	8	0
2	16	3
1	15	4
8	13	9
2	2	

'Five and six make eleven.
    And eight make nineteen.
    And four make twenty-three.
Put the "3" in the units-column of the shillings, and carry the "2" ten-shilling notes.
Now add the ten-shilling notes.
Two I am carrying and one makes three.
    And one makes four.
    And one makes five.
Five ten-shilling notes make two pounds and one ten-shilling note.
Put the "1" in the tens-column of the shillings, and carry the "2" to the pounds-column,' etc.

This method has the advantage of using the idea of an actual part of British currency, the ten-shilling note, although it is considered by some teachers to lead to more mistakes in calculation. But the idea is also helpful later when dealing with large numbers of shillings, as in some multiplication examples (see page 279).

C—*Subtraction of money*

The detailed steps in the teaching of subtraction of money are given in Analysis 5 on pages 284–6. But we ought not to limit the work to mechanical examples such as those given there. It is important, particularly in the early steps, to make sure that the children understand that what they are doing is related to everyday life. So we continue to make plenty of opportunities for 'shopping' activities in which subtraction is needed. The children are each given a sum of money and are asked to buy certain articles with it. *Before* they go to the 'shop', they work out how much change they should receive. Then they make their 'purchase' and check that the money they are given in change is correct. If it is not, then either they themselves have calculated wrongly, or the 'shopkeeper' is wrong and the mistake must be put right.

Children should be given other examples, in which they find the difference between two sums of money. These again should be based upon the information collected by the children themselves inside and outside school. For example, if there is a school fund, they may find the difference between the amounts collected in successive terms, or the difference between the amount collected by two different classes during the year. They may also find the profit or loss on the school garden or farm produce, or on an animal that has been bought and sold.

(*1*) *The method of subtraction to be used*

When the children have reached the stage of subtraction where, for example, the number of pence in the top line is smaller than the number of pence in the bottom line, we are again faced with the decision as to which method of subtraction is to be used. The stages in Analysis 5 are based on the method known as 'decomposition', but the method of 'equal additions' is just as good, if properly understood by the children. What is most important is that *we should not change the method we have previously used in dealing with numbers. If we have previously used 'decomposition', we should continue with 'decomposition' in subtraction of money.* To do otherwise would greatly confuse the children.

Both these methods of subtracting numbers, which are applied in the same way when we deal with money and measures, are fully described in Chapter XII.

(*a*) *Subtraction by 'decomposition'* —Here are standard phrases which may be used in working an example of subtraction, such as the one shown, using the method of 'decomposition'. (The example chosen is, of course, one of the later examples in Analysis 5, page 286, and should be led up to by carefully graded steps.)

	£	s.	d.
	12	6	4 −
	6	9	5
	---	---	---

'First deal with the *pence.*
I cannot take five from four.
So I use one of the six shillings (leaving five shillings), and
    change it to twelve pence.
Now I have sixteen pence.*
Five from sixteen leaves eleven.
Put the "11" in the pence-column of the
    answer.
Now deal with the *shillings.*
I cannot take nine from five.

	£	s.	d.
		25	
	1	5	16
	12	6	4 −
	6	9	5
	---	---	---
	5	16	11

So I use one of the twelve pounds (leaving eleven pounds), and change it to twenty shillings.
Now I have twenty-five shillings.
Nine from twenty-five leaves sixteen.
Put the "16" in the shillings-column of the answer.
Now deal with the *pounds.*
Six from eleven leaves five.
Put the "5" in the pounds-column of the answer.
The answer is: five pounds, sixteen shillings and elevenpence.'

(*b*) *Subtraction by 'equal additions'*—Here are the standard phrases which may be used when the same example is done by the method of 'equal additions'.

* Some teachers prefer their children not to add the shilling (twelve pence) to the fourpence. They first take the fivepence from the twelve pence and then add the fourpence to what is left. The idea is also applied in the shillings-column when using one of the pounds. The example looks like this.

	£	s.	d.
		20	
	1	5	12
	12	6	4 −
	6	9	5
	---	---	---
	5	16	11

'First deal with the *pence*.

I cannot take five from four.

So I add one shilling (twelve pence) to the fourpence in the top line (making sixteen pence*), and add one shilling to the nine shillings in the bottom line (making ten shillings).

Now return to the pence.

Five from sixteen leaves eleven.

Put the "11" in the pence-column of the answer.

Now deal with the *shillings*.

I cannot take ten from six.

So I add twenty shillings to the six shillings in the top line (making twenty-six shillings), and add one pound to the six pounds in the bottom line (making seven pounds).

Now return to the shillings.

Ten from twenty-six leaves sixteen. Put the "16" in the shillings-column of the answer.

Now deal with the *pounds*.

Seven from twelve leaves five.

Put the "5" in the pounds-column of the answer.

The answer is: five pounds, sixteen shillings and elevenpence.'

£	s.	d.
12	6	4
6	9	5

£	s.	d.
	26	16
12	6	4
7	10	
6	9	5
5	16	11

D—*Multiplication of Money*

In everyday life it is very rare indeed for people to have to perform *long* calculations in the multiplication of money. If it is needed in business the work is usually done by using a 'ready reckoner'.† Most of the everyday examples of multiplication are connected with shopping, and usually deal with small sums of money. In teaching this work to children it is most important to introduce it by 'shopping' and 'buying and selling' activities which have meaning for the children in their everyday lives. The early examples to illustrate multiplication (Chapter IX) involve buying several articles when the price of one is known, the total amount of money used being no greater than two shillings.

In multiplying so that larger totals are obtained, children should still deal with amounts of money which they understand. For example, they may find the cost of eight sheep, if one sheep

* See footnote on page 276.   † See page 280.

costs one pound, ten shillings; or they may find the amount
spent on school books for a class of thirty-two if each child's
books cost ten shillings and fourpence. It is not necessary,
however, to find practical illustrations for *every* example given
to the children. Mechanical examples should also be given so
that the children have plenty of practice in multiplying with
speed and accuracy.

(*1*) *Setting down the work*

A detailed analysis of the steps in teaching multiplication of
money are given on page 288. There are many methods in use
throughout the world. The method given here of working and
setting down is considered to be most likely to give accurate
results. It also lends itself most easily to explanation, since it
follows from the multiplication of ordinary numbers.

The method depends upon:

(*a*) The children's knowledge of the multiplication facts.

(*b*) Their ability to change from farthings to pence by dividing
by four; from pence to shillings by dividing by twelve; from
shillings to pounds by dividing by twenty. This changing can be
done 'in the head', but, in the more difficult examples, should be
properly set down so that possible errors can be seen.

(*c*) The ability to multiply 'up and down'—that is, to understand the principle that, for example, $3 \times 14 = 14 \times 3$. This
principle becomes useful when multiplying by large numbers.
For example, in multiplying 8*d.* by 47, it is possible to get the
answer by multiplying 47 by 8.

The two examples here show a standard method of setting
down and working.

In the first example there is not very much calculation since
the total of pence can be changed easily by reference to the
pence table.

(*i*) 'First deal with the *pence.*
  Seven eights are fifty-six.
  Fifty-six pence make four shillings and eightpence.
  Put the "8" in the pence-column of the answer
    and carry the "4" to the shillings-column (under
    the line).

$$\begin{array}{rr} s. & d. \\ 2 & 8 \times \\ & 7 \\ \hline 18 & 8 \\ \hline & 4 \end{array}$$

Now deal with the *shillings*.
Seven twos are fourteen.
Fourteen and the four being carried make eighteen.
Put the "18" in the shillings-column of the answer.
The answer is: eighteen shillings and eightpence.'

The next example illustrates the last step of the process given in Analysis 5 on page 291. It should, of course, be led up to by carefully graded steps. We must also remember that such examples as this *very rarely* occur in everyday life. It is best to devote most time and attention to examples where smaller amounts of money are involved.

(*ii*) This second example (£37. 16*s*. 9¾*d*. × 47) shows the process where the working is set down in columns underneath the answer line.

£	*s.*	*d.*	
37	16	9	¾ ×
(47)	(47)	47	
1778	10	2	¼
39	38	35	4)141
329	282	423	35*d*. and 1*f*.
1410	470	12)458	
1778	20)790	38*s*. and 2*d*.	
	£39. and 10*s*.		

These points should be noted:
(I) The work should be well spaced out so that confusion in the working is avoided. Some teachers like the working in each section of the example to be separated by vertical lines (as in the example shown).
(II) Instead of multiplying by the '47' it is easier to multiply by the '9', and the '16', etc.
(III) It is helpful to some children to write the '47' in each column.
(IV) The total in the farthings column (after multiplication) is changed to pence, which are put in the pence-column. The total of pence is changed to shillings (by dividing by twelve, using short division), which are put in the shillings-column. Similarly the total of shillings is changed to pounds which are transferred to the pounds-column.
(v) The arrows shown in the example are not, of course,

required to be put in by the children, but standard phrases should be used if it is found that they are still needed.

(2) Short methods

In dealing with money, particularly where multiplication is involved, there are often occasions when short methods of calculation are possible. Children should be shown these methods and encouraged to look for the occasions when they can be applied. It is a source of interest and delight to them to find that the calculation can be made quickly, but they ought also to understand the reasons for such methods. Here are four examples. The teacher in his own area may find many others.

(*i*) The cost of a dozen (twelve) articles at one penny is one shilling. Therefore the cost of a dozen (twelve) articles at any number of pennies is the same number of shillings.

For example: Because 12 articles at 1*d*. cost 1 shilling,
12 articles, at 5*d*. each, cost 5 shillings;
12 articles, at 4½*d*. (four and a half-pence) each, cost 4 shillings and sixpence (four and a half shillings).

(*ii*) The cost of twenty articles at one shilling is one pound. Therefore the cost of twenty articles at any number of shillings is the same number of pounds.

For example: 20 articles, at 9 shillings each, cost 9 pounds.

(*iii*) If a sum of money to be multiplied is near to a 'round' figure it is easier to multiply the round figure and then subtract.

For example, £2. 19*s*. 10½*d*. multiplied by 48 could first be considered as £3 multiplied by 48. Forty-eight three half-pences could then be subtracted to give the required answer, as shown here:

(*iv*) It is sometimes a good idea to build up *with the children* a ready reckoner which can be used for local purposes. For example, if the price of local vegetables (or other commodity)

£	*s*.	*d*.	
3	0	0	×
		48	
144	0	0	
	6	0	
143	14	0	

varies between 5½*d*. and 7½*d*., children may make up a ready reckoner as shown in Chart VI.

E—Division of money

In the early work dealing with money the children meet the division process very simply in the form of problems occurring

CHART VI

A READY RECKONER

	5½d.	6d.	6½d.	7d.	7½d.	etc.	etc.
1	5½d.	6d.	6½d.	7d.	7½d.	etc.	etc.
2	11d.	1s. 0d.	1s. 1d.	1s. 2d.	1s. 3d.	etc.	etc.
3	1s. 4½d.	1s. 6d.	1s. 7½d.	1s. 9d.	1s. 10½d.		
4	1s. 10d.	2s. 0d.	2s. 2d.	2s. 4d.	2s. 6d.		
5	2s. 3½d.	2s. 6d.	2s. 8½d.	2s. 11d.	3s. 1½d.		
6	2s. 9d.	3s. 0d.	3s. 3d.	etc.	etc.		
7	3s. 2½d.	3s. 6d.	3s. 9½d.				
8	3s. 8d.	4s. 0d.					
9	4s. 1½d.	4s. 6d.	etc.				
10	4s. 7d.						
11	5s. 0½d.	etc.					
12	5s. 6d.						
13	5s. 11½d.						
14	6s. 5d.						
15	6s. 10½d.						
etc.	etc.						

Note—A chart of this kind should be made up *with* the children. The figures for prices and quantities should be suited to the sales of some local commodity with which the children are familiar.

during 'shopping' activities. For example, they find that the article they want to 'buy' has a price label marked '3 for 1s.'. They find out by division how much they must pay for one article only. In the early stages this work is not very different from the division of ordinary numbers (see Chapters VIII and XIV, which it is advisable to re-read in this connexion). An understanding of the two-fold aspect of the process is necessary to a full understanding of methods of teaching division of money. Arising from this two-fold aspect of division, there are two different kinds of division problem in dealing with money.

For example:—

(a) If 15 articles cost 10 shillings (120d.), how much does one cost?
   This can be written down as 120d. ÷ 15 = 8d., i.e. a straightforward sharing example.

(b) If one article cost 1s. 3d. (15d.), how many can be bought for ten shillings (120d.)?
   This can be written as 120d. ÷ 15d. = 8. (Both amounts

must be changed to the same unit before division takes place.)

In the first example the answer is eight pennies.

In the second example the answer is eight articles.

The graded steps in teaching both these aspects of the division of money are set out in Analysis 5, page 288.

(*a*) *Division by sharing*—In the sharing examples the process is exactly as in long division except that remainders in each column have to be changed to the next unit. For example, here is a problem (*i*) in which the shillings remaining after the division has taken place must be changed to pence.

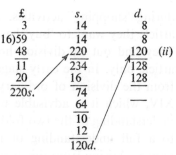

'Share 2*s*. 1*d*. between 5 boys. How much do they each get?'

In an example like this (*ii*): 'If 16 articles cost £59. 14*s*. 8*d*., what does one cost', the remainder in pounds has to be changed to shillings and the remainder in the shillings has to be changed to pence.

Note.—In dividing the 234 shillings by 16, it is necessary to deal with the 23 ten-shilling notes first.

This kind of calculation is *very seldom required*. The example is included here in order to demonstrate the *process* in full.

(*b*) *Division by grouping*—This is illustrated by the following problem: 'How many sheep, each costing £1. 2*s*. 9*d*., can be bought for £20. 12*s*. 8*d*., and how much is left over?'

It can be seen that the problem is to find out how many times the smaller sum of money is contained in the larger. The division can only take place if both sums of money are changed to the same unit. The convenient unit in this example is the penny.

Both sums must be changed to pence, and then the answer is found by long division as shown.*

£	s.	d.	£	s.	d.
1	2	9	20	12	8
20	20	264	20	400	4944
20s.	22	273d.	400s.	412	4952d.
	12			12	
	264d.			4944d.	

```
         18
273)4952
    273
    2222
    2184
      38
```

The answer is: eighteen sheep and there is 3s. 2d. (38d.) left over.

F—Summary of points to remember in teaching 'money'

1. A suitable graded scheme of work (such as that given on pages 484–91) should be followed.
2. The work, particularly at the early stages, should be based on shopping and everyday money transactions.
3. The money facts should be thoroughly learned.
4. Special attention should be paid to the accurate setting down of the work at each stage, particularly when 'changing' and 'carrying' are involved.
5. The teachers in a school (or area) should get together and decide upon the standard methods to be used for calculations.

* Again we must beware of wasting *children's* time. This type of example is rare, and is given here merely to show the process.

ANALYSIS 5

Suggested stages and steps in the teaching of money
(see Chapters IX and XVI)

Continued for Multiplication and Division

1. STAGE	2. ACTIVITIES	3. ADDITION	4. SUBTRACTION (using the method of 'decomposition')
A. Dealing with AMOUNTS UP TO 2s.	The use of the class-room shop. The making of 'rubbings' of coins. The use of the class-room bank. The use of the matching tray. The recording of simple shopping activities. The use of practice-cards.	(1) Adding *pence*. (a) Answers less than 1s. $\begin{array}{r} d. \\ 2\ + \\ 7 \\ \hline \end{array}$ (b) Answers up to 2s. $\begin{array}{rr} s. & d. \\ & 9\ + \\ & 10 \\ \hline \end{array}$ (2) Adding *shillings and pence*. (a) Early experiences. $\begin{array}{rr} s. & d. \\ 1 & 2\ + \\ & 5 \\ \hline \end{array}$	(1) Subtracting *pence*. (a) From pence. $\begin{array}{r} d. \\ 9\ - \\ 5 \\ \hline \end{array}$ (b) From shillings and pence. (i) No changing. $\begin{array}{rr} s. & d. \\ 1 & 8\ - \\ & 4 \\ \hline \end{array}$ (ii) Changing. $\begin{array}{rr} s. & d. \\ 1 & 8\ - \\ & 11 \\ \hline \end{array}$
B. Dealing with AMOUNTS UP TO £1.	The use of the class-room shop. The use of the class-room bank. The use of shopping lists. The collection of information about prices in the market, shops and newspapers. The use of everyday happenings which involve money. The making and use of simple ready reckoners.	(b) No changing. $\begin{array}{rr} s. & d. \\ 12 & 2\ + \\ 3 & 5 \\ 4 & 3 \\ \hline \end{array}$ (c) Changing pence to shillings: (i) Pence total less than 24. $\begin{array}{rr} s. & d. \\ 1 & 4\ + \\ 2 & 9 \\ \hline \end{array}$	(2) Subtracting *pence and shillings* from pence and shillings. (a) No changing. $\begin{array}{rr} s. & d. \\ 2 & 8\ - \\ 1 & 5 \\ \hline \end{array}$

Problem-type examples, on pages 288–91.

...cards', etc.

The setting down and working of many and various examples, some given in 'problem' form.

than 24.

```
        s.  d.
 3  5 —  1 10 +
 1  8    3  9
─────    2  8
        ──────
14  2 —
11  5
──────
```

(c) Dealing with ½d.'s and ¼d.'s.

(i) No changing.

```
 d.      s.  d.      s.  d.
4½ —    2  4¾ —    3  9½ —
 2      1  2¼      2  5½
───    ──────     ──────
```

(ii) Changing.

```
 d.       s.  d.
8¼ —     4  6¼ —
4¾       1  2½
───     ──────

 s.  d.      s.  d.
5  8 —      8  — —
1  6¾       1 10½
──────     ──────
```

(d) Dealing with ½d.'s and ¼d.'s.

(i) No changing.

```
 d.       s.  d.
4½ +     1  3¼ +
 5       4
───     ──────
```

(ii) Changing.

```
 d.   d.   d.        s.  d.
4½ + 4½ + 4½ +      4  4½ +
5¼   5½   5¾        5  9¼
                    1  2¾
───  ───  ───      ──────
```

Note.—At all further stages some examples should be given which involve ½d.'s and ¼d.'s. * These are not given in this analysis.

C. Dealing with AMOUNTS GREATER THAN £1.

The use of the class-room shop and the class-room bank.

The collecting of information, regarding prices of goods in shops, of farm produce, of traders' materials, of wages, of rates and taxes.

The use of the information in making up shopping lists, wage bills, tax levies, etc.

The making of all kinds of ready reckoners.

The learning of the 'facts' in the money tables through the use of

(e) First ideas of changing shillings to pounds (up to £1. 19s. 11d.).

(i) No changing of pence.

```
 s.  d.           £  s.  d.
14  6 +     then  1  3  10
 9  4            ─────────
─────
23  10
```

(ii) Changing of pence and shillings.

```
 £  s.  d.   £  s.  d.
    14  6 +     18  8 +
     9  8       17  9
   ──────     ──────
```

(3) Subtracting from *pounds, shillings and pence.*

(a) No changing.

```
 £  s.  d.    £  s.  d.
12  0  0 —   12  8  0 —
 5  0  0      5  4  0
─────────    ─────────
```

(b) Changing.

(i) Shillings to pence.

```
 £  s.  d.
12  6  4 —
 6  4  7
─────────
```

* Except, of course, in areas where the particular coin is not used.

Continued for Multiplication and Divis...

ANALYSIS 5 (cont.)

1. STAGE	2. ACTIVITIES	3. ADDITION	4. SUBTRACTION (using the method of 'decomposition')
	'practice-cards', 'flash-cards' and class-activities. The setting down and working of many and various examples, some given in 'problem' form.	(3) Adding *pounds, shillings and pence*. (a) Changing shillings to pounds. 34s. = £1. 14s. 0d. 63s. = £3. 3s. 0d. (b) Adding pounds and shillings. (i) No changing. £ s. d. 1 2 0 + 2 12 0 (ii) Changing £ s. d. 1 12 0 + 3 13 0 (c) Adding pounds, shillings and pence. (i) No changing. £ s. d. 1 12 2 + 2 3 5 (ii) Changing pence to shillings. £ s. d. 1 5 9 + 3 2 8 (iii) Changing shillings to pounds. £ s. d. 2 13 2 + 4 12 4	(ii) Pounds to shillings. £ s. d. 12 6 4 − 6 8 2 (iii) Shillings to pence and pounds to shillings. £ s. d. 12 0 4 − 6 9 5

◀ Problem-type examples, on pages 288–**91.**

and shillings to pounds.

£	s.	d.	
4	17	9	+
2	15	7	
—	—	—	

£	s.	d.	
2	13	4	+
	15	0	
7	0	11	
—	—	—	

£	s.	d.	
	17	2	+
1	4	9	
3	15	10	
—	—	—	

ANALYSIS 5 (continued from preceding pages)

1. STAGE	5. MULTIPLICATION	6. DIVISION		7. 'PROBLEM'-TYPE EXAMPLES For instance:—
		(a) SHARING	(b) GROUPING	
A. Dealing with AMOUNTS UP TO 2s. (continued from page 284).	(1) Multiplying *pence* (by numbers up to 12). (a) No changing. $\begin{array}{r} d. \\ 3\ \times \\ 2 \\ \hline \end{array}$ (b) Easy changing and carrying. $\begin{array}{r} s.\ d. \\ 3\ \times \\ 5 \\ \hline \\ \hline \end{array}$	(1) Dividing *pence*. (a) No remainders. $8d. \div 4 \qquad 4\overline{)8}\ ^{d.}$ (b) Remainders. $11d. \div 5 \qquad 5\overline{)11}\ ^{d.}$ (2) Dividing *shillings and pence* (by numbers up to 12). (a) Early experiences. $1s.\ 0d. \div 2.$	Examples such as: (1) (a) How many 2d. stamps can I buy for 8d.? (b) How many boys can be given 3d. from 11d.? (2) (a) How many sixpences must I have to make 1s. 6d.?	(1) (a) Tom has 4d. Bill has 5d. How much have they altogether? (b) Mary had 1s. 8d. She bought a melon for 4d. How much has she left? (c) Find the cost of 7 penholders at 2d. each. (d) Share 1s. 6d. between three boys. How much do they each have?
B. Dealing with AMOUNTS UP TO £1 (continued from page 284).	(2) Multiplying *pence and shillings* (by numbers up to 12). (a) No changing. $\begin{array}{r} s.\ d. \\ 1\ \ 2\ \times \\ 4 \\ \hline \end{array}$ (b) Changing and carrying. $\begin{array}{r} s.\ d. \\ 1\ \ 2\ \times \\ 8 \\ \hline \end{array}$	(b) Changing remainder in the shillings. $\begin{array}{ccc} s.\ d. & s.\ d. & s.\ d. \\ 4\overline{)6\ \ 8} & 4\overline{)5\ \ 0} & 7\overline{)12\ \ 8} \end{array}$	(b) How many tins of milk at 4d. each can I buy for 5s.? (c) How much would be left over if as many boys as possible were given 7d. from a bag containing 12s. 8d.? (d) How many 2½d. stamps can be bought for 6s. 0d.?	(2) (a) Find the sum of 4½d., 1s. 4½d., and 5s. 9d. (b) Mary spent 3s. 8d. at the shop. She gave the shop-keeper 5s. 0d. How much change did she receive? (c) Tom earned 2s. 8d. each day for five days. How much did he earn altogether.

<table>
<tr><td>

... cost £5. 5s. 3½d. What is the price of one?

</td></tr>
</table>

C. Dealing with AMOUNTS GREATER THAN £1 (*continued from page* 285).

(3) Multiplying *pounds, shillings* and *pence* (by *numbers up to* 12).

(a) No changing.
$$\begin{array}{rrr} £ & s. & d. \\ 2 & 3 & 2 \times \\ & & 5 \\ \hline \end{array}$$

(b) Changing pence to shillings only.
$$\begin{array}{rrr} £ & s. & d. \\ 2 & 3 & 9 \times \\ & & 5 \\ \hline \end{array}$$

(c) Changing shillings to pounds only.
$$\begin{array}{rrr} £ & s. & d. \\ 2 & 5 & 2 \times \\ & & 5 \\ \hline \end{array} \qquad \begin{array}{rrr} £ & s. & d. \\ 2 & 4 & 2 \times \\ & & 5 \\ \hline \end{array}$$

$$\begin{array}{rrr} £ & s. & d. \\ 2 & 15 & 1 \times \\ & & 9 \\ \hline \end{array}$$

Various multiplication examples:
$$\begin{array}{cc} d. & \\ 1\tfrac{1}{2} \times & \\ 5 & \end{array} \quad \begin{array}{cc} s. & d. \\ 2\tfrac{1}{2} \times & \\ 7 & \end{array} \quad \begin{array}{cc} s. & d. \\ 4\tfrac{1}{2} \times \\ 8 \end{array}$$

$$\begin{array}{ccc} s. & d. & \\ 1 & 4\tfrac{3}{4} \times & 3 \\ & 7 & \end{array} \quad \begin{array}{cc} s. & d. \\ 3 & 5\tfrac{1}{4} \times \\ & 6 \end{array}$$

(i) Changing remainders in the pence.
$$\begin{array}{ccccc} d. & & s. & d. & s. & d. \\ 4)\overline{10} & 8)\overline{8\ \ 6} & 5)\overline{10\ \ 7\tfrac{1}{2}} \end{array}$$

(ii) Changing remainders in shillings and pence.
$$\begin{array}{cc} s. & d. \\ 8)\overline{9\ \ 6} & 7)\overline{15\ \ 10\tfrac{3}{4}} \end{array}$$
$$\begin{array}{cc} s. & d. \\ 9)\overline{16\ \ 10\tfrac{1}{2}} & 9)\overline{16\ \ 11} \end{array}$$

(3) Dividing *pounds, shillings* and *pence* (by *numbers up to* 12).

(a) Changing remainders in the pounds.
$$\begin{array}{ccc} £ & s. & d. \\ 9)\overline{20\ \ 5\ \ 0} & 9)\overline{23\ \ 17\ \ 9} \end{array}$$

(b) Changing remainders in pounds and shillings.
$$\begin{array}{ccc} £ & s. & d. \\ 6)\overline{17\ \ 17\ \ 6} & 6)\overline{16\ \ 17\ \ 6} \end{array}$$

(c) Changing remainders in pounds, shillings and pence.
$$\begin{array}{ccc} £ & s. & d. \\ 8)\overline{18\ \ 12\ \ 6} & 8)\overline{21\ \ 15\ \ 0} \end{array}$$

$$\begin{array}{ccc} £ & s. & d. \\ 8)\overline{21\ \ 15\ \ 1} \end{array}$$

(3) (a) How many gallons of petrol can be bought for £3. 13s. 4d. if one gallon costs 4s. 7d.?

(b) The foreman paid £42. 15s. 0d. in wages. Each man received £4. 15s. 0d. How many men were there?

(c) A sheet of 4d. stamps is worth £4. 10s. 0d. How many stamps are there in a sheet?

(d) Children pay 5d. for their dinner at school. The teacher collected £3. 8s. 9d. for dinners for five days. How many children had dinner each day?

(3) (a) The 'takings' on the steamer which crosses the river were £9. 15s. 6d. on Monday, £12. 17s. 3d. on Tuesday and £7. 0s. 9d. on Wednesday. How much was taken in all during these three days?

(b) One fisherman sold his 'catch' for £4. 7s. 6d. A second sold his for £7. 4s. 6d. How much did the second get more than the first?

(c) If an engine-driver is paid 3s. 4d. an hour, what is he paid for a week in which he works 44 hours?

Note.—At all further stages some examples should be given which involve ½d.'s and ¼d.'s.* These are not given in this analysis.

* Except, of course, in areas where the particular coin is not used.

ANALYSIS 5 (cont.)

STAGE	5. MULTIPLICATION	6. DIVISION		7. 'PROBLEM'-TYPE EXAMPLES For instance:—
		(a) SHARING	(b) GROUPING	

	(d) Changing to shillings and pounds.
	
	£ s. d. £ s. d.
	2 5 9 × 2 17 9 ×
	  5 12
	
	(4) Multiplying *pounds, shillings and pence* (by *numbers greater than 12*).
	(a) Multiplying pence.
	
	£ s. d.
	      9 ×
	     25
	
	(b) Multiplying shillings.
	
	£ s. d.
	  8 0 ×
	     25
	
	(c) Multiplying shillings and pence.
	
	£ s. d. £ s. d.
	(i) 8 5 × (ii) 18 5 ×
	    16 16
		(4) Dividing *pounds, shillings and pence* (by *numbers greater than 12*).
		(a) Dividing by two-figure numbers.
		
		£ s. d. £ s. d.
		14)17 5 4 18)36 7 6
		£ s. d. £ s. d.
		27)101 0 6 14)7 6 2
		
		(b) Dividing by three-figure numbers.
		
		£ s. d.
		112)35 0 0
		£ s. d.
		112)273 0 0
				(d) A certain fertilizer costs £3. 14s. 8d. per hundredweight. How much is this per pound?

...ultiplying pounds and shillings.

	£	s.	d.			£	s.	d.
(i)	2	8	0	×	(ii)	2	18	0	×
			16					16

(e) Multiplying pounds, shillings and pence.

	£	s.	d.			£	s.	d.
(i)	12	8	3	×	(ii)	12	18	3	×
			16					16

(*Measurements*)

Imagine that you are a child and that your teacher is introducing a system of measuring length. You are told that the chief unit of length is a '*Ning*'. Smaller units are the '*Lair*', '*Rhot*', and '*Par*', whilst larger units are the '*Ish*', '*Noh*', and '*Gud*'. The units are related in the following way and can be written down in a 'table of length':—

$$3 \ Pars \ = 1 \ Rhot$$
$$10 \ Rhots = 1 \ Lair$$
$$8 \ Lairs \ = 1 \ Ning$$
$$24 \ Nings = 1 \ Ish$$
$$12 \ Ishs \ = 1 \ Noh$$
$$20 \ Nohs \ = 1 \ Gud$$

You are told to learn this 'table'. It does not interest you very much but, since you may get into trouble if you do not learn it, you make an attempt; and after a time you know it well enough to satisfy your teacher.

By reference to the 'table' you can now 'do' examples similar to the following:—

(*1*)	Nings	Lairs	Rhots	Pars	
	2	3	8	2	+
	12	5	2	1	

(*2*)	Guds	Nohs	Ishs	Nings	
	15	8	4	5	×
				7	

(*3*) Change 10,000 *Pars* to *Ishs, Nings, Lairs, Rhots* and *Pars*.

Try these examples yourself and check the answers.*
Now let us try another kind of example. (You may
find them harder than (*1*), (*2*) and (*3*), though they do
not appear so.)

    (*4*) About how long is this page (in *Lairs*)?
    (*5*) Can you guess your height in *Nings*?
    (*6*) What is the approximate length of the room in
        which you are sitting (in *Ishs*)?
    (*7*) About how far is it from your home to school
        (in *Guds*)?

We cannot answer these questions. We have no idea of
the actual length of any of the units, and so we cannot
begin to estimate any of the lengths asked for. We are
in the strange position of being able to do quite difficult
calculations in length without having any idea of what
the lengths are. The table helped us to do questions (*1*),
(*2*) and (*3*), but it does not help when we deal with real
things.

Now suppose that you are told that this line is one
Ning long:

      _____

Can you now answer questions (*4*) to (*7*)? Probably you
make a good attempt at (*4*) and (*5*), but find that (*6*) and
(*7*) are not very easy.

*You are now experiencing difficulties similar to those of
a child who has been compelled by his teacher to learn
tables of length, and to work out difficult calculations,
without having been given actual experience of:*

    (*a*) what is meant by length;
    (*b*) handling and using actual units of length;
    (*c*) seeing the relationships between units of length by
        comparison with real objects;
    (*d*) estimating the lengths of familiar objects in
        familiar units.

* (*1*) 15 Nings, 1 Lair, 1 Rhot, 0 Pars.
  (*2*) 107 Guds, 18 Nohs, 5 Ishs, 11 Nings.
  (*3*) 1 Ish, 17 Nings, 5 Lairs, 3 Rhots, 1 Par.

If we are not very careful, we are in danger of putting our pupils into this position when we teach about length or any other kind of measurement.

You have perhaps noticed that the names of the 'new' units of length used here (*Par, Rhot, Lair, Ning, Ish, Noh, Gud*) may be put together to make up the sentence, 'Parrot-learning is no good'. The words have been chosen deliberately to emphasize a very important lesson for us teachers.

Parrot-learning is no good for children (or grown-ups) in Arithmetic. We must have enough experience of using the numbers and measures to make them understandable. Far too many teachers, in the past, have insisted upon children learning like parrots. They have been satisfied if the children could repeat correctly what they have 'learned'. Whether or not the children understood what they learned by rote did not seem to matter. The same teachers often gave their children meaningless examples to work out, and were satisfied if the children got the right answer by following meaningless rules.

If we remember that 'Parrot-learning is no good', we shall try to ensure that children understand the work they are doing.

CHAPTER XVII

MORE ABOUT MEASURES

Before going on to describe in detail the later work on length, weight, capacity and time, it is well to consider in general the main aims and methods in teaching measures and measuring to children.

The ability to use measures is necessary for all those who are going on to study science and for many people engaged in various professions and trades. It is, moreover, an ability which is always useful, and sometimes necessary, in our everyday lives.

(1) 'Natural' measurement

It was from their *everyday lives* that men first chose the units they needed for measuring. They chose 'natural'* units. For example, they chose the length of a man's foot to measure the length of a room; they chose one outstretched arm to measure a length of cloth; they chose a man's stride to measure the length of a field. Moreover it was to satisfy the needs of their *everyday lives* that men agreed upon standards of measurement. They found that argument and strife were unavoidable if traders, and the people who bought from them, could not agree exactly upon what was meant by any particular unit of measure. It was easy for dishonest traders to cheat if no one knew exactly what were a foot, a yard, a pound or a pint. The ancient Egyptians found it necessary, for example, to come to an agreement whereby they could measure out the exact portions of their land after the River Nile's annual flood-waters had gone down, leaving behind them mud-covered fields where boundaries had been washed away.

The first principle to remember, then, in teaching measures to children is this: *since measures have grown out of man's needs and*

* That is, they naturally made use of the things that happened to be conveniently near; for example, parts of their own bodies, a shepherd's stick.

An example of an artificial system of measures, which did not grow out of man's natural surroundings, is the metric system invented by the French in 1792. The units in the metric system were thought out by scientists and imposed upon the people. They were not chosen by the people themselves.

from his experience, we can teach children best by using the natural situations which are to be found in the places where they live, work and play. We do not then use examples (to be found in some poor text-books) which the children cannot possibly understand. For instance, in places where wall-paper and fitted carpets are never used, it is ridiculous to expect young children to work examples about measuring wall-paper and carpeting floors. Examples should always be chosen from the area where the children live and should be based on things about which they know.

(2) Standard units and their relationship

When men were first learning to measure they found (as children do when they are learning—see Chapter X) that, if they wanted to measure the length of small objects, they needed to use a *smaller* unit than the foot. They also found that to measure a field the foot was again an inconvenient unit: they needed something *larger* (for example, the yard). For measuring longer distances they needed a still larger unit (such as the mile). Each unit was invented, in the first place, for a particular purpose, and in many cases it was not possible to change easily from one unit into another because there was no fixed relationship between them.

But when men began to agree upon *standard* units of measurement they found it necessary also to agree upon the relationship that should exist between the smaller and the larger units, to make sure that they could easily be changed. For example the length of the inch was chosen so that there would be exactly twelve of them in a *standard foot*. It was also found convenient for the yard to be thought of as three feet, which could be changed, if necessary, into thirty-six inches. The second principle of the work in measurement may now be stated: *It is necessary for children to know the agreed relationships between various units of measurement:* that is, they should know the facts in the tables of measures. Teachers should provide activities and experiences in which children can 'see' such relationships *for themselves*, can understand the need for them, and then learn them.

(3) Examples should be 'real'

It is *not* necessary for children to be able to work out difficult calculations, in which they have to change a number of units of one kind into several other units (for example: 10,000 ounces to tons, hundredweights, pounds, and ounces), or to change a number of different units into smaller units (for example: 7 miles, 30 yards, 2 feet, 6 inches to inches). Such examples rarely, if ever, occur in everyday life, nor do they often occur in the trades or the sciences.

There is no need to learn to calculate in more than two (or, at the most, three) units at a time. All measurements, speaking scientifically, are approximations. Though the units may get smaller and smaller there is never a point at which any measurement is absolutely exact. For instance, machines in industry measure lengths too small to be seen by the eye. But, if they measure to a thousandth part of an inch, it is not claimed that such a measurement is absolutely accurate, because the article being measured may be two or three ten-thousandth parts of an inch greater or smaller than the machine can allow for.

In everyday life we are continually making approximate measurements. For example, if we want to measure the distance between two towns, we are satisfied if the answer is in miles: we are not concerned with measuring to the nearest yard. If we measure a field, yards and feet are enough: we do not bother about inches. If we measure a smaller object, like a book, we may expect to use inches and simple fractions of an inch, but not thousandths of an inch. It is usually accurate enough for every-day purposes to be able to say: 'That weighs *about* two pounds' (after putting the article on the scales); 'The journey takes just under half-an-hour' (we do not time it to the exact second); 'The lorry goes *about* twenty miles to the gallon' (we cannot be sure to an exact mile, still less to a yard); 'The field is *about* three and a half acres' (it is not worth our time or trouble to count each square foot, still less each square inch of soil).

So here is the third principle we must remember in teaching measurement: *there is no need to give children difficult calculations which bring in many different units at the same time.* (For

L

example, multiply 1 mile, 3 furlongs, 25 yards, 2 feet, 6 inches, by 17.) Such examples are seldom useful and should be avoided.

(4) The importance of estimation ('guessing')
The last point to be considered is the value of getting children to make intelligent 'guesses' or estimates of the answers they are to find in measuring. This practice was suggested in Chapter X at the early stages of measuring, and it should be continued at all later stages. Estimation helps children in two ways. Firstly, it helps to direct their attention to the actual size of the unit with which they are dealing, so that they become more and more familiar with it. For example, if they are estimating the height of a room in feet, they have to think of what a foot looks like and keep it 'in the mind's eye' while they look at the height of the room. Secondly, estimation helps to stop children from giving absurd answers to their questions in measurement. For instance, if a child makes a fair estimate of the weight of an object which he has handled as about ten pounds, he is less likely, after weighing the article, to write down the weight as fifteen ounces.

So that the fourth principle to remember is: *practice in estimation should be given at all stages.*

The work in the next four chapters is concerned mainly with describing the steps in teaching measures to children, including the processes of addition, subtraction, multiplication and division. But we must remember, throughout, what is said here and in previous chapters about the necessity for the work to be as practical as possible and to be linked with the children's *everyday life*. Only in this way can our teaching have real vitality and the children's learning be permanent.

('Natural' and 'standard' lengths)

In the section preceding Chapter XVI it is suggested that our teaching is more interesting and helpful when we know a little about the history of measures, and how their names and abbreviations have come into common use. Let us consider here the measures of length discussed in the next chapter. (If we live in an area where different units of length are used, we should try to find out how our particular units of length came into being.)

Most early measures of length made use of the parts of the body. This 'rough and ready', but natural, system is still used almost everywhere, unless greater accuracy is necessary. The length of a man's stride and a man's foot, for example, have always been useful aids for work in the garden or on the farm. Both are personal and natural measures, and serve a good purpose, so long as the measurements do not have to be accepted by other people (whose 'strides' and 'feet' may be different). Other measures of length made use of the arms and the hands. For example, the length from the elbow to the tip of the middle finger was a common measure in many countries; it was called the 'cubit'. The distance between the tips of the little finger and the thumb of the outstretched hand was called the 'span'; the width of the hand across the base of the fingers was the 'palm'; the width of the finger was the 'digit'.

The early measures for longer distances were based upon happenings which occurred in everyday life. For example, the Romans used the distance covered in a thousand paces (a 'pace' was a double step) as their unit. And it is from the Latin *mille passus* (a thousand paces) that we get the present-day word *'mile'*. In England the word 'furlong' (220 yards) grew out of the expression 'furrow-long', that is, the distance that a horse or ox could pull a plough before having to pause for a rest.

Sometimes the units were divided into smaller parts. For example, the Romans divided their 'foot' into twelve parts, called *unciae*, from which we get the word '*inch*'. Simple relationships between the various units were also used. For example:—

$$4 \; digits = 1 \; palm$$
$$3 \; palms = 1 \; span$$
$$2 \; spans = 1 \; cubit$$

But when Man began to trade further afield, when he needed to build more accurately, and as he became more and more interested in science, he found that such measures were too uncertain. They varied too much from place to place. Traders found that *standard* units were necessary for fair dealing, and builders and scientists found that *standard* lengths were necessary if accurate calculations were to be made.

However, uniformity in the measures of length came slowly in most countries. Real progress came only when 'natural' units were replaced, or were more accurately defined, by the length of a particular metal bar, or by the length of special marks on a wall. Then exact copies of the standard length could be made and were available for everybody. It is interesting to note that the Roman measure of length was cut in the base of one of their famous statues in Rome, and that the '*yard*' is marked on the base of a monument in London. (The word 'yard' comes from an Anglo-Saxon word meaning a piece of wood, that is, from the idea of a piece of wood of a given length.)

The *standard yard* is now based on the length between two specified positions on a bar of platinum kept in London. This piece of metal is very carefully looked after and is kept at a given temperature so that the length does not vary. The legal measures of length now in common use (in Britain) are all based on this standard yard. For example, the '*chain*', the seventeenth-century metal measuring chain, is now defined as twenty-two standard yards.

The common legal measures are related to the standard yard thus:—

$$
\begin{aligned}
12 \ \textit{inches} \ \ &= 1 \ \textit{foot} \\
3 \ \textit{feet} \ \ &= 1 \ \textit{yard} \quad (= \quad 36 \text{ inches}) \\
22 \ \textit{yards} \ \ &= 1 \ \textit{chain} \\
10 \ \textit{chains} \ \ &= 1 \ \textit{furlong} \ (= \quad 220 \text{ yards}) \\
8 \ \textit{furlongs} \ \ &= 1 \ \textit{mile} \quad (= 1{,}760 \text{ yards})
\end{aligned}
$$

CHAPTER XVIII

FURTHER WORK ON LENGTH

In early work in measuring, as described in Chapter X, children learn by experience about units of length (the inch, the foot and the yard) and the relationships which exist between them. This involves, inside and outside the classroom, all kinds of activities in which they are intelligently 'guessing' the lengths of various objects and distances. They then see whether their guesses are accurate by using foot-sticks (marked off in inches) and yard-sticks (marked off in feet). After this kind of measuring practice some children are found to have a surprising ability to estimate distances. They have grasped the relationship between the units of length and have a 'picture in their minds' of what each unit is.

A—*Further activities*

It is most important that this practical work in measurement should be continued in learning about the other units of length. It is wrong to go on quickly to written calculations before children really understand the measures with which they are dealing. This understanding comes only from activities in which the units of measurement are constantly being used.

(*a*) *Measuring in half-inches and quarter-inches*—The foot-sticks or strips marked off in inches which were used previously should now be marked off *by the teacher* in half-inches, and later in quarter-inches. Practice should be given in measuring objects and prepared lines (see Fig. 108, page 308) to the nearest half-inch and then to the nearest quarter of an inch. We should show the children how the half and the quarter are written down, viz. $\frac{1}{2}$ and $\frac{1}{4}$. We should also explain that the '2' indicates that the inch is split up into two *equal* parts and that the '4' indicates that the inch is split up into four *equal* parts. (This is valuable information when the children begin to learn more about fractions. The children also see for themselves that, when measuring certain lines, they need to make use of the half-inch *and* the quarter-inch. For example, when they find that a line measures four inches and a half-inch and a quarter-inch, that is $4\frac{3}{4}$ inches, they are led to the conclusion that $\frac{1}{2} + \frac{1}{4} = \frac{3}{4}$.)

(*b*) *Measuring in chains*—If it is not possible to get a proper metal chain, or a measuring tape, the children may use a piece of rope or string, twenty-two yards long, marked off in yards. This can be used to measure longer distances, such as the sides of the school playing-field or games area, garden or farm plots, or the length and breadth of the school building. It is also a good idea to make, somewhere in the school grounds, two marks twenty-two yards apart, so that the children are helped to get a mental picture of the length of a 'chain'. In countries where the game of cricket is played, the children are given the helpful information that the standard distance between the wickets (that is, the length of the pitch) is exactly twenty-two yards (or one chain).

(*c*) *Measuring in furlongs*—This unit of length is best introduced by referring to the way in which the word came into being ('furrow-long', see page 299). (Similarly, the Hindus have a word meaning 'breath' to indicate the distance a man can run at full speed.)

The children should go out into the fields or on a track or road with the 'chain' (or a rope marked off in yards). They should start from a particular spot, a stake, a tree, or the corner of a building, and go on to measure ten chains, that is two hundred and twenty yards or one furlong. When this point is reached another stake should be put in the ground, or the spot should be suitably marked in some other way.

The children get a better 'picture' of the distance if they also count the number of their own strides to cover the furlong. They may also find out how long it takes to run the distance going as fast as they can.

(*d*) *Learning about miles*—The word mile is probably known to most children through their knowledge of local signposts, but it is surprising how few children (or adults) are really good judges of how long a mile is. This fact probably accounts for the wrong information which many people give to travellers who ask for directions!

Again it is important for the children to know a number of places which are about a mile from the school. It is not necessary for all of them to measure the distance, but a small group may set out to establish the fact that a mile is eight furlongs and report back to the rest of the class. They should also learn from practice that it takes them about twenty minutes to walk a mile and about eight minutes to run the same distance (unless they are great athletes!). Children who live a given number of miles from school can check these rough statements, and may contribute to a discussion as to why a mile uphill seems longer than a mile downhill.

(e) *Using athletic achievements*—Children are keen to show their ability in races and other athletic events. The teacher can use this interest to widen their experience and knowledge of measurement. For example, having found that the approximate distance round the playing-field is 440 yards the children can find out how many times they must go round the field to cover a distance of one mile.

They can also get much practice in measuring distances covered in such athletic 'events' as throwing a ball, long (broad) and high jumps, etc. Even young children become interested when they see older ones competing. And the older children often take an interest in marking out pitches, watching adult athletics, hearing of national and international records, etc.

(f) *Using the measuring-wheel*—This is an easy instrument to make. It consists of a wooden wheel, the circumference of which is known, and which can be pushed along by a handle (Fig. 106).

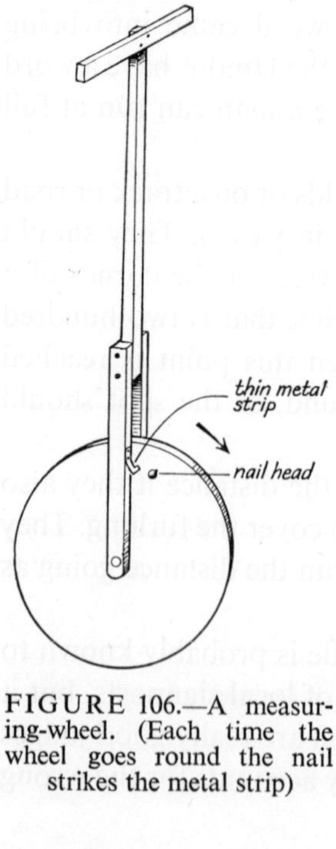

FIGURE 106.—A measuring-wheel. (Each time the wheel goes round the nail strikes the metal strip)

(Alternatively, old bicycle wheels may easily be adapted.) A piece of thin metal, fastened to the handle, strikes a nail on the wheel every time the wheel makes one turn. The children can work out the distance covered by multiplying the circumference by the number of turns that the wheel has made. (If the class has a number of wheels of different sizes the children can begin to get an idea of the relationship which exists between diameter and circumference.)

(*g*) *Using the pacing-stick*—This is a useful and simple piece of apparatus for measuring yards. It is made of two pointed sticks of equal length hinged at the top. A metal (or wooden) bar joins the two 'legs' so that the points of the sticks are exactly a yard apart (Fig. 107). (The bar may be moved to give longer or shorter distances.) The child who is measuring, for example, the length of a path, swings the pacing-stick on its point and counts the number of yards measured as he goes along.

FIGURE 107.—The pacing-stick

(*h*) *Keeping records*—Whenever they go out on visits or expeditions some of the children should carry some kind of measuring instrument. It is a good plan for them to guess the width of streams, the height of trees and buildings, the depth of cliffs, wells, etc., and then, where possible, to verify their guesses by measurement and put the information down in a note-book.

(*j*) *Drawing plans*—Simple plans of the class room and school and simple maps of the area may be made when the children are able to measure with fair accuracy. This kind of activity is discussed in more detail in Chapter XXIV.

In these activities the children are not only gaining an insight into the meaning of the various units of length, they are also getting the vocabulary and experience which help them to solve the problems they may meet from day to day, and the written problems they meet in arithmetic. They begin to realize that height and depth, width, breadth, shortness, tallness, etc., are all aspects of length, and that each particular problem requires the use of particular units of length.

B—*Changing units of length*

(*1*) *Learning the 'facts'* (the table of length)

In order to be able to calculate and work out problems involving the changing of one unit of length into another it is necessary to know the relationships between the units. This knowledge is based upon the practical work in measuring which has been described, but the children should also learn the 'facts' of length so that they know them without having to refer to apparatus like rulers and yard-sticks.

The table of length should be built up as a chart *with the children*, who should learn it thoroughly. (Chart VII shows the completed table.)

CHART VII

(A TABLE OF LENGTHS)

12 inches (in.)	=	1 foot (ft.)
3 feet (ft.)	=	1 yard (yd.)
[36 inches (in.)	=	1 yard (yd.)]
22 yards (yds.)	=	1 chain (ch.)
10 chains (ch.)	=	1 furlong (fur.)
8 furlongs (fur.)	=	1 mile (ml.)
*[1,760 yards (yds.)	=	1 mile]

The abbreviation for each unit is given in parentheses. There are only seven facts to be learnt, but the children should also be given practice in changing a number of units quickly. For example, we may give oral questions like this:

8 yards —How many feet?
3 chains—How many yards?
5 feet —How many inches?
2 miles —How many furlongs? etc.

The children soon begin to realize that in changing units of

* The more able children should eventually realize that factors of 1,760 are 22, 10, 8. Most children should also see that a furlong can be considered as 220 yards, that a half-mile is 880 yards and a quarter-mile is 440 yards.

length (in the British system) it is useful to know, and to be able to use accurately, the table of twelves, the table of threes, the table of elevens (a half of twenty-two), the table of tens, and the table of eights.

(2) Changing by written calculation

For certain examples, requiring multiplication and division, it becomes necessary to change units of length by written calculation. But it is *rarely found necessary* in everyday life, and we should not attach too great importance to this aspect of the work. When it does become necessary, this written changing should be done by the same methods as those used in dealing with money calculations. For example:

	yds.	ft.	in.
(*i*) 'Change 5 yards, 2 feet, 9 inches to inches.'	5	2	9
	3	15	204
	15 ft.	17	213 in.
		12	
		204 in.	

(*ii*) 'Change 1257 yards to furlongs, chains and yards.'

This is worked by two divisions: first, dividing by 22 to bring to chains; then, dividing the 57 chains by 10 to bring to furlongs. The answer is: 5 furlongs, 7 chains, and 3 yards.

$$
\begin{array}{r}
57 \text{ ch.}\\
22\overline{)1257}\\
110\\
\overline{157}\\
154\\
\overline{3} \text{ yds.}
\end{array}
\qquad
\begin{array}{r}
5 \text{ fur.}\\
10\overline{)57}\\
50\\
\overline{7} \text{ ch.}
\end{array}
$$

C—Length and the arithmetical processes

(1) Addition of length

The examples should be based, to begin with, upon actual measuring work which the children do. For example, in adding inches and parts of an inch, the children may be given a sheet of prepared lines, which they have to measure and add (Fig. 108).

Similarly, work-cards may be given for the other units: for example, cards with instructions, as in Fig. 109.

We should always make up such cards to suit our own class room and surroundings.

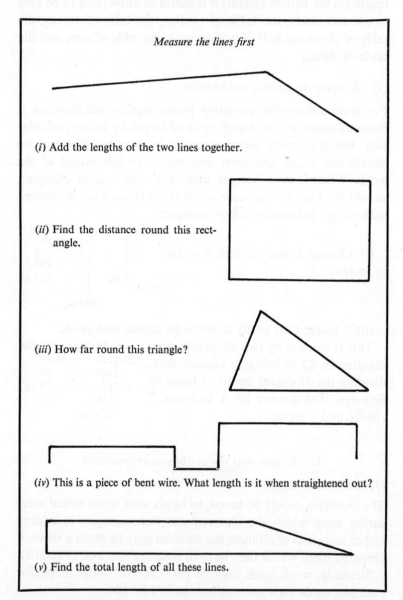

Measure the lines first

(*i*) Add the lengths of the two lines together.

(*ii*) Find the distance round this rectangle.

(*iii*) How far round this triangle?

(*iv*) This is a piece of bent wire. What length is it when straightened out?

(*v*) Find the total length of all these lines.

FIGURE 108.—A work-sheet for the measurement of lengths

Card 1. You need a yard-stick and a foot-rule.

Measure the length and breadth of the teacher's table. What is the total distance round it?

(For three children together.)

Card 12. You need a yard-stick and a foot-rule.

Each choose a different length which you are going to draw. First calculate, in your books, what the total length of these lines *should* be. Now go outside and draw your lines end to end so as to make one long straight line. Measure this line and compare it with your written answer.

Card 4. You need a chain (or string) and a yard-stick.

There are three pieces of road from the farm plot to the class-room door. Go and measure them. What is the total length of the pathways?

FIGURE 109.—Specimen work-cards (for measurement and addition of length)

The written work for card 1 may look like the example shown here. We point out to the children that the method is exactly the same as in adding shillings and pence, since the total of inches has to be changed to feet by dividing by twelve.

ft.	in.
3	4 +
2	3
3	4
2	3
11	2
1	

The written work for card 4 may look like this example (though some children may give the answer in yards only, depending on the measuring instrument they have used).

ch.	yds.
11	15 +
22	10
1	6
35	9
1	

The detailed steps in teaching addition of length are given in Analysis 6, pages 315–18. By using the suggested steps we can give suitable examples for the children to practise at each stage.

(2) Subtraction of length

The work should again be based, to begin with, on prepared sheets of lines (similar to those used for addition) and on work-cards which involve subtraction. For instance, the sheet of prepared lines may have this kind of question:

(*i*) Measure these two lines. How much longer is one than the other?

(*ii*) How much more is the length of this oblong than its width?

Two typical work-cards in subtraction are shown in Fig. 110.

Card A. Find the difference between the height and the width of the class-room door.

Card B. Measure the shadows of two trees. Which is the longer? By how much?

FIGURE 110.—Specimen work-cards (for subtraction of length)

We must make sure that, in teaching subtraction of length in written form, we use the *same method* as we used for subtraction of money and ordinary numbers. If, for example, we use the method known as 'decomposition' we should continue to use it. If, on the other hand, the children are accustomed to the method known as 'equal additions' they should not change it, if confusion and inaccuracy are to be avoided.

Here is an example of subtraction of length worked by the two methods. (A subtraction of this nature is seldom needed. The three units are included in order to demonstrate the *process* fully.)

(*a*) Using the method of 'decomposition' the suggested standard phrases are:—

'First deal with the inches.
I cannot take ten from seven.
So I use one of the two feet (leaving one foot).

yds.	ft.	in.
8	2	7 −
3	2	10

I now have nineteen* inches.
Ten from nineteen leaves nine.
Put the "9" in the inches-column of the answer.
Now deal with the feet.

yds.	ft.	in.
	4	
7	1	19
8	2	7 −
3	2	10
4	2	9

I cannot take two from one.
So I use one of the eight yards (leaving seven yards).
I now have four feet.
Two from four leaves two.

* See the note on page 172.

Put the "2" in the feet-column of the answer.
Now deal with the yards.
Three from seven leaves four.
Put the "4" in the yards-column of the answer.
The answer is: four yards, two feet, nine inches.'

(*b*) Using the method of 'equal additions' the suggested standard phrases are:—

'First deal with the inches.
I cannot take ten from seven.
So I add one foot (twelve inches) to the
   seven inches in the top line (making
   nineteen* inches), and at the same time
   I add one foot to the two feet in the
   bottom line (making three feet).
Ten from nineteen leaves nine.
Put the "9" in the inches-column of the answer.
Now deal with the feet.
I cannot take three from two.
So I add one yard (three feet) to the two feet in the top line
   (making five feet), and at the same time I add one yard to
   the three yards in the bottom line (making four yards).
Three from five leaves two.
Put the "2" in the feet-column of the answer.
Now deal with the yards.
Four from eight leaves four.
Put the "4" in the yards-column of the answer.
The answer is: four yards, two feet, nine inches.'

yds.	ft.	in.
	5	19
8	2	7 —
4	3	
3	2	10
4	2	9

(*3*) *Multiplication of length*

There are not many situations in everyday life when it becomes necessary to multiply lengths. We should, however, continue to use work-cards as a basis for multiplication examples, and should not place too much emphasis upon long calculations which tend to make the work unreal. Three typical work-cards in multiplication are shown in Fig. 111. Such cards are based on actual measuring activities, so that the children are getting practice, first in understanding and carrying out written directions, and then in making written calculations in multiplication.

* See footnote on page 175.

Card M1. Draw a square with sides of 5½ inches.
Find by multiplication the distance round the
square.

Card M2. Measure the length of a desk. If we put eight
desks end to end, how far would they reach?

Card M3. Measure the distance round the playground.
What distance would you have travelled if
you ran round it six times?

FIGURE 111.—Specimen work-cards (for multiplication of length)

The suggested method of working and setting down is the same
as for multiplication of money.

(4) Division of length

It is again necessary to emphasize the importance of relating
division examples to actual situations where division is necessary. Work-cards should be used, so that the children combine
practical measurement with written calculation. These cards and
other written problems should give practice in both forms of
division—that is, in sharing and grouping.

(a) Sharing examples (for work-cards)—

(*i*) Get a long piece of rope (or string). Tie a stone on the end.
How can you use this to find the height, from the ground, of a
branch of a tree? (If necessary the teacher can explain that the
rope can be thrown over the branch until the rope is double. The
rope is marked where it touches the ground. It is then measured
as far as the mark. This length is divided by two to give the
height of the branch.)

(*ii*) Here is a round pole with thin wire (or string) wrapped round
it. Count the number of rings of wire. Now take the wire off,
straighten it out, and measure it. How can you find the distance
round the pole? Do it.

(*iii*) Take this long strip of paper and measure its length. By
folding first, cut it into eight equal parts. Find the length of
each part *without* measuring. Then check your answer by
measurement.

(b) *Grouping examples* (for work-cards)—

(i) Take a piece of string. Measure it. Calculate by division the number of pieces six inches long that can be cut from it. What length have you left over? Test your answer by cutting up the string.

(ii) Measure the distance round the school field. How many times must you run round the field to cover a distance of at least one mile?

(iii) Measure the distance round this wheel. Now measure the length of the garden path. Find, by calculation, how many times the wheel will turn to go from one end of the path to the other. Check your answer by rolling the wheel along the path.

The detailed steps in teaching division of length are given in Analysis 6 on page 319.

As in dealing with money examples, the setting down depends upon whether the division is by sharing or by grouping. If the child understands what the question asks, he probably knows how to set it down, but the teacher should show, by going through various examples, how the working is done.

For instance, here is an example of division by sharing: 'Some thread, twenty-three yards, one foot, six inches in length,* is cut into six equal pieces. What is the length of one piece?' It is set down as shown.

The method is exactly the same as for the division of money, except for the changing of the remaining yards to feet by multiplying by three.

yds.	ft.	in.
3	2	9
6)23	1	6
18	15	48
5	16	54
3	12	54
15 ft.	4	—
	12	
	48 in.	

Here is an example of division by grouping and of how it is set down: 'How many pieces each measuring two feet eight inches may be cut from a length ten yards, one foot, nine inches?* How big is the piece left over?' The children see that this is a question of finding out how many times the smaller length is contained in the greater. Before this division can take place it is necessary to change both lengths to the

---

* Examples with three units are seldom 'real'. They are given here in order to show the *process* in full. It is a waste of time to give too much practice with this kind of example.

same unit (in this example to inches). The answer is 'eleven pieces, and a piece two feet five inches (or twenty-nine inches) left over'.

ft.	in.		yds.	ft.	in.	
2	8		10	1	9	11
12	24		3	30	372	32)381
24	32		30 ft.	31	381	32
				12		61
				372 in.		32
						29

D—Summary of points to remember in teaching length

1. A suitably graded scheme such as that given on page 315 should be followed.
2. Wherever possible the work should be based on measuring activities. Alternatively the written work should be checked by measurement.
3. Work-cards are a useful device in giving purpose to the written work, and in giving practice in dealing with 'problems' in words.
4. A perfect knowledge of the 'facts' contained in the table of length is essential.
5. Teachers in a school (or area) should agree upon the standard methods which are to be used for teaching calculations in length.

Suggested stages and steps in the teaching of length

(see Chapters X, XVII and XVIII)

1. STAGE	2. ACTIVITIES	3. ADDITION	4. SUBTRACTION
A. FEET, INCHES and YARDS.	The measuring of lengths in 'personal' units such as 'strides', 'hand-spans', etc. (leading to the need for 'standard' units). The use of the *foot-stick* to measure lengths to the nearest foot. The use of the *foot-stick, marked in inches*, to measure smaller lengths. The use of a number of foot-sticks to measure in feet and inches. The use of the *yard-'stick'* to measure longer distances to the nearest yard. The use of the *yard-stick and foot-stick* to measure lengths to the nearest foot, and, later, to the nearest inch. The use of foot-sticks marked in *inches, half-inches and quarter-inches* to measure to the nearest quarter-inch. The use of prepared *work-cards* to give varied practice in measuring and the working out of 'problems'. The use of *practice-cards and flash-cards* to learn the length 'facts'. The measuring of *athletic achievements* (e.g. high jump). The recording of *personal measurements* (e.g. height) from time to time.	*Finding the sum* of two lengths measured *by measuring* their combined length when placed end to end. *Recording* the same and similar *activities* as an addition. e.g. 4 in. + 6 in. = 10 in. in. ft. in. ft. in. 4 + 1 2 + 1 5 + 6 1 4 9 10 2 6 2 2 The *working of examples* set by the teacher (using apparatus if necessary in the early stages): (1) *Inches only.* (a) Total less than 12. in. in. 4 + 5 + 7 4 (b) Total twelve or more. ft. in. ft. in. ft. in. 8 + 9 + 9 + 5 3 8 7 7	*Finding the difference* between two measured lengths *by measuring* their difference when placed side by side. *Recording* these and similar *activities* as a subtraction. e.g. 10 in. − 7 in. = 3 in. in. ft. in. yds. ft. 10 − 1 5 − 3 1 − 7 9 1 2 3 8 1 11 The *working of examples* set by the teacher (using apparatus if necessary in the early stages): (1) *Inches only.* in. in. 9 − 11 − 4 7 (2) *Feet and inches.* (a) No changing. ft. in. ft. in. 2 9 − 2 7 − 1 4 2 4

Continued for Multiplication and Division, and Problem-type examples, on pages 319–21.

ANALYSIS 6 (cont.)

1. STAGE	2. ACTIVITIES	3. ADDITION	4. SUBTRACTION

2. ACTIVITIES

Note.—Throughout all this work: the children should 'guess', (estimate) the lengths before measuring them.

3. ADDITION

(2) *Feet and inches.*
(a) No changing.

```
ft. in.        ft. in.
1  4 +         1  5 +
   5           1  6
___            ___
```

(b) Changing inches to feet.

```
ft. in.    ft. in.    ft. in.
1  6 +     1  8 +     1  4 +
   9       1  9          8
___        ___        ___
```

(3) *Yards and feet.*
(a) No changing.

```
yds. ft.    yds. ft.
 1   1 +     2   2 +
 3   1       1   4   0
___          ___
```

(b) Changing feet to yards.

```
yds. ft.    yds. ft.
 2   2 +     3   2 +
 3   1       4   2
___          ___
```

(4) *Yards, feet and inches.*
(a) No changing.

```
yds. ft. in.
 2   1   4 +
 3   1   5
___
```

4. SUBTRACTION

```
ft. in.
2  7 -
   10
___
```

(b) Changing feet to inches.

```
ft. in.    ft. in.    ft. in.
2  7 -     2  7 -     2  8 -
1  9          10      1  5
___        ___        ___
```

(3) *Yards, feet and inches.*
(a) No changing.

```
yds. ft. in.
 3   2   8 -
 2   1   5
___
```

(b) Changing yards to feet.

```
yds. ft. in.    yds. ft. in.
 3   1   0 -     3   1   9 -
 1   2   0       1   2   5
___              ___
```

(c) Changing feet to inches and yards to feet.

```
yds. ft. in.    yds. ft. in.
 4   1   5 -     5   0   5 -
 2   2   8       2   2  10
___              ___
```

(4) Examples such as those in (1), (2), and (3), bringing in *half-inches* and *quarter-inches*.

```
in.        ft. in.      yds. ft. in.
9¼ -       2  5¼ -       4   1   0¼ -
```

B. CHAINS, FUR-LONGS and MILES.

The use of lengths of string (marked in yards), *tape measures, pacing-sticks,* and *measuring-wheels* for measuring longer distances in yards.

The use of *metal or rope chains* for measuring to the nearest chain.

The marking of a chain length in the school playground.

The measuring of a furlong along a road or path by using a chain length.

The estimation of distances in miles (use of maps and sign-posts for checking).

The measuring of tracks for races (e.g. 100 yds., 220 yds.).

The measuring of heights and depths.

The approximate measurement of *distances in terms of the time taken* (e.g. a twenty-minute walk).

The *noting down of information* about distances and lengths collected on school walks, journeys, etc.

---

(5) Examples such as those in (1), (2), (3), and (4) bringing in *half-inches and quarter-inches.*

in.	ft. in.	yds. ft. in.
4¼ +	1 2½ +	1 2 4¼ +
5¼	10½	2 1 3¾

Finding the *sum* of two or more measured lengths.

The *working of examples* set by the teacher.

(1) Adding yards.

(a) Changing yards to chains.

ch. yds.
40 +
55
61

(b) Changing yards to furlongs.

fur. yds.
150 +
275
95

(c) Changing yards to miles.

ml. yds.
1200 +
700
850

Finding the *difference between two measured lengths.*

The *working of examples* set by the teacher.

(1) *Chains and yards.*

ch. yds.	ch. yds.
4 15 —	9 2 —
2 10	4 15

(2) *Furlongs and chains.*

fur. ch.	fur. ch.
5 4 —	7 2 —
3 2	5 9

(3) *Furlongs and yards.*

fur. yds.	fur. yds.
2 55 —	7 20 —
1 27	4 55

(4) *Miles and furlongs.*

ml. fur.	ml. fur.
2 7 —	4 2 —
1 3	2 7

Continued for Multiplication and Division, and Problem-type examples, on pages 319–21.

ANALYSIS 6 (cont.)

1. STAGE	2. ACTIVITIES	3. ADDITION	4. SUBTRACTION

		(2) *Adding miles, furlongs and chains.*
		(a) Changing chains to furlongs.
		
		fur. ch. fur. ch.
		2 5 + 3 3 +
		4 7 2 5
		            1 2
		――― ―――
		
		(b) Changing furlongs to miles.
		
		ml. fur. ml. fur.
		2 3 + 4 5 +
		1 7 2 7
		            6 4
		――― ―――	

Note—It will be seen that no attempt has been made, in this work, to cover *all possible* combinations of units. The types of example suggested are deliberately restricted to the two (rarely three) units which are most likely to be used in daily affairs. Complex examples are often 'artificial' and unnecessary, and young children should not be expected to work them out as mere exercises in arithmetical calculation.

Continued for Multiplication and Division, and Problem-type examples, on pages 319-21.

1. STAGE	5. MULTIPLICATION	(a) SHARING	(b) GROUPING	EXAMPLES For instance:—
A. FEET, INCHES and YARDS *(continued from page* 315).	Finding the *sum of several equal lengths by measuring their total length* when placed end to end. Recording these and similar *activities* as a multiplication. e.g. 3×3 in. $= 9$ in. in. ft. in. yds. ft. in. $3 \times$ $3 \times$ $1 \ 6 \times$ 3 5 9 —— —— ———— 9 $1 \ 3$ $4 \ 1 \ 6$ The *working of examples set by the teacher* (using apparatus if necessary in the early stages). *(l)* Multiplying by numbers up to 12. *(a) Inches only.* (i) No changing. in. $2 \times$ 5 —— (ii) Changing inches to feet. ft. in. ft. in. $5 \times$ $8 \times$ 6 8 —— —— *(b) Feet and inches.* (i) Changing feet to yards. yds. ft. in. $1 \ 2 \times$ 5 ————	*Dividing* (e.g. by folding) a known length of material into equal parts *and measuring the length* of each part. Recording these and similar *activities* as a division. e.g. 8 in. $\div 4 = 2$ in. in. ft. in. $4)\overline{20}$ $8)\overline{4 \ 0}$ The *working of examples* set by the teacher (using apparatus if necessary in the early stages). *(l)* Dividing by numbers up to 12. *(a) Inches only.* in. in. in. $5)\overline{10}$ $7)\overline{28}$ $7)\overline{30}$ *(b) Feet and inches.* (i) No changing. ft. in. ft. in. $2)\overline{2 \ 8}$ $5)\overline{15 \ 10}$ ft. in. $5)\overline{15 \ 6}$ (ii) Changing feet to inches. ft. in. ft. in. $6)\overline{9 \ 10}$ $10)\overline{2 \ 8}$	Finding *how many times a given length is contained in a greater length* (e.g. finding how many times a six-inch length of string can be cut off a piece fifty-four inches long). *Recording* these and similar *activities* as a division. e.g. 36 in. $\div 4$ in. $= 9$. The *working of examples* set by the teacher (using apparatus if necessary in the early stages) such as: (a) How many pieces of wood, each 7 in. long, can be cut off 30 in. length? (b) How many books, each 2 in. thick, will fit in a shelf 2 ft. 8 in. long? (c) How many planks, each 8 ft. long, will stretch 24 yds. when placed end to end? (d) How many planks, each 7 ft. 6 in. long, will stretch 45 yds. when placed end to end? (e) How many rows of concrete blocks, each 8 in. high, will be needed to build a wall 6 ft. in height?	(a) Find the sum of 3 in., 4 in. and 11 in. (b) How much longer is a stick 2 ft. 6 in. in length than one 1 ft. 9 in. in length? (c) Eight bricks each $4\frac{1}{2}$ in. high are placed one on top of the other. What is the height of the stack? (d) A plank 5 ft. 9 in. long is cut into three equal lengths. How long is each? (e) How many tins, each 4 in. wide, can be placed along a shelf 7 ft. 8 in. in length? (f) Find the total height of three children whose heights are 4 ft. 7 in., 4 ft. $2\frac{1}{2}$ in. and 4 ft. 6 in. Three other children have the same total height, one is 4 ft. $4\frac{1}{2}$ in., a second is 4 ft. $8\frac{1}{2}$ in. What is the height of the third child? (g) A piece of rope 19 ft. 6 in. long goes exactly three times round a tree-trunk. What is the distance round the trunk?

ANALYSIS 6 (cont.)

1. STAGE	5. MULTIPLICATION	6. DIVISION		7. 'PROBLEM'-TYPE EXAMPLES For instance:—
		(a) SHARING	(b) GROUPING	

5. MULTIPLICATION

(ii) Changing inches to feet and feet to yards.

```
yds. ft. in.        yds. ft. in.
 2   5 ×             2   3 ×
     7                  7
```

(c) Yards, feet and inches.

```
yds. ft. in.        yds. ft. in.
 1   1  2 ×          2   2  8 ×
        4                   4
```

(d) Examples such as those in (a), (b) and (c), bringing in half-inches and quarter-inches.

```
 in.                yds. ft. in.
 2¼ ×                1   2¼ ×
  5                       9
```

```
yds. ft. in.
 2   1  8¾ ×
        10
```

(2) Multiplying by numbers greater than 12.

```
yds. ft. in.        yds. ft. in.
 2   5 ×             2   1  3½ ×
    16                     18
```

6. DIVISION

(a) SHARING

(c) Yards, feet and inches.
(i) Changing yards to feet.

```
    yds. ft. in.        yds. ft. in.
7)9  1  0          7)9  1  8
```

(ii) Changing yards to feet and feet to inches.

```
    yds. ft. in.        yds. ft. in.
8)19  1  5         8)17  1  2
```

(d) Examples such as those in (a), (b) and (c), bringing in half-inches and quarter-inches.

```
    in.        ft. in.
5)11¼      6)2  4¾
```

```
    yds. ft. in.
7)9   1  2½
```

(2) Dividing by numbers greater than 12.

```
    ft. in.        yds. ft. in.
14)16  6      15)17  2  5
```

```
    yds. ft. in.
25)80   0   0
```

(b) GROUPING

(f) A man's step is 27 in. long. How many steps will he take in walking 100 yds.?

7. 'PROBLEM'-TYPE EXAMPLES For instance:—

(h) A farmer is putting up a wooden fence 5 ft. 6 in. in height with lengths of fencing each 5 ft. 6 in. long and 9 in. wide. The length of the fencing is 20 yds. How many pieces of fencing will he need? What total length of timber will he use?

(i) Forty canes, each 5 ft. long, and sixty canes, each 6 ft. long, are to be cut up to make marking pegs, each 7 in. long, for the sports field. How many pegs can be made?

MILES (continued from page 317).

The working of examples set by the teacher.

(I) Multiplying yards.

(a) Changing to chains.

ch. yds.	ch. yds.
15 ×	15 ×
7	14

(b) Changing to furlongs.

fur. yds.	fur. yds.
25 ×	15 ×
9	30

(2) Multiplying chains and yards.

fur. ch. yds.	fur. ch. yds.
3 10 ×	5 19 ×
6	14

(3) Multiplying miles and furlongs.

ml. fur.	ml. fur.
7 ×	3 5 ×
14	12

(I) Dividing chains and yards.

ch. yds.	ch. yds.
4)8 16	14)5 6

(2) Dividing furlongs, chains and yards.

fur. ch. yds.

8)9 4 15

(3) Dividing miles, furlongs and yards.

ml. fur. yds.

6)8 3 55

...ample) is *contained in a larger length.*

The *working of examples set by the teacher.*

(a) How many times must a chain measure be moved in measuring a distance of 360 yds.?

(b) How many men will be needed to carry a torch from one village to another, five miles away, if each man runs about 440 yds.?

(c) The distance round a running track is 352 yds. How many times round the track must a man run to cover four miles?

round a five-sided field, if the sides measure 2 ch. 15 yds., 3 ch. 4 yds., 4 ch. 17 yds., 2 ch. 10 yds. and 1 ch. 19 yds.?

(b) The height of the highest mountain in the world is 29,000 ft. How many miles is this (to the nearest mile?)

(c) A football field is 110 yds. long and 78 yds. wide. A boy runs round it three times. Has he run a mile? If not how much further has he to go?

Note—It will be seen that no attempt has been made, in this work, to cover *all possible* combinations of units. The types of example suggested are deliberately restricted to the two (rarely three) units which are most likely to be used in daily affairs. Complex examples are often 'artificial' and unnecessary, and young children should not be expected to work them out as mere exercises in arithmetical calculation.

Most people find it easy to understand that if two objects balance each other when placed on a pair of scales then the weight of each object is the same. Also, that if one of the objects happens to be a two-pound weight, then the other has a weight of two pounds.

It is less easy to explain clearly what is really meant by 'weight'. Nor should we attempt it with young children. Older children, however, are interested to know (particularly now there is much talk of space travel) that the Earth is always trying to pull (or attract) all other objects towards it. The pull (or force) on a particular object (for example, an orange, an aeroplane, etc.) depends upon the distance of the object from the centre of the Earth, and also upon the amount and the kind of substance of which the object is made. The weight of an object is a measure of the pull of the Earth on it. If two objects balance each other when placed on scales, it means that the pull of the Earth is the same on each; in other words they each have the same weight. The weight of an object is more directly measured when a spring balance is used (see Fig. 114); in this case the pull of the Earth on the body being 'weighed' stretches the spring. The weight is indicated by the distance that the spring is stretched.

It was only about three hundred years ago that the idea of the Earth pulling other objects towards itself first began to be understood. So it is not surprising that the records of early weighing (which go back at least five thousand years) all show the use of the balance together with metal 'standard' weights. We do not know exactly how they first came into being, but the Babylonians, Egyptians, and Romans all had a 'standard' similar to the present-day pound weight. (It is from the Roman word *pondus*—a weight—that we obtain the word 'pound'. It is also from the word *libra*, the Roman pound, that we have the abbreviation 'lb.')

The Romans divided their standard 'pound' into twelve equal parts (in the same way as they divided their 'foot'), each part being called an *uncia*, that is 'a twelfth part'. The words 'ounce' and 'inch' are derived from this. (The abbreviation 'oz.' comes from the Italian word *'onza'*, which also came from the Latin *uncia*.)

For many years the number of ounces to the pound varied from place to place. It also differed in various trades. For example, although nowadays almost everybody uses sixteen ounces to the pound the goldsmith and others still use twelve. The legal standard for the pound-weight is now the weight *in vacuo** of a piece of platinum carefully preserved in London.

The word 'stone' suggests the possible use of a number of stones for weighing larger weights. For many years the number of pounds in a stone varied greatly and depended upon the kind of produce being weighed. Only in comparatively recent years has it been standardized at fourteen pounds.

The 'hundredweight' was originally a hundred pounds, but it gradually increased because of the practice of traders to add a little extra ('for good measure'). The variations became so confusing that in the seventeenth century it was agreed that the extra weight should always be twelve pounds and the hundredweight became standardized at one hundred and twelve pounds. The Romans had a weight a hundred times as heavy as the *libra* which they called the *centum pondium*. It is from the words *centum* and weight that the abbreviation 'cwt.' is obtained.

Until about a hundred years ago the ton was called a 'tun', a name which is still used by wine merchants

---

* *In vacuo*—in a space from which all the air has been pumped out.

to describe a large cask. In America and some other countries a ton is two thousand pounds (and the hundred weight is one hundred pounds). To avoid confusion this ton is sometimes called a 'short ton' and the hundred-pound weight is called a 'cental'.

This brief historical account of how British weights came into being can be used as interesting information for children in areas where these measures are used. In other areas, teachers should find out how their own standard weights developed. It is likely to be an interesting story.

CHAPTER XIX

FURTHER WORK ON WEIGHT

In the early work described in Chapter X, children learn about pounds and ounces. They use scales (perhaps made by the teacher) and shop weights, where they can get them, to weigh all kinds of objects in pounds and ounces. They practise making up packets of sand, clay, pebbles, etc., each packet being an exact weight of ounces or pounds. Play methods are also used to enable the children to estimate weights. They learn to use their muscle-sense in balancing activities, which show them that they cannot always estimate weights by looking: they find that sometimes a small object is heavier than a larger one.

These activities are designed to give a good background for the work to be done in later stages. It is important for us to remember that the later written work in weight should also be accompanied by practical activities which help the children to understand fully what they are doing.

A—*Further activities*

(*a*) *Weighing fractions of a pound*—The children notice that some of the shop weights are marked '$\frac{1}{2}$ lb.' (a half-pound) and '$\frac{1}{4}$ lb.' (a quarter-pound). By balancing on the scales they learn that a quarter-pound is four ounces (a quarter of sixteen) and that a half-pound is eight ounces (a half of sixteen). They are already familiar with the idea of the fractions half, quarter, three-quarters, from their knowledge of length; so it is easy for them to grasp the idea, again by weighing, that '$\frac{1}{2}$ lb.' added to '$\frac{1}{4}$ lb.' (making '$\frac{3}{4}$ lb.') is balanced by twelve ounces (three-quarters of sixteen).

We may then show two interesting little experiments which may prove helpful to the children in their everyday lives.

(*i*) Any number of ounces up to fifteen may be weighed out by using four weights only, namely 1 oz., 2 oz., 4 oz. ($\frac{1}{4}$ lb.), 8 oz.

($\frac{1}{2}$ lb.). The children may join in this by suggesting ways in which various weights can be made up. For example,

$$13 \text{ oz.} = 8 \text{ oz.} + 4 \text{ oz.} + 1 \text{ oz.}$$
$$7 \text{ oz.} = 4 \text{ oz.} + 2 \text{ oz.} + 1 \text{ oz.}$$

(*ii*) Scales can be used to divide an amount of sand, sugar, clay, etc. into two or four equal parts. For example, a pound of sugar is shared between both sides of the scales until they balance. There are then eight ounces on each side.

(*b*) *Learning about stones, quarters and hundredweights**—The need for units of weight greater than a pound is seen when children begin to discuss their own weights, the weight of animals, and of sacks of corn, fruit, vegetables or other produce. They find that small scales and pound-weights are of no use for this purpose. We should then introduce the idea of the *stone*-weight which weighs the same as fourteen pounds. We should give the children practice in picking up small sacks of produce of a stone-weight so that they can 'feel' what it is like. This helps them to estimate the weights of other objects and of animals in terms of stones. In comparing their own weights the children

FIGURE 112.—A see-saw. (An aid to learning about weight)

may make use of a piece of play apparatus known as the 'see-saw' (Fig. 112). This can easily be made by placing a plank of wood across a log. The two children being compared must sit at

* Once again it must be pointed out that this book deals with the *British* system. Teachers should apply the same principles and similar methods to the weights commonly used in their own areas.

equal distances from the centre of the plank.* They can then see which is the heavier.

Since the *hundredweight* is too heavy for most children to pick up, they can only get experience of it from watching adults carrying loads of about that weight. We have to tell them that the hundredweight is equal to eight stones or a hundred and twelve pounds. But it is possible for them to pick up a weight equal to a quarter of a hundredweight, which is known as a *quarter*, and can be balanced by two stones or twenty-eight pounds.

We may also introduce *tons* by discussions about lorries, trains, ships and the goods they carry.

(*c*) *Spring balances*—In some places the spring balance is the usual means of measuring weight. Children may be used to the

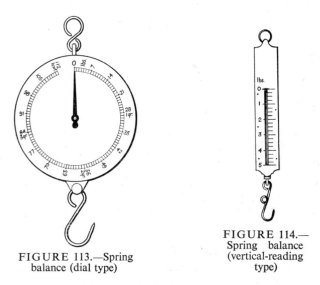

FIGURE 113.—Spring
balance (dial type)

FIGURE 114.—
Spring balance
(vertical-reading
type)

kind with a large dial (Fig. 113) showing, for instance, amounts up to a hundredweight. Or they may be familiar with the equally common, but smaller kind (Fig. 114), weighing up to a few pounds and graduated, perhaps, in 8, 4 or 2 ounces.

* The children see that if the distances are unequal, it is possible for a smaller weight to outbalance a heavier. This gives a background for later work in science when the principle of levers is studied.

Even in these places it may be best to start with the idea of balancing, and to introduce the spring balance later although this gives a more direct method of measuring the pull of the earth on an object.

If possible, children should play and experiment with the stretching of thin strips of rubber, 'elastic', and spiral springs, in order to gain understanding of the spring balance. Whether or not they have opportunities of using this balance themselves, the children should be given experience, if necessary through expeditions, of seeing when and how it is used.

(*d*) *Collecting information about weight*—It is a great help towards acquiring general knowledge and arithmetical ability if children are encouraged to collect all kinds of information about weight. Each child has a note-book, which he uses at school and at home, to write down anything he has noticed or found out. Here are some of the items which may be included:

(*i*) My own weight month by month. (If we have no weighing machine in the school, we may be able to get permission to visit a shop or store which has one.)

(*ii*) My dog's (or other animal's) weight month by month. (The animal may be weighed in a basket, but great care must be taken to avoid any cruelty.)

(*iii*) A list of the people who deal in ounces and pounds.

(*iv*) A list of the people who deal in stones, quarters and hundredweights.

(*v*) A list of things weighed in tons; in hundredweights; in stones; in pounds; in ounces.

(*vi*) A list of interesting weights (for example: three English pennies weigh one ounce; an English half-crown weighs half an ounce).—The child may notice references to weight on the sides of lorries and railway trucks.

(*vii*) A list of different kinds of weighing machines.

(*viii*) The meaning of 'gross weight'.

(*ix*) The meaning of 'net weight'.

(*x*) The weight of water contained by a pint bottle. The weight of sand contained by the same pint bottle.

(*xi*) Accounts of special activities or problems. For example, why does a piece of wood float in water while a piece of metal of the same size sinks? (They are both weighed. Then an equal volume of water is weighed. What do we notice about these three weights?*)

B—*Changing units of weight*

(*1*) *Learning the 'facts' in the table of weight*

The arithmetical facts of weight measures are not so easy for children to learn as the facts of length measures, mainly because they cannot be 'seen' so easily. For example, if a child forgets the number of inches in a foot, or the number of feet in a yard, he can visualize the foot-ruler and the yard-stick and arrive at the answer. This is not possible with the units of weight. The relationships between the various units have to be learned, so that they are perfectly known. The knowledge can then be used in written calculations and everyday transactions.

CHART VIII

(A TABLE OF WEIGHTS*)

16 ounces (oz.)	= 1 pound (lb.)
	$\left\{\begin{array}{l} 4 \text{ oz.} = \frac{1}{4} \text{ lb.} \\ 8 \text{ oz.} = \frac{1}{2} \text{ lb.} \\ 12 \text{ oz.} = \frac{3}{4} \text{ lb.} \end{array}\right\}$
14 pounds (lb.)	= 1 stone (st.)
2 stones (st.)	= 1 quarter (qr.)
(or 28 lb.	= 1 qr.)
4 quarters (qrs.)	= 1 hundredweight (cwt.)
(or 8 st.	= 1 cwt.)
(or 112 lb.	= 1 cwt.)
20 hundredweight (cwt.)	= 1 ton

* *British* weights.

Much of the learning of these facts comes through the experience of weighing which the children have had from the beginning. But with most children it is necessary to fix the facts by

* The experience gained in this activity may not give the child a full understanding of the principle at this stage. But when he has learned more about volume (discussed in Chapters XXIV and XXVII) he should have a background which will help him to understand the idea of 'specific gravity', which he may later meet in his science lessons.

M

using other methods too. The Table should be built up *with the children* into a chart which, when completed, may be used for reference if necessary (Chart VIII). The facts can also be put on flash-cards (Fig. 115) and used in games (see Chapter XV). The teacher should also make use of class-activities, quick oral questioning, etc., until the facts are known.

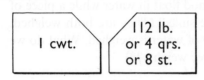

FIGURE 115.—A flash-card (for weight-changing)

Suitable size: 3″ × 2″

(2) Changing by written calculation

The method used is similar to that used for the other measures. It is rarely necessary to deal with more than two (or at the most three) units at a time. Most teachers rightly prefer to deal with the work as it becomes necessary and do not emphasize its importance by giving unreal examples. The method is shown in these examples:

```
cwt.        qrs.
  5           3
  4          20
20 qrs.      23
             28
            460
            184
            644 lb.
```

(i) Change 5 cwt. 3 qrs. to pounds.—The hundredweights are changed to quarters by multiplying by four, and the quarters are changed to pounds by multiplying by twenty-eight.

(ii) Change 572 lb. into hundredweights.—The pounds are changed to hundredweights by dividing by one hundred and twelve (long division).

```
         5 cwt.
112)572 lb.
    560
     12 lb.
```

C—*Weight and the arithmetical processes*

(1) Addition of weight

It is not possible to allow every child in a class to take part *at the same time* in practical activities in weighing. There are not enough scales and weights to go round, and there may not be enough room. It is, however, important for all the children to take their turns in using the scales and any other weighing instruments which are available. This can be done if we give a child (or a pair of children) a work-card (Fig. 116) to use, while the rest of the class are doing written work from the blackboard.

> *1A*   Weigh 6 oz. of sand.
>   Weigh 9 oz. of sand.
>   Weigh 5 oz. of sand.
>   Add these in your book.
>   Now weigh them together.

> *6A*   Weigh your Reading Book.
>   Now weigh your History Book.
>   Now weigh your Geography Book.
>   What is the total weight?
>   Test your answer.

> *10A* Weigh ½ lb. 'corn'.
>   Weigh ¾ lb. 'sugar'.
>   Weigh 1¼ lb. 'rice'.
>   Weigh 2 lb. 'flour'.
>   How heavy are all your goods
>   together?

> *12A* Here are three parcels.
>   Weigh them together.
>   What would it cost to send them by
>   post as one parcel?

FIGURE 116.—Specimen work-cards (addition of weights)

The setting down of the addition examples is similar to that used for the other measures. When the stage is reached for changing and carrying to take place we should make sure that this is done correctly. Here is an example:

The total of twenty-seven ounces is changed to one pound eleven ounces.

lb.	oz.
7	6 +
8	9
10	12
26	11
1	

(2) Subtraction of weight

The practical work concerned with the subtraction of one weight from another illustrates very clearly the nature of subtraction (see Chapter XII). It also emphasizes the need for children to understand that the words which indicate that subtraction is necessary often take different forms. For example, the children may be given tasks like these (using the scales and weights):

(*i*) 'Put one pound two ounces on one side, and twelve ounces on the other. How much more is on the one side than on the other?' The child takes off weights from the heavier side until the two sides balance, and then decides how much has been *taken off*.

(*ii*) 'How much must I add to the twelve ounces to make one pound two ounces?' In this case the child adds weights to the twelve ounces until the two sides balance. Then he decides how much he has *put on*.

There are, of course, many ways of expressing the same problem. But the teacher shows that whatever method has been used to indicate that the difference between two quantities has to be found, it can be worked out *on paper* as a subtraction. The ability to do this by calculation is useful because scales are not always available.

1S   Get a large tin and a small one.
Fill them with sand.
Weigh them.
Which is the heavier?
By how much?

2S   What is the difference in weight between a bottle filled with water and the same bottle filled with soil?

10S   Weigh a dry brick.
Now soak it in water.
Weigh it again.
What weight of water has the brick taken up?

12S   Weigh this bottle.
Fill it with water.
Weigh it again.
Now work out the weight of the water.

FIGURE 117.—Specimen work-cards (subtraction of weights)

As in addition, individual children (or pairs of children) in turn should use work-cards in subtraction (Fig. 117), and the teacher should show how the working can be set down. The

method should be the *same* as that used for other measures.
(In the example shown here, three units
are included in order to demonstrate the
process.)

tons	cwt.	qrs.
6	7	2 −
4	14	3

Using the 'decomposition' method, the
working appears as shown here.

tons	cwt.	qrs.
	26	
5	6	6
6	7	2 −
4	14	3
1	12	3

The same example worked by the method
of 'equal additions' is set down like this.

tons	cwt.	qrs.
	27	6
6	7	2 −
5	15	
4	14	3
1	12	3

(3) Multiplication of weight

The detailed steps in the teaching of multiplication are given on
pages 340–5. The methods used are similar to those used for other
measures, and the teacher should continue to try to provide real
situations where multiplication takes place. Some of these situations can be connected with the shopping activities described
earlier. For example, the children are provided with bills on
which they have to work out the separate amounts and find the
total. ('What weight of meat is required weekly for mid-day
meals, in a school of 149 children, if each child has 7 oz. per
week?'—The children go on to find the cost.) Other activities, to
be worked individually, are given on work-cards (Fig. 118),

1M Weigh a parcel.
What is the weight of six parcels
like this?

5M Weigh six pennies.
What would be the weight of five
shillings' worth?

FIGURE 118.—Specimen work-cards (multiplication of weight)

which ask the children to weigh an object and then find the

weight of several similar objects by calculation. The method of working and setting down is shown in these two examples:

	lb.	oz.
(i) 'The weight of a sheet of metal is six pounds three ounces. What is the weight of eight similar sheets?'	6	3
		8
	49	8
	1	

(ii) 'A truck holds ten tons three hundredweights of timber. A train pulls twenty-six such trucks. What is the total load of timber?'

tons	cwt.
10	3
	26
263	18
3	20)78
260	3 tons 18 cwt.
263	

(4) Division of weight

As in dealing with money and the other measures, the main difficulty that children meet is caused by the two-fold nature of division. It is important for them to realize that there are these two aspects. The teacher can help this understanding by giving them work-cards and problems cards which require both types of example to be used.

(a) *Division by sharing*—For example, a work-card may state: 'Weigh this bag of beans. If you share it between six boys, what weight of beans should each boy get?' This is set down as a division example like that shown here. Children may then weigh out each boy's share, according to an instruction on the card.

	lb.	oz.
		9
6)	3	6
	16	48
	48 oz.	54
		54
		—

(b) *Division by grouping*—This is necessary, for instance, when we are asked to find how many times a given weight is contained in another larger weight. For example, 'A sack of corn weighs one hundredweight three stones. How many full sacks can be taken from a store of corn weighing nine and a quarter tons?' (Three units are given here for demonstration purposes.)

tons	cwt.
9	5
20	180
180 cwt.	185
	8
	1480 st.

134
11)1480
11
38
33
50
44
6

In this example both amounts have to be changed to the same unit (in this case stones) before the division takes place. One hundredweight three stones is easily seen as eleven stones. The other amount has to be changed by calculation. The number of sacks is then found by the ordinary process of division of numbers. The answer is one hundred and thirty-four sacks.

D—*Summary of points to remember in teaching weight*

1. A suitable graded scheme such as that given on page 336 should be followed.
2. The work should be based on actual weighing experiences.
3. The children should be encouraged to take an interest in the weights they see around them.
4. The weight 'facts' should be known perfectly.
5. Particular attention should be paid to accurate setting down, particularly where 'changing' and carrying are involved.
6. The teachers in a school (or within an area) should decide upon the standard methods to be used for the arithmetical processes and should keep to them in all the work on measures.

ANALYSIS 7

Suggested stages and steps in the teaching of weight
(see Chapters X, XVII and XIX)

1. STAGE	2. ACTIVITIES	3. ADDITION	4. SUBTRACTION
A. POUNDS and OUNCES.	Lifting various objects; the use of the words 'light' and 'heavy'. The use of scales to balance quantities of various substances. The use of pound-weights of substances in common use (e.g. sugar) to weigh a pound-weight of other substances. The use of standard pound-weights to measure pound-weights of various substances. To show that pound-weights of different substances have different shapes and sizes. To find the number of ounces in a pound by balancing ounce-weights and a pound-weight. The use of ounce-weights to make up given weights of sand, clay, etc. The use of scales to balance ounce-weights with ½ lb., ¼ lb., and ¾ lb. weights. Making up sets of weights. Weighing objects and substances using 1 oz., ¼ lb., ½ lb. and 1 lb. weights. Dividing given quantities of substances (e.g. sand) by balancing.	Finding the total weight of two or more known weights of a given substance by weighing. Recording these and similar activities. e.g. 4 oz. + 5 oz. = 9 oz. $$\begin{array}{r}\text{oz.}\\4+\\5\\\hline 9\end{array}\qquad\begin{array}{rr}\text{lb.}&\text{oz.}\\1&4+\\2&7\\\hline 3&11\end{array}\qquad\begin{array}{rr}\text{lb.}&\text{oz.}\\1&12+\\1&14\\\hline 2&10\end{array}$$ The working of examples set by the teacher (using scales, if necessary, in the early stages). (1) Ounces only. (a) No changing needed. $$\begin{array}{r}\text{oz.}\\4+\\7\\\hline\ \end{array}\qquad\begin{array}{r}\text{oz.}\\3+\\5\\6\\\hline\ \end{array}$$ (b) Changing ounces to pounds. $$\begin{array}{rr}\text{lb.}&\text{oz.}\\&8+\\&10\\\hline\end{array}\qquad\begin{array}{rr}\text{lb.}&\text{oz.}\\&8+\\&6\\&10\\\hline\end{array}$$	Finding the difference in weight between two objects or two amounts of known weight, by: (a) adding known weights to the lighter to make it balance the heavier; (b) (for substances such as sand or clay) removing sufficient of the heavier to balance the lighter and weighing the remainder. Recording these and similar activities as subtraction examples. e.g. 10 oz. – 4 oz. = 6 oz. $$\begin{array}{r}\text{oz.}\\10-\\4\\\hline 6\end{array}\qquad\begin{array}{rr}\text{lb.}&\text{oz.}\\2&4-\\1&3\\\hline 1&1\end{array}\qquad\begin{array}{rr}\text{lb.}&\text{oz.}\\3&4-\\1&8\\\hline 1&12\end{array}$$ The working of examples set by the teacher. (1) Ounces only. $$\begin{array}{r}\text{oz.}\\14-\\8\\\hline\ \end{array}\qquad\begin{array}{r}\text{oz.}\\20-\\14\\\hline\ \end{array}$$ (2) Pounds and ounces. (a) No changing needed. $$\begin{array}{rr}\text{lb.}&\text{oz.}\\4&7-\\3&14\\\hline\end{array}\qquad\begin{array}{rr}\text{lb.}&\text{oz.}\\3&14-\\ \end{array}$$

Problem-type examples, on pages 340–5.

Collecting information about common uses of various weights.	lb. oz. lb. oz.
	2 3 + 1 4 +
	4 7 10
	        2 0
	___ ___
	
	(b) Changing ounces to pounds.
	lb. oz. lb. oz.
	2 7 + 1 10 +
	3 10 2 10
	        15
	___ ___
		lb. oz. lb. oz.
		3 4 - 2 10 -
		1 6 1 12
		___ ___

B. STONES, QUARTERS, HUNDRED-WEIGHTS and TONS.	Making up *stones* of produce and materials *by weighing out fourteen separate pounds.* *Collecting information* about local produce and materials normally sold by the *stone* and, where possible, the handling of these weights. *Collecting information* about produce and materials usually sold by the *quarter, hundredweight* or *ton.* The making of *booklets* in which are recorded all kinds of information about weights (e.g. weight of a truck or train; safe load for a bridge, etc.).	

The *working of examples* set by the teacher. (As far as possible the work should be based on local examples.)

(Addition)	(Subtraction)
(1) *Stones and pounds.* (a) No changing needed. st. lb. st. lb. 2 4 + 9 + 1 8 2 2 ___ ___ (b) Changing pounds to stones. st. lb. st. lb. st. lb. 2 8 + 5 8 + 2 9 + 4 10 7 6 13 3 10 ___ ___ ___ (2) *Stones and hundredweights.* (a) No changing needed. cwt. st. cwt. st. 4 3 + 5 4 + 12 4 2 ___ ___	(1) *Stones and pounds.* (a) No changing needed. st. lb. st. lb. 4 10 - 5 7 - 2 4 4 ___ ___ (b) Changing stones to pounds. st. lb. st. lb. st. lb. 5 6 - 6 2 - 4 9 - 2 8 4 12 3 12 ___ ___ ___ (2) *Stones and hundredweights.* (a) No changing needed. cwt. st. cwt. st. 5 4 - 12 7 - 2 3 5 ___ ___

ANALYSIS 7 (continued from preceding pages)

Continued for Multiplication and Division

1. STAGE	2. ACTIVITIES	3. ADDITION	4. SUBTRACTION
		(b) Changing stones to hundredweights.	(b) Changing hundredweights to stones.

3. ADDITION

(b) Changing stones to hundredweights.

```
cwt. st.    cwt. st.    cwt. st.
 5   6 +     7   5 +     9   7 +
 2   4      10   3       5   6
```

(3) Hundredweights and quarters.
(a) No changing needed.

```
cwt. qrs.    cwt. qrs.
 4   1 +      5   2 +
10   2        5   1
```

(b) Changing quarters to hundredweights.

```
cwt. qrs.   cwt. qrs.   cwt. qrs.
 7   3 +     8   3 +     5   3 +
 4   2      10   1       1   3
```

(4) Quarters and pounds.
(a) No changing needed.

```
qrs. lb.    qrs. lb.
 1   6 +     6  15 +
 2  14       2  11
```

(b) Changing pounds to quarters.

```
qrs. lb.   qrs. lb.   qrs. lb.
 1  20 +   20 +       24 +
 1  16      2   8      1  20
```

4. SUBTRACTION

(b) Changing hundredweights to stones.

```
cwt. st.    cwt. st.    cwt. st.
 5   0 —     8   2 —    14   2 —
 2   5       4   6      13   6
```

(3) Hundredweights and quarters.
(a) No changing needed.

```
cwt. qrs.    cwt. qrs.
 4   3 —     15   3 —
 2   1             2
```

(b) Changing hundredweights to quarters.

```
cwt. qrs.   cwt. qrs.   cwt. qrs.
 7   0 —    12   1 —    16   2 —
 4   2       7   3           3
```

(4) Quarters and pounds.
(a) No changing needed.

```
qrs. lb.    qrs. lb.
 2  14 —     3  18 —
 1   8            9
```

(b) Changing quarters to pounds.

```
qrs. lb.   qrs. lb.   qrs. lb.
 3   0 —    3   8 —    2   5 —
 1   8      2  20         24
```

blem-type examples, on pages 340–5.

tons cwt.
2   5 +
4 10
───────

tons cwt.
9 15 +
    4
───────

(b) Changing hundredweights to tons.

tons cwt.   tons cwt.   tons cwt.
4 15 +   12   5 +   2 15 +
8 10   5 15   12 17
                         14
───────   ───────   ───────

(6) Examples in which three units are used (*if* such examples arise in common usage).

e.g.   tons cwt. qrs.
          2   4   3 +
          4   10   2
        ──────────────

tons cwt.
7 14 —
5   5
───────

tons cwt.
17 12 —
     8
───────

(b) Changing tons to hundredweights.

tons cwt.   tons cwt.   tons cwt.
6   0 —   14 6 —   8   2 —
2 15   8 14   17
───────   ───────   ───────

(6) Examples in which *three units* are used (*if* such examples arise in common usage).

e.g.   cwt. qrs. lb.
          5   2   10 —
          2   3   7
        ──────────────

ANALYSIS 7 (continued from preceding pages)

STAGE	5. MULTIPLICATION	6. DIVISION		7. 'PROBLEM'-TYPE EXAMPLES For instance:—
		(a) SHARING	(b) GROUPING	

A. POUNDS and OUNCES (continued from page 336).	Finding the *total weight* of a number of equal objects of known weight *by weighing*. *Recording* these activities as multiplication examples. e.g. 3 oz. × 5 = 15 oz.
	
	oz.
	3 ×
	5
	—
	15
	
	lb. oz.
	1 6 ×
	   4
	—
	5 8
	
	The *working of examples* set by the teacher.
	(1) Multiplying *by numbers up to 12*
	(a) *Ounces only.*
	(i) No changing needed.
	oz. oz.
	4 × 5 ×
	3 4
	— —
	
	(ii) Changing ounces to pounds
	lb. oz.
	4 ×
	6
	—
	
	lb. oz.
	8 ×
	6
	—
	
	(b) *Pounds and ounces.*
	(i) No changing needed.
	lb. oz.
		Dividing a known weight of a substance (such as sand, clay, etc.) into *two equal parts by balancing* the two parts on scales. Weighing each part. Dividing each of these parts into *two further equal parts.* Weighing each of these parts. *Recording* these activities as division examples.
		
		e.g. 24 oz. ÷ 2 = 12 oz.
		     24 oz. ÷ 4 = 6 oz.
		
		The *working of examples* set by the teacher.
		(1) Dividing by numbers up to 12.
		(a) *Ounces only.*
		oz. oz.
		8)48 8)53
		
		(b) *Pounds and ounces.*
		(i) No changing needed.
		lb. oz. lb. oz.
		4)12 8 6)18 12
		
		(ii) Changing pounds to ounces.
		lb. oz. lb. oz.
		3)10 2 10)9 10
			Finding, *by weighing, how many times a given quantity of known weight, can be obtained from a larger quantity.*
			e.g. Finding how many 4 oz. packets of tea can be made up from 24 oz. of tea.
			Recording these activities as division examples.
			e.g. 24 oz. ÷ 4 oz. = 6
			e.g. 3 lb. ÷ 6 oz. = 8
			The *working of examples* set by the teacher.
			(1) *No changing of units.*
			(a) How many children can be given 2 oz. of sugar from a bag containing 16 oz.?
			(b) A small tin of beans weighs 5 oz. How many tins will together weigh 700 oz.?
			(2) *Changing of units.*
			(a) How many 10 oz. packets of seed can be made up from a bag containing 14 lb.? How much will be left over?
			(b) The total weight of a
				(a) A baby weighed 8 lb. at birth. He gained 3 oz. in the first week, 2 oz. in the second, 5 oz. in the third, and 8 oz. in the fourth week. What did he weigh at the end of the fourth week?
				(b) A basket of fruit weighed 4 lb. 5 oz. The basket weighed ¼ lb. What was the weight of the fruit?
				(c) A shop-keeper has 54 two-ounce bars of chocolate and 84 quarter-pound bars of chocolate on his shelf. What is the total weight of the chocolate?
				(d) Mother used 24 lb. of fruit to make 32 jars of jam. What weight of fruit did each jar contain?
				(e) A crate of eggs weighs 70 lb. The crate itself weighs 10 lb. If the weight of an egg be taken as 2 oz. how many eggs are contained in the crate?

weighs 1½ lb. Each tin of cocoa weighs 5 oz. How many tins are there in the box?

lb. oz.   lb. oz.

18)21 10   20)14 8

lb. oz.

24)56 0

B. STONES, QUARTERS, HUNDRED-WEIGHTS and TONS (*continued from page 337*).

```
           lb. oz.   lb. oz.   lb. cz.
           2  6 ×    2 10 ×    1  3 ×
              5         5         4
```

(2) Multiplying by *numbers greater than 12.*

```
           lb. oz.   lb. oz.   lb. oz.
           1  2 ×    3 12 ×       6 ×
             20         16        64
```

The *working of examples* set by the teacher. (As far as possible the work should be based on local examples.)

(*1*) Multiplying by *numbers up to 12.*

(*a*) Multiplying *pounds.*

(*i*) No changing.

```
           lb.
            8 ×
           10
```

(*ii*) Changing to stones.

```
           st. lb.
            8 ×
           10
```

The *working of examples* set by the teacher. (As far as possible the work should be based on local examples.)

(*1*) Dividing by numbers up to 12.

(*a*) Dividing *stones and pounds.*

(*i*) No changing needed.

```
           st. lb.    st. lb.
          3)6  9     4)4 12
```

(*ii*) Changing stones to pounds.

```
           st. lb.    st. lb.    st. lb.
          6)7  4     4)6  0     5)3  8
```

The *working of examples* set by the teacher. (As far as possible the work should be based on local examples.)

(*a*) *Stones and pounds.*

A farmer feeds 5 lb. of grain to his hens each day. How many days will a bag containing 4 st. last him?

(*b*) *Quarters and pounds.*

How many 4 lb. bags of beans can a shopkeeper make up from a partly-filled sack weighing 3 qrs. 15 lb.?

(*a*) What is the total weight of three children whose weights are 6 st. 8 lb., 6 st. 10 lb. and 7 st. 12 lb.?

(*b*) A boxer weighs 191 lb. How much weight must he lose to bring his weight down to 13 st.?

(*c*) An aeroplane can carry a load of 4 tons. If it already has a load of 2 tons 5 cwt. on board, how many crates each weighing 64 lb. can it take?

(*d*) A farmer buys 2 tons of grain for his hens. Each bird is given 3 oz. each

ANALYSIS 7 (cont.)

1. STAGE	5. MULTIPLICATION	6. DIVISION — (a) SHARING	6. DIVISION — (b) GROUPING	7. 'PROBLEM'-TYPE EXAMPLES For instance:—
	(iii) Changing to quarters. qr. lb. 8 × 10	(iii) Changing stones to pounds and pounds to ounces. st. lb. oz. st. lb. oz. 8)5 5 0 12)1 0 0	(c) Hundredweights and stones. How many sacks of seeds each weighing 6 st. can be carried on a truck which can carry 5 cwt.?	day. If he has 200 hens, how long will the grain last?
	(iv) Changing to hundredweights. cwt. lb. 20 × 8	(b) Dividing quarters and pounds. (i) No changing needed. qrs. lb. 3)3 15	(d) Hundredweights and quarters. How many bags of cement each weighing 1 cwt. 1 qr. are needed for a job which requires 10 cwt.?	(e) A bucket weighs 3 lb. When full of water it weighs 18 lb. A metal water tank weighs 65 lb. when empty. What will be the total weight of the tank if 20 buckets of water are poured into it?
	(v) Changing to stones and hundredweights. cwt. st. lb. 13 × 12	(ii) Changing quarters to pounds. qrs. lb. 9)2 7	(e) Tons and hundredweights. How many trips will a lorry have to make to move 20 tons of sand if it carries 1 ton 15 cwt. each trip?	(f) The fire of a boiler burns 20 lb. of fuel in 24 hours. It is kept burning day and night for four weeks. If the fuel cost 7 shillings a cwt. how much is the total cost?
	(vi) Changing to quarters and hundredweights. cwt. qrs. lb. 13 × 12	(iii) Changing quarters to pounds and pounds to ounces. qrs. lb. oz. 10)3 2 0		
	(b) Multiplying stones and pounds. (i) No changing. st. lb. st. lb. 1 2 × 2 1 ×	(c) Dividing hundredweights and stones. (i) No changing needed. cwt. st.		

7)15 6   12)7 4

(iii) Changing hundred-
weights to stones and
stones to pounds.

cwt. st. lb.

10)13 5 0

(a) Dividing *hundredweights
and quarters.*
(i) No changing needed.

cwt. qrs.

3)12 3

(ii) Changing hundred-
weights to quarters.

cwt. qrs.

7)15 3

(iii) Changing hundred-
weights to quarters to
pounds.

cwt. qrs. lb.

12)8 2 0

(e) Dividing *tons and hundredweights.*
(i) No changing needed.

tons cwt.

9)18 0

1 3 ×
     6

(iii) Changing pounds to
stones and stones to
hundredweights.

cwt. st. lb.

2 8 ×
   12

(c) Multiplying *quarters and
pounds.*
(i) No changing.

qrs. lb.   qrs. lb.

1 8 ×   2 4 ×
   3   6

(ii) Changing pounds to
quarters.

qrs. lb.

1 18 ×
     2

(iii) Changing pounds to
quarters and quarters
to hundredweights.

cwt. qrs. lb.

2 10 ×
    10

ANALYSIS 7 (cont.)

1. STAGE	5. MULTIPLICATION	6. DIVISION		7. 'PROBLEM'-TYPE EXAMPLES For instance:—
		(a) SHARING	(b) GROUPING	

	(d) Multiplying *hundredweights and stones.*
	(i) No changing.
	
	cwt. st.
	4 2 ×
	   3
	——
	
	(ii) Changing stones to hundredweights.
	
	cwt. st.
	2 3 ×
	   7
	——
	
	(iii) Changing stones to hundredweights and hundredweights to tons.
	
	tons cwt. st.
	6 5 ×
	  10
	——
	
	(e) Multiplying *hundredweights and quarters.*
	(i) No changing.
	
	cwt. qrs.
	4 1 ×
		(ii) Changing tons to hundredweights.
		
		tons cwt.
		8)12 0
		——
		
		(iii) Changing tons to hundredweights and hundredweights to quarters.
		
		tons cwt. qrs.
		8)29 2 0
		——
		
		(iv) Changing to other units (e.g. stones and/or pounds) if the need arises.
		
		(2) Dividing by numbers *greater than 12.*
		The repetition of the steps in (1) with the omission of (i) in each case.		

cwt. qrs.
$$2 \quad 2 \times$$
$$8$$

(iii) Changing quarters to hundredweights and hundredweights to tons.

tons cwt. qrs.
$$5 \quad 3 \times$$
$$12$$

(f) Multiplying *tons and hundredweights.*

(i) No changing.

tons cwt.
$$2 \quad 2 \times$$
$$8$$

(ii) Changing hundred-weights to tons.

tons cwt.
$$5 \quad 7 \times$$
$$12$$

(2) Multiplying by *numbers greater than 12.* The repetition of the steps in (*I*) with the omission of (*i*) in each case.

(*Units of capacity*)

Tables showing measures of capacity such as the following are sometimes given in English books. (*Of course they are NOT intended to be taught like this in schools.*)

Dry goods measure

2 pints	= 1 quart		3 bushels	= 1 sack
2 quarts	= 1 pottle		4 bushels	= 1 coomb
4 quarts	= 1 gallon		8 bushels	= 1 quarter
2 gallons	= 1 peck		12 sacks	= 1 chaldron
4 pecks	= 1 bushel		5 quarters	= 1 wey
2 bushels	= 1 strike			(or load)
			10 quarters	= 1 last

Wet measure

4 gills	= 1 pint		54 gallons	= 1 hogs-head (beer)
2 pints	= 1 quart			
4 quarts	= 1 gallon		63 gallons	= 1 hogs-head (wine)
9 gallons	= 1 firkin			
18 gallons	= 1 kilderkin		72 gallons	= 1 puncheon
36 gallons	= 1 barrel			
42 gallons	= 1 teice		2 hogsheads	= 1 butt (or pipe)
			2 butts	= 1 tun

Many English people, especially those who live in the towns and cities, have not even heard of some of these measures, which belong to the *British system*! Such people probably wonder whether these 'strange' measures are still used, and, if so, by whom and for what purpose. Moreover, they have little idea of the size of the unknown measures.

If we are not careful, we are likely to put our children in a similar position when we expect them to learn much simpler tables of capacity. For instance, we may expect them to learn a few of the more common measures in the form of 'tables' like the following:—

Dry goods measure		Wet (liquid) measure	
2 pints	= 1 quart	4 gills	= 1 pint
4 quarts	= 1 gallon	2 pints	= 1 quart
2 gallons	= 1 peck	4 quarts	= 1 gallon
4 pecks	= 1 bushel	8 pints	= 1 gallon
8 bushels	= 1 quarter		

These may have as little meaning for children as the longer tables have for us. Perhaps most people know these *liquid* measures (possibly excepting the gill). It would be interesting, however, to find out:—

(i) How many grown-ups know even this shortened table of *dry* goods measure.

(ii) How many, if any, make use of the table in their everyday lives.

(iii) How many *teachers* know the table before they have to teach 'capacity'.

(iv) How many teachers have themselves handled, or even seen, for example, a peck or a bushel of any kind of produce.

The absence of real experience of the units on the part of the teacher, in common with most other people, often makes the teaching of dry measures of capacity unreal and meaningless in school. Without real experience we have little to offer the children—except the working of 'made-up' examples on the various measures.

Once again, it is suggested that work of this kind loses most of its value if the children have no real idea of the approximate sizes of the various units. It is better for the teacher and children to look around the village, town or area to find where the various measures are being used, and wherever possible to handle produce measured in the different units. In this way the children get a 'picture' in their minds of how big the units are.

This is all that most children need. Other children, who may have to do calculations, will find this work made more real and interesting.

If we find it difficult, in our own neighbourhood, to obtain evidence of the use of some of the units, we should consider very carefully whether we need teach them to most of the children. As far as possible we should select units which are being *used* 'on the spot'.

The wet and dry measure units mentioned in this section are now based on the standard (British) gallon, which is defined as 'a vessel containing ten pounds weight of distilled water weighed in air with the water and air at a temperature of 62° Fahrenheit, and the barometer at a pressure of thirty inches of mercury'. It should be noted, however, that the *American* (United States) *gallon* for liquids is based on an earlier 'standard'. (It is less than the British standard gallon. 1 U.S. gallon = 0·83 British gallon, or 1 British gallon = 1·2 U.S. gallon.)

CHAPTER XX

FURTHER STEPS IN CAPACITY*

Teachers should realize, from the work described in Chapter X, that very few children will ever need to be able to work out difficult calculations in capacity. It is important, therefore, that they should continue to deal with *practical* problems. They should be given opportunities to increase their knowledge by the use of all kinds of materials and containers.

A—*Further activities*

(*a*) *Making pots*—In areas where clay is found the children may make pots of various shapes and sizes. The pots may be left to bake in the sun, or may be dried or 'fired' according to local custom. When we decide upon the size of a pot to hold, for example, a pint or a quart of liquid, it is essential for the children to estimate the capacity. So they must first have formed an idea of what a pint or a quart means. Sometimes they have to make a mark on the inside to show the level to which a pint or a quart of liquid (or sand) fills it. Tins or bottles may be used in the same way. The correct level may be marked by a scratch, or a strip of gummed paper.

(*b*) *Making a booklet*—Children should be encouraged to notice and record things which have some connexion with capacity. This increases their interest, as in the case of other measures, and helps them to relate their arithmetic to everyday life. They may have a book with each of the following (or similar) questions at the top of a page:—

> (*i*) What is measured in half-pints and pints?
> (*ii*) What is measured in pints and quarts?
> (*iii*) What is measured in gallons?
> (*iv*) What is measured in pecks and bushels? †

* This chapter deals with *British* liquid and dry measures. But the same principles and methods apply in other parts of the world. Teachers should adapt them to their own system.

† In Britain dry materials (for example, grain, seeds, soft fruits, etc.) are measured in pints, quarts, pecks and bushels. But there is little need for most

Other pages may have drawings and descriptions of interesting containers, together with an estimate of how much each holds. Older children may make records such as the following:—

How much water is carried from the well to my father's house each day?

How much water is consumed by the street or village each day, from mains supply, pumps, or wells?

How much water for each person is allowed in time of drought? How is this calculated?

How much water is consumed by various animals each day?

How much petrol is needed for a lorry travelling a certain distance?

What is meant by 'miles per gallon', and what is the different 'm.p.g.' for various vehicles seen in the district?

(c) *Work-cards*—It is not possible for all the children to do practical work at the same time, particularly if the class room is small. It is therefore advisable to let them work in small groups. To carry out the tasks given to them, they need dry materials (sand, small stones, etc.) and water. There is a danger that the work-cards (for example, Fig. 119) may get wet, so if possible they should be protected (for example, by coating with a clear varnish). Some of the work should be

3C
How many spoonfuls in this tin of sand?
How many half-pint drinks can I serve from two quarts?
Each child in the class drinks half a pint of milk per day. How much does this cost at sixpence per pint?
Take out seven pints from a gallon. What is left?
What is the weight of a pint of water?

FIGURE 119.—A specimen work-card, for capacity

linked with simple shopping and costs, and with the weighing described in Chapter XIX.

children to be concerned with them. As a rule each area has its own container for various kinds of produce, and this is the local 'measure'. For example, some children and adults have had experience of earning money by picking tea, beans, cocoa, coffee, nuts, etc., at so much per basket. Fishermen, also, often sell their fish in baskets of a particular size (for example, in Britain, the 'cran' = $37\frac{1}{2}$ gallons).

B—*Changing units of capacity*

(*1*) *Learning the facts*

After the children have had this practical experience of the various measures they find it easy to remember the few facts concerned. But, as before, we should build up the table of liquid measure (Chart IX) and dry measure (Chart X) *with the children.* They are helped to remember the quart if they are told that the word stands for a quarter (that is, a quarter of a gallon). Comparison can be made here with the meaning of 'a quarter' in weight.

CHART IX	CHART X
A TABLE OF	A TABLE OF
LIQUID MEASURES	DRY MEASURES

4 gills = 1 pint (pt.)	2 pints (pts.) = 1 quart (qt.)
2 pints (pts.) = 1 quart (qt.)	4 quarts (qts.) = 1 gallon (gal.)
4 quarts (qts.) = 1 gallon (gal.)	2 gallons (gal.) = 1 peck (pk.)
(or 8 pts. = 1 gal.)	4 pecks (pks.) = 1 bushel (bush.)

Each fact should be put on to flash-cards (Fig. 120) and learned through games and class activities.

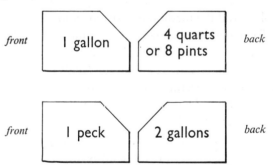

FIGURE 120.—Flash-cards, for the facts in tables of capacity

(*2*) *Changing the units by calculation*

As with other measures the children should gain the ability to change quickly from one unit to a number of smaller units (and *vice versa*), but it should rarely be necessary to make long calculations on paper. If it does become necessary to do this, the teacher should explain that the method and form of setting down are the same as those used for money, length and weight. For example:—

(*i*) How many pints are contained in a tank which holds nineteen gallons, three pints?
Change nineteen gallons, three pints to pints.

gal.	pts.
19	3
8	152
152	155 pts.

(*ii*) I have a hundred and sixty-nine quart tins of grain. How much is this in bushels, etc.?
Change one hundred and sixty-nine quarts to bushels, pecks, etc.

```
4)169 qts.
2) 42 gal. 1 qt.
4) 21 pecks
     5 bushels 1 peck
5 bushels, 1 peck, 1 quart
```

C—*Capacity and the arithmetical processes*

The formal setting down and working of examples in capacity is best left till as late as possible in the junior school. The work is best introduced as a means to make systematic the things the children already know from practical experience. They should not think of these calculations as something new which has to be learned but has little connexion with the work they have done before.

The detailed steps in teaching are given in Analysis 8, on pages 354–8, and the method of working and setting down is the same as for length and weight. An example of each process is given here for reference, but it should be remembered that these examples are taken from the end of the Analysis and should have been led up to by carefully graded steps.

(*1*) *Addition*—One drum of oil has 9 gallons, 2 quarts; another has 3 gallons, 3 quarts; and another 5 gallons, 2 quarts. If all the oil is poured into one drum how much is there altogether?

gal.	qts.
9	2 +
3	3
5	2
18	3
	1

(*2*) *Subtraction*—A water tank contains 56 gallons. The family use up 14 gallons, 3 quarts. How much is left? The examples show
(*a*) the method of decomposition;
(*b*) the method of equal additions.

	(*a*)		(*b*)	
	gal.	qts.	gal.	qts.
	5 4			4
	56	0 −	56	0 −
	14	3	5	
	41	1	14	3
			41	1

(*3*) *Multiplication*—A certain size of jar contains 3 quarts, 1 pint. If I put 9 jars of water into a tank how much is there altogether?

	gal.	qts.	pts.
	3	1	
		9	
	7	3	1
		4	9

(*4*) *Division*—(*a*) *By sharing*. A water supply of 33 gallons is to be rationed among 12 people. How much will each person get?

	gal.	qts.
	2	3
12)33	0
	24	36
	9	36
	4	36
	36	..

(*b*) *By grouping*. A bucket holds 7 pints. How many times can I fill it from a tank containing 54 gallons, and how much is left over?

Here the 54 gallons must be changed to pints before the division can take place. The answer is 61; and 5 pints are left over.

```
gal.
 54        61
  8     7)432
432 pts.   42
          12
           7
           5
```

D—*Points to remember in teaching capacity*

1. It is best to follow a graded scheme of work such as that suggested on pages 354–8.
2. The work should be kept as practical as possible, particularly in the early stages, and the amounts involved should be sensible.
3. Children should be encouraged to notice and make records of interesting information about the capacity of all kinds of vessels, utensils, etc., which they come across.
4. Teachers within a school or within an area should agree on standard methods to be used in teaching the arithmetical processes and should keep to them.

ANALYSIS 8

Suggested stages and steps in the teaching of capacity
(see Chapters X, XVII and XX)

1. STAGE	2. ACTIVITIES	3. ADDITION	4. SUBTRACTION
A. EARLY EXPERIENCES of filling and emptying containers.	The *use of containers* of various shapes and sizes (e.g. tins, bottles, jugs). Filling these containers with liquids (generally water), sand or sawdust. The *filling of one container* by using another container as a measure (e.g. finding how many jugs of water are required to fill a bucket). *Comparing the sizes* of different containers by finding how many 'tins' of water or sand are needed to fill them.		
B. Learning about PINTS, QUARTS and GALLONS. (*a*) *Liquid measure.*	The *use of a pint measure* to find the capacity of vessels of various shapes and sizes. The *use of pint and half-pint measures* to find the capacity of a container to the nearest half-pint. *Marking of the water levels in a container* when filled with various amounts of water (in pints and half-pints). The use of such a marked container as a measure. The *filling of a quart measure* by using pint and half-pint measures.	(*1*) *Adding pints and quarts.* (*a*) No changing needed. (*i*) qts. pts. 2 1 + 3 0 ——— 5 1 (*ii*) qts. pts. 2 $1\frac{1}{2}$ + 2 0 ——— (*b*) Changing pints to quarts. (*i*) qts. pts. 1 1 + 1 1 ——— 2 (*ii*) qts. pts. 2 1 + 1 0 ——— 1 1	(*1*) *Subtracting pints and quarts.* (*a*) No changing needed. qts. pts. 3 1 — 2 0 ——— (*b*) Changing quarts to pints. (*i*) qts. pts. 3 0 — 1 1 ——— 1 1 (*ii*) qts. pts. 4 0 — 3 1 ———

Problem-type examples, on pages 357–8.

(a) No changing needed.

gal. qts.
3 3 —
1 1
———

(b) Changing gallons to quarts.

(i) gal. qts.   (ii) gal. qts.
3 0 —   4 2 —
1 3   3 3
———   ———

(3) *Using three units* (as the need arises).

gal. qts. pts.
3 0 0 —
   3 1
————

N.B. Practice in changing should be given at each stage.

---

gal. qts.
2 1 +
1 2
———

(b) Changing quarts to gallons.

(i) gal. qts.   (ii) gal. qts.
3 3 +   2 3 +
1 2   2 0
———   ———
                    2

(3) *Using three units* (as the need arises).

gal. qts. pts.
3 1 +
2 0
3 1
————

N.B. Practice in changing should be given at each stage.

(ii) a pint measure, (iii) a half-pint measure.

The *measuring of larger quantities* of liquids by using a gallon measure (together with quart and pint measures later).

The *checking of the capacities* of standard containers (e.g. petrol tins, oil drums, milk churns).

The *collecting of information* of all kinds about capacity.

The use of *practice-cards, flash-cards* and *work-cards* in learning the 'facts'.

(b) *Dry measure.*

The *repetition of selected activities* from those given above using grain, beans or sand in place of water.

C. Learning about OTHER MEASURES.

(a) Liquid measure: GILLS.

The *use of the gill measure* to make up pints and quarts.

The *measuring of small quantities* of liquids in gills and in pints and gills.

The *collecting of information* about the use of gills.

ANALYSIS 8 (cont.)

1. Stage		2. Activities	3. Addition	4. Subtraction
(b) Dry measure: PECKS and BUSHELS.		The use of quart, pint and gallon *measures to make up pecks and bushels* of grain or beans. The *handling of* pecks and bushels of grain or beans. The *collecting of information about* the use of pecks and bushels. The use of *work-cards.* The use of *practice-cards* and flashcards in learning the 'facts'.	*Note*—It is recommended that practice, through graded examples, in calculations with units of this kind, should be given *only when the need arises.* In many places such units are seldom used, and 'sums' which involve them are therefore meaningless to most children.	

Continued for Multiplication and Division, and Problem-type examples, on pages 357–8.

1. STAGE	5. MULTIPLICATION	6. DIVISION	7. 'PROBLEM'-TYPE EXAMPLES
A. EARLY EXPERIENCES of filling and emptying containers (*continued from page* 354).			(After experience of many and varied activities, such as those given in column 2, and together with the working of graded examples, such as those given in columns 3, 4, 5 and 6.) For instance: (*a*) A water tank contained 10½ gallons of water. A further 3 gallons 3 quarts were put in. How much did the tank then contain? (*b*) An oil-drum contained 12 gallons of oil. Some was used and it was found that 10½ gallons were left in the drum. How many pints of oil had been used? (*c*) A store-keeper sold fifty bottles, each containing ¾ pint of fruit juice. How much did this amount to in gallons and quarts? (*d*) Seven and a half gallons of water is shared between twenty men. How much do they each receive? (*e*) How many quart packets of seeds can be made up from a bag containing one bushel?

B. Learning about PINTS, QUARTS and GALLONS.
(*a*) *Liquid measure* (*continued from page* 355).
	(*1*) *Multiplying quarts and pints.*
	(*a*) Changing pints to quarts.
	
	(*i*) qts. pts. (*ii*) qts. pts.
	  2 1 × 3 1 ×
	     5 4
	   ————— —————
	
	(*iii*) qts. pts.
	   3 1 ×
	     16
	   —————
	
	(*b*) Changing quarts to gallons.
	(*i*) gal. qts. (*ii*) gal. qts.
	   3 × 3 ×
	   4 14
	 ————— —————
	
	(*c*) Changing pints to quarts and quarts to gallons.
	(*i*) gal. qts. pts. (*ii*) gal. qts. pts.
	   3 1 × 2 1 ×
	    4 24
	 ——————— ———————
	 ——————— ———————
		(*1*) *Dividing quarts and pints.*
		(*a*) Sharing.
		
		(*i*) qts. pts. (*ii*) qts. pts.
		  7 1 ÷ 5 6 0 ÷ 5
		
		(*b*) Grouping.
		'How many half-pint bottles can be filled from a jar holding five quarts of liquid?'
		
		(*2*) *Dividing gallons and quarts.*
		(*a*) Sharing.
		
		(*i*) gal. qts. (*ii*) gal. qts.
		  5 2 ÷ 7 5 2 ÷ 8
		
		(*b*) Grouping.
		'How many quart-bottles of oil are needed to fill a container which holds three and a half gallons?'
		
		(*3*) *Dividing gallons, quarts and pints.*
		(*a*) Sharing.
		
		gal. qts. pts.
		(*i*) 4 3 1 ÷ 9
		
		gal. qts. pts.
		(*ii*) 24 0 0 ÷ 15	

ANALYSIS 8 (cont.)

1. STAGE	5. MULTIPLICATION	6. DIVISION	7. 'PROBLEM'-TYPE EXAMPLES
	(2) *Multiplying gallons and quarts.* (*a*) No changing needed. gal. qts. 2 1 × 3 (*b*) Changing quarts to gallons. (*i*) gal. qts. (*ii*) gal. qts. 3 2 × 3 2 × 5 15 (3) *Multiplying gallons, quarts and pints.* (*i*) gal. qts. pts. (*ii*) gal. qts. pts. 2 3 1 × 2 3 1 × 8 28	(*b*) Grouping. 'How many three-pint tins can be filled from an eight-gallon drum of oil?'	
(*b*) *Dry measure* (*continued from page* 356).	*Note*—It is recommended that practice, through graded examples, in calculations with units of this kind, should be given only when the need arises. In many places such units are seldom used, and 'sums' which involve them are therefore meaningless to most children.		

SOMETHING TO THINK ABOUT—11
(*Time*)

Man was aware, probably in the very distance past, of the regularity of light and darkness, of the moon's phases, and of the changes in the seasons. For a very long time, however, he did not understand the reasons for these regular changes. It is only during the last thousand years that he has come to realize, and to accept the idea, that the earth is round and spins on its axis, and that the axis itself slowly turns; that the earth moves round the sun; and that the moon moves round the earth. But man's lack of understanding did not prevent him from using these regular happenings to help him to measure time. (It is interesting to note that, unlike all other measures, the day and the year are natural units: man had no part in deciding upon their size. Time is also the only measure which has the same units all over the world.)

At first, time was measured in terms of days (of light) or nights (of darkness)—our present word 'fortnight' probably originated in the idea of fourteen nights. But gradually the word *day*, in terms of time, has come to be used to mean the sum of the hours of darkness and light: more exactly it is the time taken for the earth to turn once round its axis.

Man has always been fascinated by the moon. Before he knew that the apparent changes in its size and shape are due to its movement round the earth, he often attributed to it mysterious and magical powers. In many countries the coming of the new moon was the occasion for a holiday and for rejoicing. The regular growing and dying away (waxing and waning) of the moon provided man with another unit in which to measure time. (The phrase 'many moons ago' is still in common use.) It was natural that man should try to measure the moon's movements in days. At first the full cycle was reckoned as thirty days, but this figure was found to be not quite exact. More careful measurement gave twenty-nine and a half days. (It is now known that the length of the lunar month, as this unit is called, is not constant. In our present-day units, it varies from 29 days, 7 hours, 20 minutes to 29 days, 19 hours, 30 minutes.)

The fractional part of the day in the lunar month has always been a cause of difficulty, and often confusion, in the making of calendars. Had man himself been able to arrange the length of the lunar month, he would certainly have arranged it to be an exact number of days. For everyday convenience the length of a calendar month must be an exact number of days, so, at the best, it must be slightly more or less than a lunar month.

The length of the year, that is, the time taken for the earth to move once round the sun, adds further confusion to the work of the calendar makers. Here again, man would like to have arranged for a year to be an exact number of days, but once again an awkward fraction of a day appears. Thus it was impossible to build up a simple table of time, as may be done for man-made measures (for example, 12 in. = 1 ft., 3 ft. = 1 yd., 22 yds. = 1 chain, etc.). It was only when man introduced other units of time that he was able to arrange for them to be related to each other in a simple manner. For example:—

$$60 \text{ seconds} = 1 \text{ minute}$$
$$60 \text{ minutes} = 1 \text{ hour}$$
$$24 \text{ hours} = 1 \text{ day}$$
$$7 \text{ days} = 1 \text{ week}$$

The story of the many ways in which man, in various parts of the world, and over the centuries, tried to fit the lengths of the lunar month and the year into a workable calendar, is too long to tell here. It is only possible to say how the present calendar is made up.

Nowadays, no attempt is made to link calendar months with lunar months although the idea of having twelve months in the year does come from earlier attempts to do this (12 lunar months = $12 \times 29\frac{1}{2}$ days = 354 days). The twelve months cannot be equal in length if their total is to be 365 days. Also, even numbers were not favoured in the early days, though later some were brought in. So we now have months varying from 28 days to 31 days.

The exact length of a year, however, is 365 days, 5 hours, 48 minutes, 45 seconds, and for an exact calendar some arrangement must be made to allow for the extra fraction of a day. If this fraction is regarded as a quarter of a day, allowance can be made for it by adding one whole day to every fourth year. It has been so arranged that these years occur when the number of the year is exactly divisible by four. For example, the year 1956 was such a year. Similarly the years 1960, 1964, 1968, etc. This arrangement gives us our 'leap year'. But there is still a small difference: the length of the year is $11\frac{1}{4}$ minutes less than $365\frac{1}{4}$ days. During a hundred years these $11\frac{1}{4}$ minutes amount to almost $18\frac{3}{4}$ hours. During four hundred years they amount to just over three days. Allowance is made for this growing difference between the calendar year and the actual year by leaving out the extra day three times in every four hundred years. (For convenience, these omissions are arranged when the centuries change. For example, the years 1700, 1800, 1900 were *not* leap years but the year 2000 will be a leap year.)

When the allowances are made the present calendar year differs from the actual year by about only three hours in four hundred years.

N

CHAPTER XXI

MORE ABOUT TIME

Although children do not easily grasp the idea of time it gradually develops through their normal everyday experiences. It is important to remember this in our teaching. The child's difficulties are not so great if the work is continually related to what is going on around him, and if formal calculations are left till the last year of the primary school course.

A—*Further activities*

(*1*) *Telling time in different ways*

Children learn to tell the time quickly by short periods of daily revision of the work described in Chapter X. Here are some other activities which widen and strengthen the child's knowledge.

(*i*) The children make small cardboard clocks. The hands are held together by a drawing pin. The teacher calls out various times: 'Set your clock at ten minutes past eight.' 'Now show me a quarter to eleven.' Sometimes the children can test each other, referring to the teacher's wall-clock (Fig. 79, page 138) for the answers.

(*ii*) Written questions are put on the blackboard for the children to work out. For example, 'Show the following times: twenty past three, five minutes to twelve', etc. The children are each provided with a small circle of cardboard to enable them to draw a series of circles in their books. These circles are then filled in by drawing the hands at the correct position.

(*iii*) Children enjoy acting as clocks. In turn they stand at the front of the class but with their backs turned to it. They hold up their arms (one of their hands holding a stick to indicate that it is the minute hand) in a particular position. The rest of the class write down the time shown (Fig. 121).

(*iv*) When the children are perfect at 'telling the time' (and *not* before) it is an interesting exercise for them to try to tell the time by looking at a clock through a mirror. This requires the ability to make judgements about spatial relationships, but it is enjoyed by the more able children.

(*v*) The children should also learn to express the time in other ways. For example, they should make use of their knowledge of the table of fives to learn the 'sixty-minute clock'. They learn that 'twenty-five minutes to six' can be expressed as

FIGURE 121.—Clock acting ('nine o'clock')

'five thirty-five' (5.35). They should now also learn to tell time exactly to the nearest minute. Instead of saying: 'Just after quarter to three', they should be able to say: 'Two forty-seven' (2.47), or 'Thirteen minutes to three'. This becomes necessary when they are learning to deal with time-tables of trains, buses, etc.

(*vi*) The children should learn why 'a.m.' and 'p.m.' are used.* This knowledge becomes necessary, they find, because of the confusion which is sometimes caused when a time is stated without any indication of whether morning or evening is meant. When the children are used to this idea they can be introduced to the twenty-four-hour clock (Fig. 122), and can make calculations concerning it. This is particularly helpful in

FIGURE 122.—
The twenty-four-hour clock

shipping areas, and where the children have some knowledge of air-fields and air-travel.

* 'a.m.' and 'p.m.' stand for the Latin *ante meridiem* and *post meridiem*, meaning before and after mid-day (noon). The English word 'meridian' comes from the same source.

(2) Estimating time

Children do not find it easy to estimate time, mainly because the impression they gain of the passage of time depends upon what they are doing. A child who has a difficult and boring task to do says later that he 'spent ages' over it, whereas we may have estimated that this task should take fifteen minutes. (We should bear this fact in mind if we set home-work!) On the other hand we all know how disappointed children are because an interesting lesson has 'finished too soon'. Practice can be given in estimating time with questions like these:—

How long can I hold my breath? (seconds)
How long does it take to walk a certain distance? (minutes)
How long does it take to run the same distance? (minutes)
How long does it take to cycle the same distance? (minutes)
How long will it take to tidy up the room at the end of the day? Can we beat this estimate? (minutes)
How long does it take to learn a poem, or a part in a play? (hours—reckoned as number of lessons), etc.

But before this estimation is possible the children should be given opportunities to concentrate on the passage of short periods of time. For example:—

(i) They should learn to count seconds. This is difficult at first and most children are too quick. A useful way of learning the interval between one second and another is to count like this, without a break in normal (but not slow) speech and keeping a regular rhythm: 'Hundred and <u>one</u>, hundred and <u>two</u>, hundred and <u>three</u>, hundred and <u>four</u>, hundred and <u>five</u>.' If the emphasis is placed on the numbers underlined, five seconds will have gone by. Thus the children get an idea of seconds by rhythmic counting.

When the opportunity occurs we may get the children to count how many seconds pass, after a flash of lightning, before the thunder is heard. Then older children, with our help, may find how far away the storm is. (The speed of sound is 1,100 feet per second.)

(ii) The children should experience what it is like to sit still, in silence, for an exact minute. (They may listen to all the sounds

going on outside, as an introduction to a lesson about sounds, or about the words used to describe different kinds of sounds.)

(*iii*) Children may look at the class time-table and discuss why it is that some periods of half-an-hour seem longer than others.

(*iv*) Older children may be shown how they can measure each other's rate of pulse-beat. They need a stop-watch or a watch with a second's hand. A child puts his fingers tightly on his partner's left wrist. When he feels the regular beat, he counts them until a half-minute has gone by. He then doubles this number to find out how many pulse-beats there are in a minute. (Similarly, children may find their rates of breathing, at rest, and after running fast.)

(*3*) *Collecting information about time*

As with the other measures, children should be encouraged to make a little booklet in which they collect information. This increases their general knowledge of the world in which they live and gives a basis for understanding written problems. Such a booklet may include:—

(*i*) A section on clocks and time-pieces through the ages. Early man's calculation of time; the water-clock; the sand-clock; a candle marked for every hour that it burns. When were watches and clocks of the modern type first made? Where is the largest clock? What is the smallest watch?

(*ii*) How does a clock pendulum work? What does it do? (The children give an account of their own experiments with simple pendulums of various lengths.*)

(*iii*) Interesting information about travelling times, from time-tables or newspapers. For example, 'By aeroplane it takes twenty hours to reach Nigeria from England.' 'A river boat takes seven days to travel down the River Congo from Kabalo to Stanleyville.'

---

* The 'simple' pendulum (a small heavy bob swinging at the end of a strong thread) has a 'period' of 1 second for a length of about 9¾ inches and 2 seconds for a length of about 39 inches. (The 'period' is the time of one complete to-and-fro swing. It is usual to take the time for twenty complete swings and then divide by twenty to find the 'period'.)

(*iv*) Time-charts connected with History or Science dealing with years B.C. and A.D. (We explain these letters.)

(*v*) Time connected with Geography and Astronomy. Discussions about longitude and the rotation of the earth, and the position of the earth with regard to the sun, the moon and the stars, may lead to interesting notes in the booklet. For example, the older children may enquire why 'the time' in Zanzibar and New York is different.

B—*Changing units of time*

There is rarely any need for the children to work out long calculations, changing days and hours to minutes, etc. If, for examination purposes, this must be taught, then the teacher should follow the methods outlined for the other measures (Chapters XVIII–XX).

But children should learn the *facts* of time, in order to be able to carry out simple calculations when necessary. The facts are shown as a table in Chart XI. This chart should be built up *with the children*, drawing upon the experience gained from various activities. The facts should then be thoroughly learned.

CHART XI

A TABLE OF UNITS OF TIME

60 seconds (sec.)*	= 1 minute (min.)*
60 minutes (min.)	= 1 hour (hr.)
24 hours (hrs.)	= 1 day
7 days	= 1 week
4 weeks	= 1 month (lunar)†
365 days	= 1 year ⎫†
366 days	= 1 leap year ⎬

It is usual to speak of a year as 52 weeks, but in fact: 1 year = 52 weeks and 1 day, 1 leap year = 52 weeks and 2 days.

When the children are shown a yearly calendar they notice that only one month of the year (February) has twenty-eight

---

* Symbols for minutes (′) and seconds (″) are sometimes used. The origin of these symbols is obscure, but it is likely that they were 'borrowed' from the Egyptian symbols indicating minutes and seconds in the measurement of angles. The same symbols are also used, of course, to denote feet and inches.

† See page 361.

days (four weeks). The other months are different. From the calendar they should count the number of days in each month. Then they can be taught this simple rhyme which helps them to 'fix the facts' about days and months:—

> 'Thirty days have September,
> April, June and November.
> All the rest have thirty-one,
> Excepting February alone
> Which has twenty-eight days clear,
> And twenty-nine each leap year.'

It is advisable to have in the class room, if possible, three kinds of calendar. That shown in Fig. 123 is a daily reminder of the date, which children can copy as a heading for the day's work. They should take turns in changing this each day. A

FIGURE 123.—
A day-by-day calendar

FIGURE 124.—
A month-by-month calendar

calendar of the kind shown in Fig. 124 gives the days and dates of the month. This must be changed at the end of each month. The third calendar should be one for the whole year. This may be useful for reference in the solving of written problems.

C—Calculations on time

As with the other measures, there is more purpose in working mechanical exercises on time if they are related to actual situations. We should show how the working is set down, and should devise graded examples (as given in Analysis 9, page 372). It is advisable also to give the children work-cards. These require them to add, subtract, multiply or divide, but also give meaning to what they are doing.

(*a*) *Work-cards in addition of time*—Fig. 125 shows two typical examples.

(*a*)

2TA	You need the class time-table

Work out the time spent each day of the week on physical activities (P.E., Games, Play, etc.).
Which day do you have most?
Which day do you have least?

(*b*)

4TA	You need the calendar for the year

How many weeks and days are there altogether in the months January, February, March and April, in a leap year?

FIGURE 125.—Work-cards, for addition of time

The working for part of the card in Fig. 125(*a*) is set down like this:

Monday	hrs.	min.
P.E.		35 +
Games	1	15
Play-breaks		30
Mid-day play	1	5
	3	25
	1	

(*b*) *Work-cards in subtraction of time*—Typical examples are shown in Fig. 126.

(*a*)

4TS	You need a school time-table

How much time do you spend at school each day?
(Use the idea of the twenty-four-hour clock if you wish).

(*b*)

10TS	You need a railway time-table

Find out which is the fastest train between your nearest railway station and the next big town.

FIGURE 126.—Work-cards, for subtraction of time

In dealing with the card shown in Fig. 126(*a*) the children should be shown that the work can be set down more easily if the idea of the twenty-four-hour clock is used. For example, if school starts at 9.15 a.m. and ends at 4.10 p.m. the latter can be thought of as 16.10 hours, and the subtraction (using the method of decomposition) can be set down like this.

hrs.	min.
5	70
1̸6̸	1̸0̸ −
9	15
6	55

Another method is to find the length of time from 9.15 a.m. to 12.0 noon, and then add on the 4 hrs. 10 mins. of the afternoon. The working may be set down as shown here.

hrs.	min.		hrs.	min.
1	60			
1̸2̸	0 −		2	45 +
9	15		4	10
2	45		6	55

(c) *Work-cards in multiplication of time*—Examples are shown in Fig. 127.

(a) | 1TM   You need a school time-table.
How much time do you spend in school each day? (Leave out the mid-day break.) Now work out how much time you spend in school in a week.

(b) | 12TM   You need a calendar for June and the school time-table.
How many days in June did you go to school?
Work out how much time you spent at school altogether during this month.

FIGURE 127.—Work-cards, for multiplication of time

In dealing with the card shown in Fig. 127(a), the working may be set down as shown (supposing the daily time spent in school to be 5 hours 35 minutes and that there are 5 school days per week).

hrs.	min.		
5	35 ×		2
	5		60)175
27	55		120
2	175		55

(d) *Work-cards in division of time*—Examples are shown in Fig. 128.

(a) | 5DT In a relay race there are four men in each team and each man runs the same distance. The time of the winning team is 5 minutes 12 seconds. What is the approximate time that each man is running?

(b) | 9DT A fruit picker collects a basket of fruit and empties it about every 15 minutes. How many baskets of fruit does he deal with if he works 54 hours 30 minutes in a week?

FIGURE 128.—Work-cards, for division of time

In dealing with the card in Fig. 128(a), the work is set down like this. The answer is 1 minute 18 seconds.

	min.	sec.
	1	18
4)5	12	
	4	60
	1	72
	60	72
	60	

The card in Fig. 128(b) is an example of division by grouping. The working is set down as shown. The answer is 218 baskets. Some children are able to 'see' that the answer may be obtained by working in quarter-hours. They work out the number of quarter-hours in 54 hrs. 30 mins.

hrs.	min.	
54	30	218
60	3240	15)3270
3240	3270	30
		27
		15
		120
		120

(e) *Other possible work-card activities*—Teachers may have many other ideas for making the work practical. The examples, and, to some extent, the methods, depend upon the area in which the children live, and the kind of experiences they have from day to day. Here are several further suggestions which may help in the making up of work-cards:

(i) Children may use a calendar to find how long it is to their next birthday celebration, or to some coming festival.*

* It is important for children to learn that, in reckoning the time from one date to another, only *one* of the dates should be included (unless the word 'inclusive' is mentioned in the question).

(*ii*) Information about postal arrangements may provide examples of mail or parcel delivery dates to other countries.

(*iii*) Railway, bus or shipping time-tables may be used to find, for instance:

(I) 'How long can you spend in a relative's home if you take the first train of the day and return by the last train of the day?'

(II) 'What is the quickest time in which you can make a particular return journey?'

(III) 'What is the difference between the times taken by a stopping train and an express train (for a given journey)?'

(*iv*) Children can be encouraged to construct their own time-tables. For example they may make a record of a day's events, or of a journey (real or imaginary).

(*v*) Older children may be able to make calculations concerning speeds—that is, to deal with measurements of time and length in the same problem. They are interested in timing athletic races at school, and where possible should be introduced to the use of the stop-watch. Even young children who have seen the inside of cars and lorries are immensely interested in 'speedometers'.

(*vi*) Some children enjoy competitions in speed of writing or reading. These can be timed and the number of letters or words per minute may be calculated.

D—*Points to remember in teaching about time*

1. It is advisable to follow a suitably graded scheme such as that shown on pages 372–6.
2. The work should be based upon the children's experiences in their everyday lives.
3. The children should be encouraged to take an interest in all the methods by which time is measured.
4. The time 'facts' should be known perfectly.
5. Accurate setting down of written work should be insisted upon.
6. Teachers in a school (or within an area) should together decide upon the standard methods to be used in calculation and should keep to them.

ANALYSIS 9

Suggested stages and steps in the teaching of time
(see Chapters X and XXI)

Continued for Multiplication and Division

1. STAGE	2. ACTIVITIES	3. ADDITION	4. SUBTRACTION
A. Getting to know about time through REGULAR HAPPENINGS; the CLOCK, the DAY, the WEEK, the MONTHS, the SEASONS, the YEAR.	Noting the *positions of the hands of the clock* at important times each day (e.g. the beginning and end of school). The *use of model clocks* to show these times. *Writing the date* (day, month, year) on the blackboard each day. The use of *stories and rhymes* about the seasons.		(1) *Subtracting hours and minutes.* (a) No changing needed. (i) hrs. min. 3 30 − 1 20 ; (ii) hrs. min. 3 30 − 3 15 ; (b) *Changing hours to minutes.* (i) hrs. min. 3 10 − 1 40 ; (ii) hrs. min. 4 2 − 3 15 ; (iii) hrs. min. 12 0 − 7 15
B. LEARNING 'TO TELL THE TIME' (in five-minute intervals). (a) The positions of the HOUR-HAND. (b) The positions of the MINUTE-HAND. (i) 'Past,' (ii) 'To.' (c) Using the minute- and hour-HANDS TOGETHER. (a) 'Past' the	The use of *model clock-faces:* (a) Hour-hand only. (b) Minute-hand only. (c) Hour- and minute-hands together. The examination of the class and school time-tables. The recording of a personal time-table for a particular day.	(1) *Adding minutes.* (a) No changing needed. (i) min. 25 + 15 ; (ii) min. 10 + 7 32 ; (b) *Changing minutes to hours.* (i) hrs. min. 40 + 30 ; (ii) hrs. min. 35 + 45 45 45	

Problem-type examples, on pages 375–6.

C. Learning more about DAYS, WEEKS and MONTHS.		

The *keeping of diaries* of all kinds.
Example:
  (i) Class diaries.
  (ii) Weather diaries.
  (iii) Garden or farm diaries.
  (iv) Personal diaries.
The *drawing of simple graphs* concerned with time.
e.g. (i) Growth of a plant.
  (ii) Daily temperatures.
  (iii) Length of the shadow of a stick at various times of the day.

(a) No changing needed.

(i) hrs. min.	(ii) hrs. min.
2 10 +	3 5 +
3 5	5 35
	10

(b) Changing minutes to hours.

(i) hrs. min.	(ii) hrs. min.
2 40 +	1 40 +
3 30	2 50
	40

(3) Adding days and hours.
(a) No changing needed.

(i) days hrs.	(ii) days hrs.
2 10 +	2 4 +
1 8	1 12
	4

(b) Changing hours to days.

(i) days hrs.	(ii) days hrs.
2 20 +	4 20 +
1 16	1 12
	18

(4) Adding weeks and days.
(a) No changing needed.

weeks days
2   3 +
4   2

(a) No changing needed.

days hrs.
4 12 –
1   8

(b) Changing days to hours.

(i) days hrs.	(ii) days hrs.
3 7 –	2 5 –
1 14	1 8

(iii) days hrs.
3   0 –
2 10

(3) Subtracting weeks and days.
(a) No changing needed.

weeks days
4   5 –
2   3

(b) Changing weeks to days.

(i) weeks days	(ii) weeks days
3 4 –	7 0 –
1 6	1 3

(4) Subtracting minutes and seconds.
(a) No changing needed.

min. sec.
14 35 –
10 12

D. Learning to TELL THE TIME MORE EXACTLY and RECORDING IT in different ways.		

(a) Using 'PAST' and 'TO' the hour (e.g. 18 minutes past 5).
(b) Using only HOURS AND MINUTES
(c) Using *a.m.* and *p.m.*
(d) Using the 24-HOUR CLOCK (e.g. 14.47).

The *further use of model clock-faces* and outline drawings of clock-faces.
'Acting as clocks' by the children.
The reading of time-tables in which the terms *a.m.* and *p.m.* are used.
The reading of time-tables in which the 24-hour clock is used.
The collecting of interesting information about time (e.g. the time taken to run a mile).
The estimation of the time taken for various activities.
The use of stop-watches (if available): methods of counting in seconds.

ANALYSIS 9 (cont.)

1. STAGE	2. ACTIVITIES	3. ADDITION	4. SUBTRACTION

E. Learning and using the TIME 'FACTS'.	The use of *work-cards* dealing with everyday activities involving time. The use of *time-tables* of various kinds (e.g. 'bus, train, high and low tide, air travel, postal arrangements). The learning of helpful *rhymes*. The use of *practice-cards* and *flash-cards* to learn the 'facts'.	(b) Changing days to weeks.
		 (i) weeks days (ii) weeks days
		 2 6 + 3 6 +
		 1 4 1 4
		             5
		
		 (5) *Adding minutes and seconds.*
		 (a) No changing.
		 min. sec.
		 14 35 +
		  2 12
		
		 (b) Changing seconds to minutes.
		 (i) min. sec. (ii) min. sec.
		 12 40 + 3 58 +
		  8 33 4 2
		            3 59
		            4 8
		
		 (6) *Adding three units* (when the need arises).
		 hrs. min. sec.
		 1 4 15 +
		 1 5 49
		
		 N.B. Practice in 'changing' should be given at the various stages.
			(b) Changing minutes to seconds.
			 (i) min. sec. (ii) min. sec.
			 4 2 − 6 5 −
			 2 47 5 57
			
			 (iii) min. sec.
			 9 0 −
			 2 13
			
			 (5) *Subtracting three units* (when the need arises).
			 hrs. min. sec.
			 4 5 39 −
			 3 39 15
			
			 N.B. Practice in 'changing' should be given at the various stages.

Continued for Multiplication and Division, and Problem-type examples, on pages 375–6.

TABLE 2 (cont.)

1. STAGE	5. MULTIPLICATION	6. DIVISION	7. 'PROBLEM'-TYPE EXAMPLES
A. Getting to know about time through REGULAR HAPPEN-INGS; the CLOCK, the DAY, the WEEK, the MONTHS, the SEASONS, the YEAR (*continued from page 372*).			(After experiencing the various activities listed in column 2, and together with the working of many graded examples such as those in columns 3, 4, 5 and 6.) For instance:— (a) A boy runs four times round the school running track. His times for the four laps are 27 sec., 29 sec., 29 sec., 29 sec. and 28 sec. What is his total time?
B. LEARNING TO 'TELL THE TIME' (in five-minute intervals) (*continued from page 372*). (a) The positions of the HOUR-HAND. (b) The positions of the MINUTE-HAND. (i) 'Past,' (ii) 'To.' (c) Using the minute- and hour-HANDS TOGETHER. (i) 'Past' the hour. (ii) 'To' the hour.	(1) *Multiplying hours and minutes.* (a) No changing needed. (i) min. (ii) hrs. min. $12 \times$ 1 $7 \times$ $\underline{}4$ $\underline{}7$ (b) *Changing minutes to hours.* (i) hrs. min. (ii) hrs. min. $15 \times$ 2 $20 \times$ $\underline{}7$ $\underline{}4$ (iii) hrs. min. 2 $35 \times$ $\underline{}9$ (2) *Multiplying days and hours.* (a) No changing needed. days hrs. 2 $5 \times$ $\underline{}3$	(1) *Dividing hours and minutes.* (a) Sharing. (i) No changing needed. hrs. min. 6 $18 \div 3$ (ii) Changing hours to minutes. hrs. min. 9 $6 \div 7$ (b) Grouping. 'The school cleaners take 15 minutes to sweep and dust a class-room. How many class-rooms will they clean in 1½ hours?' (2) *Dividing days and hours.* (a) Sharing. (i) No changing needed. days hours 6 $15 \div 3$ (ii) Changing days to hours. days hours 20 $15 \div 9$	(b) The bus for the town leaves the village at 9.37 a.m. and arrives at 11.13 a.m. How long does the journey take? (c) The machine in the mill makes a yard of fabric every three minutes. How many hours will it take to make a thousand yards? (d) The farmer calculates that he takes 25 minutes to hoe one row of plants. How many complete rows will he hoe in four hours? (e) A motor-cyclist travels 19 miles in 40 min. 51 sec. Two villages on his route are 3 miles apart. How long would he expect to take in covering this part of his journey?

C. Learning more about DAYS, WEEKS and MONTHS (*continued from page 373*).

(b) Changing hours to days.

(i) days hrs.
1 7 ×
   4

(ii) days hrs.
2 16 ×
   9

(b) Grouping.
A petrol engine can run for nine hours on a can of petrol. How many cans will it need to run for three days?

(3) *Multiplying weeks and days.*
(a) No changing needed.

weeks days
4 2 ×
   3

(3) *Dividing weeks and days.*
(a) Sharing.

weeks days
4 2 ÷ 3

(b) Changing days to weeks.

(i) weeks days
2 2 ×
   9

(ii) weeks days
2 5 ×
   7

(b) Grouping.
'The river boat takes five days to go down the river and return. It takes another day to load again. What is the greatest number of trips it can make in four weeks?

D. Learning to TELL THE TIME MORE EXACTLY and RECORDING IT in different ways (*continued from page 373*).
(a) Using 'PAST' and 'TO' the hour (e.g. 18 minutes past 5).
(b) Using only HOURS AND MINUTES (e.g. 2.47).
(c) Using *a.m.* and *p.m.*
(d) Using the 24-HOUR CLOCK (e.g. 14.47).

(4) *Multiplying minutes and seconds.*
(a) No changing.

min. sec.
5 12 ×
   4

(4) *Dividing minutes and seconds.*
(a) Sharing.
(i) No changing needed.

min. sec.
18 45 ÷ 6

(ii) Changing minutes to seconds.

min. sec.
47 13 ÷ 12

(b) Changing seconds to minutes.

(i) min. sec.
2 14 ×
   9

(ii) min. sec.
3 37 ×
   7

(iii) min. sec.
4 24 ×
   5

(b) Grouping.
'The water wheel turns round once every seven seconds. How many times does it turn in thirty minutes?'

E. Learning and using the TIME 'FACTS' (*continued from page 374*).

(5) *Using three units* (as the need arises).

weeks days hrs.
2 14 ×
   5

(5) *Using three units* (as the need arises).
(a) Sharing.
'An aeroplane took 1 hr. 6 min. to travel 300 miles. How long did it take to travel one mile?'
(b) Grouping.
'A car goes one mile in 1 min. 4 sec. How far will it go in 1½ hrs. if it continues at the same speed?'
N.B. (i) *Practice* in 'changing' should be given at the various stages.
(ii) Examples involving remainders should be included at each stage.

N.B. Practice in 'changing' should be given at the various stages.

CHAPTER XXII

INTRODUCING FRACTIONS

A—*The first approach*

When we begin to deal with fractions, we should *not* give the impression that this is a *new* piece of arithmetic, separate from ordinary number and therefore difficult to learn. Rather, the children should be shown that they already know something about fractions. Now they need to learn how to write them down and how to use them.

In their home surroundings and during their early years at school children hear and use language which indicates that fractions are being used. Here, for example, are some common phrases and experiences with which children may already be familiar.

(*i*) 'Break that cake in half and give a *half* to your brother.'
(*ii*) 'We shall need a piece of wood *half* as big again.'
(*iii*) 'I can get there in a *quarter* of the time if I am not delayed.'
(*iv*) 'It only takes a *quarter* of an hour to reach the field if you hurry.'

The names of some fractions (usually 'half' and 'quarter') may also be used or heard by children when they go shopping with their parents; for example, when buying dress lengths, making clothes, and sometimes in cooking.

In school, too, fractions are mentioned in the earlier years. *Before* they reach the stage of dealing with fractions as a separate topic in arithmetic, children usually meet them in connexion with measurement of all kinds. For example:—

(*i*) They measure in half-inches and quarter-inches, perhaps even in tenths.
(*ii*) They may write down the sign for half-penny and farthing and do calculations with them.
(*iii*) They may deal with half-pounds and quarter-pounds in weight.
(*iv*) They may deal with vessels containing, for instance, half a pint.
(*v*) They learn to tell the time in half- and quarter-hours.

It is important that *we emphasize to the children the fact that they already know a lot about fractions. This gives them confidence to go on learning more.*

It is also necessary for the teacher to decide how far he should go in the teaching of fractions to young children. It is probably wise at the primary school stage to deal mainly with those fractions which are met with in everyday life. The old text-books used to give, for children to work out, examples which were ridiculous if applied to everyday situations.* If we examine the occasions in everyday life when fractions are used, we find that almost all of them are concerned with halves, quarters and thirds. Eighths, tenths and twelfths are used in measurement and in business, but not by everybody.

It is wise, therefore, in the primary school, to limit our work to these simple fractions. The children then gain a much greater understanding of what fractions mean, because they are dealing with familiar ideas. This understanding has its effect later, especially for those children who come to study mathematics involving more difficult fractions. It helps to prevent the mistakes which so often occur in older children's work through lack of real understanding of the meaning of fractions.

B—*The idea of fractions*

When the children realize that they already know something of fractions we should begin to enlarge upon this knowledge. We must give the children various practical activities to show what fractions are, explain what the word means, and show how they are written down.

The word 'fraction' comes from the Latin *frangere* which means 'to break'.† The idea then develops that a whole object or a whole quantity is broken up into *equal* parts. These *equal* parts are then considered as fractions of the whole. For example:—

(*i*) If we break a stick into two equal parts, each of these parts is a half of the whole (written as $\frac{1}{2}$).

---

* One such example on time has the answer: $5\frac{17}{23}$ seconds after 6 o'clock.

† The word is also met in our word 'fracture'. When a bone is 'fractured', it is broken.

(*ii*) If we share twenty-four articles between four people we break up the whole twenty-four into four equal shares (each share being six articles) and we write each share as $\frac{1}{4}$ (one-quarter of the whole).

(*iii*) If we empty a large can of water into three smaller tins, so that there is the same amount in each, we have 'broken' the quantity of water into three equal parts, and we write each part as $\frac{1}{3}$ (one-third of the whole).

This explanation should be accompanied by *varied* activities, in which the children are themselves dealing with fractions in a practical way. It is important in these early stages that the children should take part in a *variety* of activities. Otherwise there is a danger that they may connect fractions only with *particular* shapes or figures, instead of realizing that fractions may apply to any quantity or any object. For example, some teachers merely show fractions by dividing up a rectangle: their children often fail to apply their knowledge to other things. They sometimes find it difficult to see, for instance, that 'a quarter' can refer to a quarter of a gallon, a quarter of the class, a quarter of a shilling, a quarter of twenty, a quarter of an inch, etc.

Here are some possible methods of approach.

(*1*) *Folding and cutting*

(*a*) *Paper strips*—Four strips of paper of equal size are given to each child. The first is labelled 'One whole'. The next is folded or cut into two halves, each labelled '$\frac{1}{2}$'. These are placed on the desk below the 'One whole' so that the child can see that the two halves together make a strip as big as the whole. The next strip is folded or cut, first into halves and then into quarters. Each piece is labelled '$\frac{1}{4}$', and placed on the desk as in Fig. 129. Similarly the next strip is folded into eight equal parts and each part is labelled '$\frac{1}{8}$' and placed on the desk. The child compares the whole one, each time, with the number of parts. We ask 'How many halves in a whole one?' 'How many quarters?' 'How many eighths?' 'How can we write these down?' The children may then be asked to hold up two quarters, three eighths, seven eighths, one whole one and a half, one whole and five eighths, etc. If they are successful with this, we may repeat the exercise by writing fractions on the blackboard (for example, $\frac{1}{2}$, $\frac{3}{4}$, $\frac{5}{8}$, $1\frac{1}{4}$),

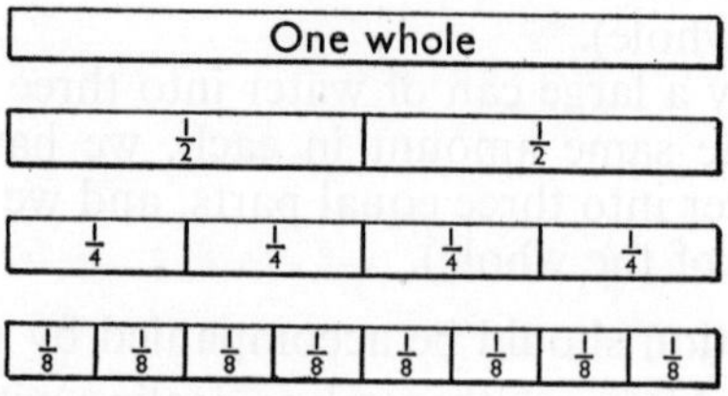

FIGURE 129.—Fraction strips (paper folded and cut)

and asking the children to hold up the quantity shown. Such exercises show whether the children understand the spoken and written language of these fractions.

(b) *Pieces of string*—Four pieces of string of equal length are given to each child, who is told to put the first piece on the desk. This is to be thought of as a whole piece, but this time it is not possible to label it. The next piece is folded and cut so that there are three equal parts, each part being called 'a third'. We write '$\frac{1}{3}$' on the blackboard. The next piece is folded in the same way, and then folded again so that, when it is cut, there are six equal parts. Each part is called 'a sixth', and written as '$\frac{1}{6}$'. The last piece is again folded and cut, this time into twelfths. All are placed on the desk so that the parts may be compared with the whole. As before, we question the children on the value of each fraction, and ask them to hold up various quantities, such as 'two thirds', 'three sixths', 'seven twelfths', and get them to recognize the quantities, put in number form, such as $\frac{2}{3}$, $\frac{3}{6}$, $\frac{7}{12}$, etc.

(2) *Fractions in measurement of length*

(a) *Inches and fractions of an inch*—This is mainly a repetition of an activity with which the children are familiar. (See Fig. 73 and pages 302–3.) They are given a card of prepared lines, of varying length, and are required to measure them accurately to a fraction of an inch, and to write down the measurement. The children obviously need rulers marked in halves, quarters, eighths, tenths, and twelfths. So we first discuss the ruler and how the fractions of an inch are marked. It should be realized, however, that small fractions of an inch are difficult for younger children to deal with and it is wiser to keep to halves and quarters in the early stages.

(*b*) *Drawing lines, using fractions of an inch*—This is a development from measuring, but is more difficult. The children learn to make the exact beginning and ending of the lines required by putting in pencil points and then joining up the points. They may also mark off a given length from longer lines. For example, 'On this line mark two points which are $2\frac{3}{8}$ inches apart.'

(3) *Fractions of shapes*

(*a*) *Circles*—Dividing and cutting up circles helps children to realize that they are dealing with the relationship of the part to the whole. This is easier to see than when cutting up squares

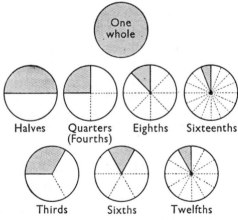

FIGURE 130.—Fractions of a circle (coloured, or cut out, and labelled)

and rectangles, where the *shape* of the fractional part is often the same as that of the whole.

It is a good plan to let the children make a series of small circles of the same size by drawing round a coin or counter. These may then be coloured, or cut out, and labelled as in Fig. 130. In each case the children are asked to compare the fractional pieces with the whole, as when dealing with strips. These circles can later be used for learning the 'equivalence' of fractions (see page 384).

(b) *Squares or rectangles*—These may be made of cardboard. Each child should have a square (or rectangle) labelled 'one whole'. He is then given another smaller shape, preferably of a different colour (see Fig. 131), and asked what fraction the

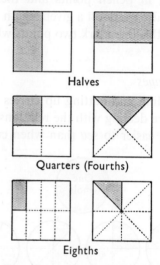

Halves

Quarters (Fourths)

Eighths

FIGURE 131.—Fractions of a square. (A small, coloured, fractional piece of cardboard is used by the child to find out how many are needed to cover the white cardboard square)

smaller part is of the other. He does this by trying it out on the whole piece and finding how many are needed to cover the whole. Children may eventually notice that, for example, a quarter of a square may be another smaller square or it may be a small triangle. This is an interesting discovery which is valuable when they begin to deal with areas.

(c) *Using squared-paper*—It is a very useful and rewarding exercise for children to mark off a particular shape on squared-paper (preferably the kind with one-inch squares). This represents a whole (for example, a rectangle eight squares long and three squares deep). It is then shaded or coloured to show various fractional amounts. For example, in Fig. 132 the teacher has asked the children to colour $\frac{1}{4}$ in blue, $\frac{1}{8}$ in red, and $\frac{5}{12}$ in green. The children learn a great deal for themselves from

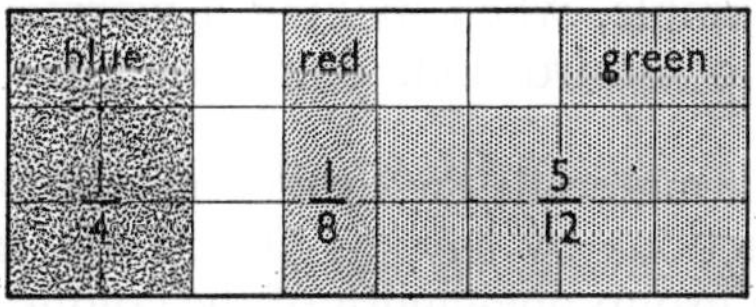

FIGURE 132.—Fractional shapes on squared-paper

this activity. They begin to realize that all three amounts can be thought of as twenty-fourths. This is a background of experience which helps them to understand the need for changing to common fractions when they come to add and subtract.

(4) Drawing activities

Instructions are put on the blackboard, or given individually on small work-cards, requiring the children to represent fractions in drawings. Here are a few simple examples:—

(i) Draw a cake. Show that a quarter of it has been cut out.
(ii) Draw a bottle half-filled with water. Now draw another bottle half-empty.
(iii) Mother has made a large piece of chocolate. Draw it, and show how it would be cut for six of us to have an equal piece each. What fraction do we each get?
(iv) Draw twenty oranges in a pile. Now draw a fifth of this amount.
(v) Draw a clock-face. Show by shading how far the minute-hand travels in a quarter of an hour. How many minutes is this?

(5) Making use of everyday happenings

We should make use of any opportunity during the school day to draw the children's attention to the everyday use of fractions. For example:—

(i) In cutting up or dividing solids of any kind into equal amounts: for example, at meal-times.
(ii) In filling up and emptying bottles of liquid. It is particularly useful if a medicine bottle is sometimes used. This is one of the

few occasions when unusual fractions are met. For example, a bottle may be marked on the side to indicate that it contains twenty-one doses.

(*iii*) In filling up a box with equal quantities of varying substances. For example, when making a wormery the box may have layers of one-third soil, one-third sand, and one-third gravel.

(*iv*) In giving out materials the teacher may draw the children's attention to fractions by saying: 'There are eight groups, so please give each group one-eighth of the coloured chalks in this box.'

C—*Changing fractions*

When the work so far described is understood, the majority of children begin to realize that fractions can be put into 'families' and that it is possible to change one fraction for a number of smaller ones (and vice versa). That is, they have grasped the principle of 'equivalence'. It is sometimes necessary for the teacher to demonstrate this again, particularly to the less able children, and give activities which provide further experience of changing fractions.

(1) Teachers' apparatus for showing equivalence of fractions

(a) Fraction-board—A wooden board has ledges arranged as shown in Fig. 133(*a*). Strips of three-ply wood or stout cardboard slide along the ledges, their sizes being arranged and marked to represent 'One whole' and simple fractions of this whole.

The teacher shows the class how a fraction may be replaced

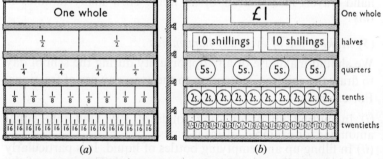

(*a*) (*b*)
FIGURE 133.—Fraction-boards: (*a*) Number, (*b*) Money

by or changed into another: for example, a quarter equals two-eighths; a quarter equals three-twelfths, a third equals four-twelfths. Individual children then change the strips, and the results of the changing are then written down: for example, $\frac{1}{2} = \frac{2}{4} = \frac{4}{8} = \frac{8}{16}$.

The board is useful when children begin to add and subtract fractions. It is also helpful in showing the relationships between fractions of the units of money or measures: for example, fractions of £1 are shown in Fig. 133(*b*).

The same apparatus may be used as a number-board (Fig. 17, page 35) or a fraction-board.

(*b*) '*Sewed circle*' —Three circles, made of stiff paper, and of the

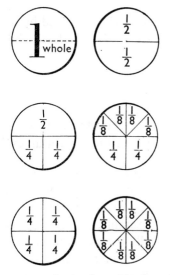

FIGURE 134.—'Sewed circles' for fractions. (The three circles of stiff paper are put on top of each other, sewed across the middle, and marked as shown)
Suitable diameter: 8″

same size, are sewed across the middle and marked, as in Fig. 134, with various fractions. The teacher can demonstrate that the whole may quickly be changed to two halves, four quarters, eight eighths, etc.

(2) *Children's activities*

(a) *Fraction boxes*—Each group of three or four children is provided with a box. The box contains:—

(i) Rectangular pieces of coloured card. One represents a whole; the others are cut to represent different fractions of the whole and are marked accordingly.

(ii) A series of instruction cards which tell the children to work out little problems with fractions and to write down the answers. For example:—

1. Measure the three-quarter piece with eighth pieces. Write down how many there are.
2. Add the quarter to the three-quarters. What do they make?
3. If you cover up some of the whole one with an eighth piece, what is left?

(b) *The changing game*—This is played by the children in pairs, as described on pages 49 and 58. Each child has a number of pieces of card marked with their fractional values. The first child says, for example, 'Please change three quarters for me.' His partner decides what is equal to three-quarters (for example, six-eighths). The pair exchange pieces, after making sure, by measuring, that the six eighths fit exactly over the three quarters. It is then the partner's turn to ask for an exchange.

(3) *Statements about 'equivalence'*

After these activities the children should be ready for a formal statement about equivalence of fractions. The teacher puts on the blackboard, for example, $\frac{1}{4} = \frac{2}{8} = \frac{4}{16}$ and asks: 'What do you notice?' Eventually the children see that *if we multiply the top and bottom of the fraction by the same number, the value of the fraction is unchanged.*

Similarly, we may put on the blackboard: $\frac{8}{12} = \frac{4}{6} = \frac{2}{3}$. We ask: 'What do you notice?' The idea is then shown formally that: *if we divide the top and bottom of a fraction by the same number, the value of the fraction is unchanged.* This is an important principle for the children to understand. Failure to understand lies at the root of many errors in fractions, particularly in 'cancelling'.*

* A word in this sense often incorrectly used. See page 449.

(4) Fractions of measures

If the children grasp the idea of a fraction as a part of a whole, there is no limit to the kind of whole to which the work can be extended. For instance, it is useful to learn how to calculate the fractional parts of the various units of money (Fig. 133(b)) and measures. Many of these are already known to the children from everyday use: for example:—

a half ($\frac{1}{2}$) of a shilling = 6d.;

a half ($\frac{1}{2}$) of a pound note = a ten-shilling note;

a quarter ($\frac{1}{4}$) of a hundredweight = 28 pounds.

It is also necessary, from time to time, to be able to calculate fractional parts of various amounts. For example: 'For helping to harvest fruit a group of eight of us were paid £2. I shall get one-eighth ($\frac{1}{8}$) of this. How much shall I get?' The teacher should link this with the division process, emphasizing that the bottom figure, 8, in the fraction, tells us into how many equal parts the whole £2 is to be divided. The top figure, 1, tells us how many of these equal parts the one child will get. In this example the children have to change the two pounds into forty shillings. They then find $\frac{1}{8}$ of 40s. by dividing 40 by 8. (There is no 'cancelling' at this stage.)

Later the teacher should introduce examples such as this: 'The pay for three days work is twenty-four shillings. I work for two days only, so I get two-thirds of the amount. How much is this?' When reading this example the teacher and class should lay special stress on the word 'two' when saying 'two-thirds'. The children already know how to find one-third of twenty-four shillings. Two-thirds will be twice that amount. In this way they come to see that in calculations of this nature there is an understandable order and method of working.

First we divide by the bottom number* in the fraction in order to find the value of one part. Then we multiply by the top number* of the fraction, which tells how many parts we have

---

* At some stage, depending on the age and ability of his children, the teacher may introduce the words *denominator* and *numerator*. The importance lies, not in knowing the names, but in knowing what they are and what they do.

Later, it can be shown that it is sometimes more convenient to multiply first and then divide.

This kind of work may be extended to fractional calculations of all the measures, but it is advisable to keep the fractions and amounts to reasonable numbers, and, at this stage, to choose examples which are worked out *easily*. Remainders tend to confuse children who are already finding fractions difficult enough.

(5) *Mixed numbers and improper fractions*

When the children measure and draw lines in inches and fractions of an inch (see pages 380–1), they write down their answers as *mixed numbers*. For example, when they measure a line which is three inches and 'a bit more', they may find the 'bit more' to be a quarter of an inch. This is added to the three inches and they say the line is three and a quarter inches long. A *mixed number* is a number of wholes and a fraction of a whole expressed together.

Now, if the children measure the same line again with a ruler marked off in quarter-inches, they can give the length of the line as thirteen quarter-inches or $\frac{13}{4}$ inches. This is an *improper fraction* where the top is greater than (or equal to) the bottom: for example, $\frac{12}{3}$, $\frac{100}{15}$, $\frac{8}{8}$. A *proper fraction* is one which is less than one whole: for example, $\frac{2}{3}$, $\frac{5}{8}$, $\frac{3}{4}$.

A certain amount of practice is needed, for later work in fractions, in changing mixed numbers to improper fractions and vice versa. At this stage it is recommended that children simply do this at a practical level. For example:—

(*i*) 'You have $2\frac{3}{4}$ pounds of sugar. How many quarter pounds is this? How can you write this as an improper fraction?'

(*ii*) 'A tin contains 43 pints of water. A pint is $\frac{1}{8}$ of a gallon. How many gallons and fractions of a gallon does the tin contain?'

D—*Addition of fractions*

A great deal of the early work in adding and subtracting fractions takes place at the time when children are trying out fractional parts of squares, rectangles, circles, etc. They learn from experience, for example, that if they add $\frac{1}{2}$ and $\frac{2}{8}$ they have

$\frac{3}{4}$ of a whole. The teacher has to show how these findings can be written down. It is wise to approach this formal setting down in carefully graded steps (see Analysis 10, page 454), and to allow the children to refer, when they need, to the fraction apparatus.

(1) Adding fractions of the same kind

There is usually little difficulty in such additions, if care is taken to use the correct language in 'reading' the examples given. For instance, in an example like this: $\frac{1}{8} + \frac{2}{}$, it is important to stress the words 'one' and 'two'. Thus the example reads 'one-eighth, add two-eighths'. Children may do this just as easily as they learnt 'one bean, add two beans' in their very early schooldays. The importance of using language which helps the child's understanding is frequently mentioned in this book. Nowhere is it more important than in dealing with fractions. For instance, it is wise to begin teaching examples such as '$3\frac{1}{8} + 2\frac{3}{8}$' by getting the children to read it aloud, making sure that they understand what they are being asked to do: 'Three whole ones and one-eighth, add two whole ones and three-eighths'. It then becomes obvious that the whole ones must be added first and the fractions afterwards, like this: $3\frac{1}{8} + 2\frac{3}{8} = 5 + \frac{1}{8} + \frac{3}{8} = 5\frac{4}{8} = 5\frac{1}{2}$.*

(2) Adding fractions of different kinds

Again, at the next stage, children are already prepared for adding fractions of different kinds because of their early practical activities. They have learnt to change one fraction for another of different kind, and they have used squares, circles, etc., to add these fractions together.

The children begin this stage by adding fractions of the same 'family' such as $\frac{1}{2} + \frac{3}{8}$, that is, by working examples in which *only one* of the fractions has to be changed. They should be given practice at this stage until they realize that it is necessary to find the common fraction before the addition takes place. Then they should be ready to deal with examples, such as

---

* It should be noted that a common method of setting down, $5\frac{1+3}{8}$, is avoided here, because this does not help children's understanding.

$\frac{1}{2} + \frac{1}{3}$, in which *both* fractions have to be changed. Here we should refer to the fraction board again, and show that both $\frac{1}{2}$ and $\frac{1}{3}$ can be changed for sixths. This should be done with several different examples, until the children see that the fraction board is unnecessary. They find that, at this stage, dealing with simple examples, multiplying the two bottom numbers together gives a guide to finding the common fraction.

After written practice of this kind we may set an example like this: $\frac{1}{4} + \frac{1}{6}$. The children at first may say that the common fraction is twenty-fourths, and are prepared to carry on with the calculation. But we insist on returning to the fraction-board. The board is not big enough to show twenty-fourths, but it does show twelfths. The children can see that both the quarter and the sixth may be changed to twelfths. By writing down the many fractions into which a quarter and a sixth may be changed, this may also be shown clearly in figures:—

$$\frac{1}{4}, \frac{2}{8}, \boxed{\frac{3}{12}}, \frac{4}{16}, \frac{5}{20}, \boxed{\frac{6}{24}}, \frac{7}{28}, \text{etc.}$$
$$+\;\;\;\;\;\;+\;\;\;\;\;\;\;\;\;\;\;+$$
$$\frac{1}{6}, \boxed{\frac{2}{12}}, \frac{3}{18}, \boxed{\frac{4}{24}}, \frac{5}{30}, \frac{6}{36}, \frac{7}{42}, \text{etc.}$$

This leads to a discussion of the need to look for the *simplest* common fraction, and we should give practice in this before proceeding further.

E—*Subtraction of fractions*

The work of subtraction follows the same lines as that for addition, namely:—

(*a*) Subtracting fractions of the same kind, for example: $\frac{5}{8} - \frac{2}{8}$.

(*b*) Subtracting fractions of different kinds, for example:

    (*i*) $\frac{1}{2} - \frac{1}{8}$, where *one* fraction has to be changed
    (*ii*) $\frac{1}{4} - \frac{1}{6}$, where *both* fractions have to be changed, and it is necessary to find the lowest common fraction into which they must be changed.

The work should go on *at the same time* as the work in addition. Detailed steps in teaching are suggested in Analysis 10, pages 454–7.

F—*Multiplication of fractions*

If the children understand the meaning of ordinary multiplication (see Chapter VII), beginning to multiply fractions presents no new idea. Just as 5×4 can be thought of as five fours, so $5 \times \frac{1}{4}$ can be thought of as five quarters and be written down as $\frac{5}{4}$.

We should show again that multiplication is a form of continuous addition, and then go on to point out that, for example, $4 \times \frac{2}{3} = \frac{2}{3} + \frac{2}{3} + \frac{2}{3} + \frac{2}{3} = \frac{8}{3}$. This leads to the idea of multiplying the top of the fraction by the multiplier, that is,

$$4 \times \tfrac{2}{3} = \frac{4 \times 2}{3} = \tfrac{8}{3} = 2\tfrac{2}{3}.$$

The next stage concerns the multiplying of a mixed number by a whole number, for example: $3 \times 2\frac{1}{2}$.

It is suggested that children should learn *two* ways of dealing with this:

(*i*) By saying: 'Three twos and three halves.'
$3 \times 2 = 6$ and $3 \times \frac{1}{2} = 1\frac{1}{2}$. $6 + 1\frac{1}{2} = 7\frac{1}{2}$. Therefore, $3 \times 2\frac{1}{2} = 7\frac{1}{2}$.

(*ii*) By making the mixed number into an improper fraction like this: $3 \times 2\frac{1}{2} = 3 \times \frac{5}{2} = \frac{15}{2} = 7\frac{1}{2}$.*

The work on fractions described in this chapter is limited to the early stages. Emphasis is placed first on a thorough *understanding* of the meaning of fractions through *practical* experiences. Then *simple* calculations are carried out in addition, subtraction and multiplication. In Chapter XXVI the work is developed further, showing how children may be introduced to more difficult ideas in the multiplication and division of fractions.

* This method is inconvenient when dealing with large numbers.

(*Decimal fractions*)

Most civilizations used some kind of fractions, but there was always much difficulty in working out calculations in which fractions appeared. It must be remembered that the people of earlier times did not have the number system we use nowadays. Calculations with ordinary whole numbers were complicated enough. Bringing in fractions made them even more difficult.

The only way that the early mathematicians could find to calculate fractions was to deal with them separately, and in a different way from whole numbers. Many centuries went by before a way was found of dealing with them at the same time, as we do today by using decimal fractions.

The Egyptians, for example, worked only in unit fractions, that is, fractions with a '1' at the top. They used to change all their fractions to sums of unit fractions. For example, two-fifths would be changed to $\frac{1}{4} + \frac{1}{10} + \frac{1}{20}$. A 'table' has been found which was used by the Egyptians in order to make such changes quickly.

The Romans, on the other hand, tried to deal with the difficulty, especially when dealing with measures (for example, length and weight), by dividing their standard units into twelve equal parts. Each twelfth then became a new smaller standard unit, and measurements were usually made to the nearest small unit. (We have noted that 'inch' and 'ounce' both come from '*uncia*'—a twelfth.)

The Greeks had two different systems of fractions. One of these was used in everyday calculations, and the other by the mathematicians and scientists. Much of the work of the latter was concerned with the measurement of angles, for which they used the degree as a unit. To indicate parts of a degree they used a system, similar to the decimal system, in which they divided a degree into sixty parts. Each of these sixtieths was then divided into a further sixty parts. (Nowadays we call these parts of a degree 'minutes' and 'seconds'.) This is similar to the decimal idea of dividing the unit into tenths and then tenths of a tenth, etc.

The Hindus used decimals in the Middle Ages. But when our present number system spread from India to other parts of the world about a thousand years ago, the mathematicians of that time did not immediately make use of the decimal nature of the number system in order to express fractions. They were still largely concerned with astronomy and the measurement of angles and they continued to use minutes and degrees for the measurement of fractional parts.

Gradually, however, with the growth of commerce and navigation, the need for simpler calculation was felt. The merchant needed it for compound interest. The surveyor needed it for working out square roots when dealing with heights and distances. The idea of using decimal fractions in everyday calculations came as a result of trying to meet these needs.

Tables of square roots and compound interest, using decimal fractions, were available early in the sixteenth century, but it was not until 1585 that a first account of their nature and use was published.

In this it was shown that, by using the decimal system, it was possible to deal with whole numbers and fractions at the same time: calculations could be made by using the same methods as were used for whole numbers. In this way the calculations were simplified and time was saved.

The early writers on decimal fractions also described another advantage of their use. They realized that it is

o

possible to be as exact (or as approximate) as the circumstances of the work justify or require. This makes it possible to shorten calculations by working to a particular number of decimal places.

It is well to remember this in our teaching today.

CHAPTER XXIII

OTHER KINDS OF FRACTION

A—DECIMAL FRACTIONS

In this chapter only the *early stages* of learning about decimal fractions are considered. Most children should learn what decimal fractions mean, and be able to make very simple calculations with them. (They meet them from time to time in everyday life and in their reading about rainfall, temperatures, and the achievements of athletes, etc.) This knowledge is sufficient at the primary school level. For those children who go on to secondary education, where they use decimal fractions in mathematics and science, it is equally important that the early work should be clearly understood.

We may ask ourselves 'Why do we use decimal fractions, particularly in science, and later in mathematics, in preference to ordinary fractions?' There are, perhaps, five main reasons:—

(*i*) Because they are a natural extension of our 'tens' number system: Hundreds, Tens, Units, Tenths, Hundredths.
(*ii*) Because they are often easier to deal with than other families of fractions, when we have to make calculations. This is particularly true when dealing with mixed numbers, and when comparing the values of different fractions.
(*iii*) Because there is a close link between decimal fractions and the metric system of measurement (see Chapter XXVII).
(*iv*) Because it is easier to work to a particular degree of accuracy in the measurement of length, weight, time, etc.
(*v*) Because a knowledge of decimal fractions is necessary in later mathematics for dealing with logarithms.

But we are concerned here only with the early stages, and, as always, we must make sure that the children understand the *meaning* of the words and symbols used.

(Children may be taught, quite easily, to add, subtract, multiply and divide decimal fractions by following certain rules. But this does not help them to realize that they are dealing with *fractions*, nor to understand the values of the various figures. A lack of understanding often accounts for the absurd answers which children sometimes give to problems, or in calculations. To be unable to 'see' the absurdity of an 'answer' is a serious matter at any time. It is particularly so for those children who reach the stage of making calculations from the results of experiments in science.)

(*1*) *Introducing decimal fractions* (*tenths*)

It should be noted that the full expression, 'decimal fraction', has been used here. It is wise to use it when introducing 'decimals' to children. They are not then worried by thinking that this is a new and difficult topic. They are encouraged to think of a decimal as a particular kind of fraction, written in a special way. They are less likely to think of decimals as a separate branch of arithmetic with its own strange language.

With this in mind, it is probably best to introduce decimals *not* as an extension of the ordinary 'tens' number system, but as fractions, about which the children already know. The following methods are suggested:

(*a*) *Measuring and drawing lines*—Each child is given a card, or a sheet of paper, on which lines have been drawn* as in Fig. 135. Each line should be a number of inches and an *exact* number of tenths. The children already know how to measure a line and write down its length in inches and tenths of an inch. (For example, the first line is $2\frac{8}{10}$ inches.) We then say: 'Now, there is another way in which you can write down two inches and eight-tenths of an inch. It is rather quicker than the usual way, and the method is very useful. You will see how useful it is when we have to measure more accurately than we have done so far.' We then write 2·8 inches, and the children copy this by the side of the $2\frac{8}{10}$ inches. We go on to explain that the dot (or 'point')

---

* If these sheets cannot be duplicated an alternative method of preparing several sheets at once is this: the lines are drawn on one sheet of paper. This is placed on top of several plain sheets clipped tightly together. A strong pin (or the pointed end of a pair of compasses) is pressed through the point where the first line begins and through the sheets beneath. Keeping this pin in position, another pin is pressed through the other end of the line. The process is repeated for the other lines. By joining each pair of holes on each sheet several copies of the original set of lines may be obtained.

is used to separate the whole number from the tenths, and that instead of giving the length of the line as two and eight-tenths inches, we can now say, 'two point eight inches', which means exactly the same.

The next few lines are measured and marked in the same way, first using common fractions, and then decimal fractions.

Next the children are given practice in drawing lines for themselves. For example, we write on the blackboard: 'Draw five

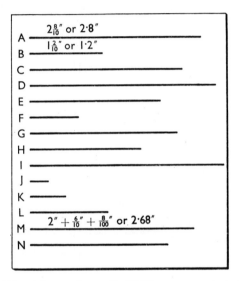

FIGURE 135.—A 'measuring card'. (Children measure in tenths, later in tenths and hundredths, and decimal fractions)

lines, 2·7"; 3·5"; 4·2"; 1·9"; 5·1"; and mark the length of each in decimal fractions and ordinary fractions.' To do this correctly the children have to realize that the figure after the decimal place represents tenths. The lines are carefully checked, either by the children themselves, working in pairs, or by passing round strips of cardboard cut to the required length.

(b) *Using squared-paper*—The squares on the paper must have sides which are divided into tenths. (Here we consider only the vertical tenths: that is, each large square is divided into ten equal columns.) The children are asked to shade in various amounts, such as 3·5; 2·3; 4·9; ·6* (Fig. 136), as when learning about common fractions (page 382).

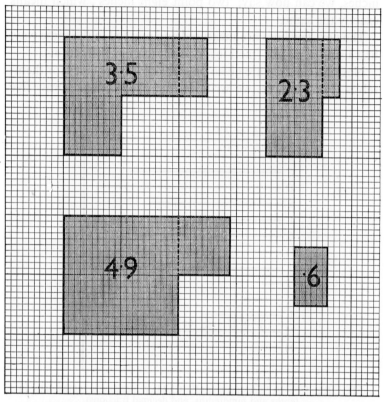

FIGURE 136.—Decimal fractions on squared-paper (tenths)

(c) *Expressing parts of a pound as decimal fractions*—The children are already familiar with the idea of writing a number of shillings as a fraction of a pound. We now show (using question and answer methods) how this can be put down as a decimal. For example:—

$$6 \text{ shillings} = £\tfrac{6}{20} = £\tfrac{3}{10} = £·3*$$
$$14 \text{ shillings} = £\tfrac{14}{20} = £\tfrac{7}{10} = £·7*$$

* If, at any stage, children are found to lose the 'point' in decimal fractions without whole numbers, they should be taught to put a nought in the units column, that is, to write '0·6' instead of '·6', etc.

Similarly, we show how to turn a decimal fraction of a pound into shillings:—

$$£·1 = £\tfrac{1}{10} = 2 \text{ shillings}$$
$$£·8 = £\tfrac{8}{10} = 8 \times 2s. = 16 \text{ shillings}$$

(This can be adapted to the coinage in any country provided that it is easily sub-divided into tenths.)

(2) Simple calculations in decimal fractions
(a) Addition—This may be based on the addition of the lengths of lines measured in inches and tenths of an inch. For example, 'One line measures 1·8 inches. Another measures 2·4 inches. If we put them together to make one line, how long is it?'

A similar approach may be made by the use of squared-paper, whole squares and decimal fractions of squares being added together by shading. 'Answers' may then be checked by practical measurement.

The children are shown how this work may be set down in the same way as the ordinary addition process. It is important, however, that they should not only get practice in setting down and working examples like this. They should also be able to state the example and to give the answer *in words*. For instance, the example shown here may be read: 'Add one point eight and two point four.' When the answer is obtained we expect the children to say it aloud as 'Four point two' (or 'Four and two tenths'). To make the work clearer, we put the word 'units' at the top of the units column and the word 'tenths' at the top of the column following the decimal point. This is a useful way of leading to a full discussion of place-value in connexion with hundredths (see page 400).

Units	Tenths	
1 ·	8	+
2 ·	4	
4 ·	2	
₁		

(b) Subtraction—This process may also be introduced through the measurement of length. For example:—

'How much longer is line A than line B?'
'If I cut off 2·6 inches from a piece of string measuring 8·9 inches, how much is left?'

The work is set down as before, the teacher making sure that the same methods and standard working are used as in ordinary subtraction.

Units	Tenths	
8 ·	9	−
2 ·	6	
6 ·	3	

(c) *Multiplication* (by whole numbers up to twelve)—We may begin by considering the total of several equal sums of money expressed as decimal fractions, or the total length of several equal lines. For instance:—

Tens	Units	Tenths	
	3 ·	2	×
		4	
1	2 ·	8	

'Here are four lines, each 3·2 inches long. What is the total length?'

'A hurdle is 8·5 feet long. What is the length of six such hurdles placed end to end?'

'What is the distance round a square with sides each 5·6 inches long?'

(d) *Division* (by whole numbers up to twelve)—Again we use examples: for instance, 'A line measuring 6·4 inches has to be divided into four parts. What is the length of each part?'

It is suggested that the same methods should be followed as in the ordinary division process (see Analysis IV, page 232).

The children's understanding of what they are doing should be tested frequently. For instance, in the example shown we may point to the '24' and ask: 'What are these? Twenty-four what?' The children should be able to answer that they are twenty-four *tenths*.

	Units	Tenths
	1 ·	6
4)	6 ·	4
	4	
	2	4
	2	4
	·	·

(3) *Introducing hundredths*

(a) *By measuring and estimating lengths of lines*—The children are told that it is sometimes necessary (for example, in the making of car and aeroplane engines) to work accurately with fractions smaller than a tenth. (They are already used to fractions such as $\frac{1}{12}$ $\frac{1}{16}$, $\frac{1}{24}$. They may have used rulers to measure lines in twelfths and sixteenths of an inch.) We now ask the children to return to the sheet of prepared lines (Fig. 135). The length of the last few lines on the sheet have been specially arranged so that they are not an exact number of tenths of an inch. The children first measure these lines to the *nearest tenth* of an inch. When they look carefully, they see that some lines are just short of a tenth while others are just a bit more than a tenth. These 'little bits over' help the children to begin to appreciate the approximate nature of many measurements, and the need for more accurate measurement.

We now get the children to look at one of the lines (M) again. Its length is between $2'' + \frac{6}{10}''$ and $2'' + \frac{7}{10}''$. We draw an

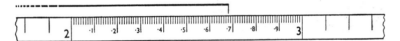

FIGURE 137.—Measuring to hundredths: a blackboard enlargement

enlarged picture of the line and the ruler on the blackboard (Fig. 137), and divide the seventh tenth into a further ten equal parts. The children see that the length of the line is $2'' + \frac{6}{10}''$ + about 8 of the extra small parts. But what is the length of each of these little parts? We divide all the tenths in the third inch into ten equal parts. Thus there are ten equal small parts in each of the ten tenths; that is, one hundred of them in one inch. In other words, each small part is one-hundredth of an inch. The length of the line to the nearest hundredth is thus $2'' + \frac{6}{10}'' + \frac{8}{100}''$. (This is valuable work on common fractions, quite apart from its relation to decimal fractions.) Wooden rulers are not normally divided into hundredths of an inch (though metal rulers sometimes show them). So the children can only attempt to measure to the nearest hundredth of an inch by imagining that the particular tenth at the end of the line is divided into ten hundredths, and then estimating the number needed. It is remarkable how proficient children become after a little practice at estimating in this way.

As each line is measured the result is written, in inches, tenths, and hundredths, above the line. (We must take care to include some examples in which there are no tenths and others with no whole inches. Where there are no tenths the length should be written as, for example, $4'' + \frac{0}{10}'' + \frac{4}{100}''$.)

Underneath each line the children write the length as a decimal fraction. We have to explain, of course, where the hundredths are put.

(b) *Using squared-paper*—The squared-paper used to demonstrate tenths may now be used to show hundredths. First, a large square is seen, as before, to be divided into tenths (vertically). Now, on looking closely, the children can see that the tenth is itself divided (horizontally) into ten parts. So that each tiny square is a tenth of a tenth. The children may not yet know how to work this out in figures: $\frac{1}{10}$ of $\frac{1}{10} = \frac{1}{10} \times \frac{1}{10} = \frac{1}{100}$. But they should realize that a tiny square is one-hundredth of the whole square. They may prove by counting (perhaps in tens), that there are a hundred hundredths in the whole square.

Practice should then be given, as before, in shading particular amounts, for example: $\frac{2}{10}$ and $\frac{5}{100}$; $\frac{7}{10}$ and $\frac{8}{100}$; three whole ones and two tenths and five hundredths; etc. The children soon understand that, for example, $\frac{2}{10}$ and $\frac{5}{100}$ may be written and thought of as $\frac{25}{100}$.

Next, we show how these may be written in the form of decimal fractions, and the children should again be given practice in shading particular amounts written as decimals (Fig. 138).

(4) Decimal fractions as an extension of the H.T.U. notation

It is at this point in the work that we may explain more fully why tenths and hundredths are written in this special way. We show how, if the H.T.U. notation is extended to the right, the tenths-column occupies the first place and the hundredths-column the second place. Replacing H.T.U. by 100, 10, 1 at the top of the columns (as in Fig. 139) helps to make this clear.

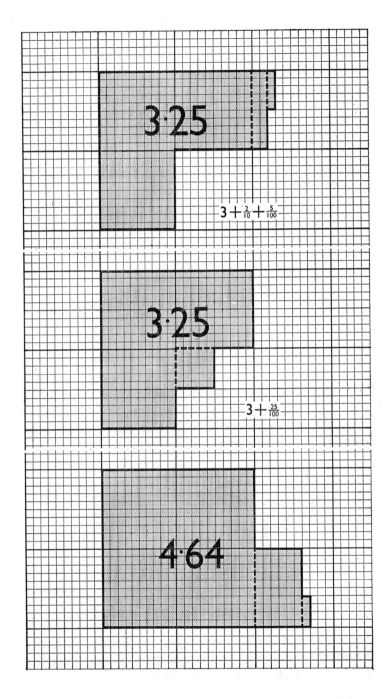

FIGURE 138.—Decimal fractions on squared-paper (hundredths)

The children's understanding of the work should be tested by oral and written questions such as:

(*i*) Write down as a decimal fraction: $\frac{3}{10} + \frac{5}{100}$.

(*ii*) Write down as decimal fractions: $\frac{40}{100}$; $\frac{3}{100}$; $1\frac{9}{100}$.

(*iii*) What is the value of each figure with a ring round it?

     3·4③;   ①0·15;   32⑥·05.

(If in doubt, children should refer to a chart (as in Fig. 139) where the notation is shown.)

H.	T.	U.	Tenths	Hundredths
100	10	1	$\frac{1}{10}$	$\frac{1}{100}$
		5	4	2
	2	4	6	
2	4	1	7	
	1	6	0	5

FIGURE 139.—Decimals as an extension of the H.T.U. notation

The place-value slide (see Fig. 91, page 195) is useful for helping the children. For instance, we first show a '2' under the units; when we move it along to stand for two tens we have to put a nought in the empty units place. Now, having rubbed out the nought, we move the slide so that the '2' comes under 'Tenths' (Fig. 140), thus representing two tenths. When we move

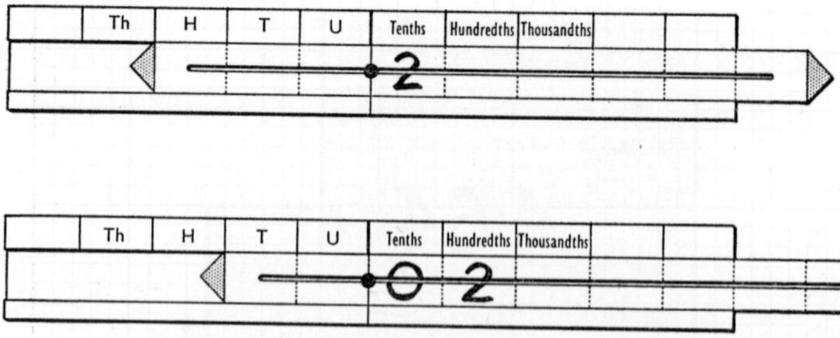

FIGURE 140.—The place-value slide used for decimals

it further, so that the '2' becomes two hundredths, we have to put a nought in the empty tenths position. Children should have individual practice with the apparatus in this way. When they understand the idea, they may go on to use it with two- and three-figure numbers. Later, we may use the slide to demonstrate the quick methods of multiplying and dividing decimal fractions by ten, and later by a hundred, etc. For instance, we write 26·8 on the slide: to multiply by ten we move the slide one place to the left, and at once see the answer as 268; to divide by ten we move the slide one place to the right, and immediately have the answer 2·68.

When the children properly understand the extension of place-value to cover tenths and hundredths they readily see that, when necessary, further places of decimals may be used.

(5) Changing common fractions to decimal fractions

Sometimes decimal fractions have to be changed to ordinary fractions. This change is easy for children who already understand place-value. They merely have to recognize the fraction (tenths, hundredths, etc.) represented by the figures on the right

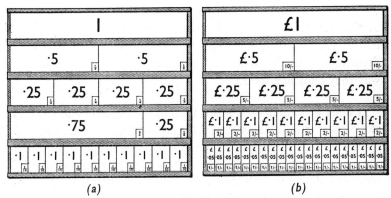

(a)   (b)

FIGURE 141.—Fraction-boards, used for decimals: (a) Number, (b) Money (the pound)

of the decimal point. For example, they know immediately that ·2 means $\frac{2}{10}$ or $\frac{1}{5}$ and that ·25 means $\frac{25}{100}$ or $\frac{1}{4}$.

But more frequently it becomes necessary to change ordinary fractions into decimals. For instance, the change is helpful when dealing with percentage (see next page) and it is very important when comparing the size of various fractions; for example, when putting the following fractions in order of size, $\frac{7}{8}$, $\frac{12}{15}$, $\frac{9}{11}$, $\frac{15}{19}$.

It is not suggested that work of this nature is suitable for primary school children, but it should be possible for them to change simple fractions to decimals. Much of this they learn from experience. They quickly learn, for example, that:

$$\tfrac{1}{2} = \cdot 5; \qquad\qquad \tfrac{1}{4} = \cdot 25; \qquad\qquad \tfrac{1}{5} = \cdot 2.$$

The use of decimal fraction-boards (Fig. 141) often helps to make these simple relationships clear. But they may also learn the *procedure* for changing *any* fraction into a decimal fraction.

The procedure may be introduced by referring again to the meanings of the symbol $\tfrac{3}{4}$ (see page 441): $\tfrac{3}{4}$ *may* mean $3 \div 4$, or $\tfrac{1}{4}$ of 3, or $4)\overline{3}$. When $\tfrac{3}{4}$ is put down as an example of ordinary division, the children realize that they cannot divide three units by four so they must change the three units to thirty tenths before dividing by four. Similarly, when they find a remainder of two tenths they change these to twenty hundredths and again divide by four. In this way they change $\tfrac{3}{4}$ to ·75.

	Units	Tenths	Hundredths
		· 7	5
4)	3	· 0	
	2	8	
		2	0
		2	0
		–	–

It must be emphasized again that, in the primary school, it is sufficient if children understand the *idea* of decimal fractions and if they are able to recognize the value of those simple ones which they may meet. They are also extending their knowledge of place-value, and the structure of our number system. This knowledge and understanding is essential if, at the secondary stage, they are going to deal successfully with more difficult calculations in decimals.

B—PERCENTAGES

As when learning about fractions and decimals, the children's main difficulty in percentages is caused by failure to understand fully the language used. 'Percentage' is a long word, and children are sometimes afraid of it because they think it means something new and difficult. It is most important that they should realize from the beginning that percentage is merely another form of fraction: that percentages arise from, and are closely connected with, the fractions and decimal fractions which are already familiar.

The emphasis again, at the primary school, must be on *understanding*. It is unwise for us to give children 'rules' for calculating percentages, unless they understand the meaning of the necessary words and phrases. Children who do not understand are likely to be in difficulties if they meet a problem which requires a little more than the mere application of a 'rule'. Further, the children should be familiar with some of the uses of percentages in everyday affairs.

In the primary school, therefore, it is better to concentrate on a thorough understanding of the *ideas* rather than on much practice in calculations. The children then have a good foundation upon which they can build.

(1) Why teach 'percentages'?

In his life outside the class room, the child is most likely to come across the term 'percentage' in the conversation of grown-ups and when reading newspapers. He may understand merely that the word has something to do with quantities of things or amounts of money. For example, he may hear the common percentages (25%, 50%, 75%) mentioned in news stories on the radio. He may hear the phrase '99% of the people' to indicate 'nearly everybody'. He may understand a phrase like '100% attendance' to mean 'everybody was there'.

Gradually, his understanding may increase until, for instance, he is able to compare his own examination marks in various subjects. If he goes on to study subjects such as science or agriculture, he must be able to calculate percentages, in order to understand the results of his experiments. When he grows up he may need to know, for example, about interest rates and discount expressed in percentages.

(2) The idea of percentage

Various methods of expressing the relationship between two quantities have already been discussed. For example, if twenty-five children out of thirty are present in one class, and thirty-two out of forty in another, we can say that there are seven more children present in one class than the other. On the other hand we can think of the attendances as fractions of the total numbers, and say that $\frac{25}{30}$ (that is, $\frac{5}{6}$) are present in the first class and $\frac{32}{36}$ (that is, $\frac{8}{9}$) in the second. To compare these two fractions we change them both to eighteenths, and say that the attendances are respectively $\frac{15}{18}$ and $\frac{16}{18}$ of the totals.

If we wish to compare these attendances with that of a class where thirty-three out of thirty-five children are present, it becomes necessary to compare the fractions $\frac{5}{6}$, $\frac{8}{9}$ and $\frac{33}{35}$. This can be done by changing them to $\frac{525}{630}$, $\frac{560}{630}$ and $\frac{594}{630}$. But these are not easy fractions to work with, nor can we easily get an accurate idea of their size. The difficulty increases if we have to consider other fractions as well as these three. The working is simplified, and we find it easier to see the relative sizes of the various fractions, if we make a habit of changing such fractions to hundredths. We choose hundredths because of the tens-nature of our number system. We can 'see' the size of $\frac{72}{100}$, for example, more easily than that of $\frac{18}{25}$. We can think of it as just over seven-tenths.

Returning to our first example, we find that when we try to change $\frac{5}{6}$ to hundredths there are not an exact number of hundredths; but it is sufficient for our purpose to use $\dfrac{83 \cdot 3}{100}$ or even $\frac{83}{100}$. Likewise $\dfrac{88 \cdot 9}{100}$ (or $\frac{89}{100}$) and $\dfrac{94 \cdot 3}{100}$ (or $\frac{94}{100}$) are sufficiently accurate values for $\frac{8}{9}$ and $\frac{33}{35}$ respectively.

Expressed in this way the three attendances are approximately $\frac{83}{100}$, $\frac{89}{100}$ and $\frac{94}{100}$ of the totals. When the attendances of other classes are expressed in this way it becomes easier to see their relative values.

Another way of thinking of these fractions is to say that:

'If there were 100 children in the first class 83 would be present. If there were 100 children in the second class 89 would be present. If there were 100 children in the third class 94 would be present.'

Or, more shortly:

'83 per hundred, 89 per hundred, and 94 per hundred were present.'

Another word for hundred is cent, so that the results can be expressed as: 83 per cent, 89 per cent, and 94 per cent.

In a still shorter form these are usually written as 83%, 89%, 94%.

(3) Explaining percentage to children

It is not suggested that such an example is suitable for children. But we ourselves, as teachers, must have full understanding before we can explain the idea.

(a) *Introduction*—It is perhaps best to begin by revising work which the children have already done in fractions. For instance: 'Which is the biggest of these fractions: $\frac{3}{4}$, $\frac{2}{3}$, $\frac{5}{8}$?' The children know that it is necessary to bring them to a common denominator, that is, in this case, to twenty-fourths: $\frac{18}{24}$, $\frac{16}{24}$, $\frac{15}{24}$. It is then quite easy to put these fractions in order of size.

(b) *The next step*—We may put on the blackboard a list of a child's examination marks. How can we find out his best mark?

> *Reading:*   7 out of 10 ($\frac{7}{10}$ of full marks)
> *Arithmetic:* 13 out of 20 ($\frac{13}{20}$ of full marks)
> *History:*   16 out of 25 ($\frac{16}{25}$ of full marks)
> *Geography:* 33 out of 50 ($\frac{33}{50}$ of full marks)

The fractions are easily compared if we change them to hundredths like this: $\frac{70}{100}$, $\frac{65}{100}$, $\frac{64}{100}$, $\frac{66}{100}$. (We are imagining that, in each case, the marks are 'out of a hundred'.) Now another way of saying seventy-hundredths of the total (or seventy out of a possible hundred) is 'seventy per cent'.* and it is written 70%.

---

* *Per cent* means 'by the hundred' or 'for each hundred'. Children should be asked to think of the meaning of other words which include 'cent'. For example, the coin 'a cent', century, centipede, centurion, centimetre, etc.

Similarly, $\frac{65}{100}$ (65 out of 100) = 65 per cent or 65%
and $\frac{64}{100}$ (64 out of 100) = 64 per cent or 64%
and $\frac{66}{100}$ (66 out of 100) = 66 per cent or 66%.

(c) *Looking for examples of percentage*—We encourage the children to find examples of percentage in everyday life. These should be fully discussed *without* any *written* calculations being made. For instance:

(*i*) A newspaper report says that one football team (A) has a higher percentage of wins than another team (B). We look at the results of the games played by these teams and find that team A has won 13 out of 18 games (that is $\frac{13}{18}$). Team B has won 11 out of 16 games (that is $\frac{11}{16}$). These fractions have been turned to a percentage by the newspaper writer, and he knows which is the more successful team.

(*ii*) 'A savings bank pays three per cent.' What does this mean?

(*iii*) A newspaper advertisement says: 'Buy now and save ten per cent of the cost.' What does it mean?

(*iv*) A man has a new car. He expects to sell it next year. The salesman says its value will go down by seven per cent; if he does not sell it for two years, the value will go down by twenty per cent. What does this mean?

Discussion of this kind is very valuable, because it gives the children a sensible and practical approach to the idea of percentages. This is a sure foundation for the calculations to come later.

(d) *Changing fractions to percentages*—The children soon begin to remember the percentage value of the easy fractions. For example: $\frac{1}{2} = 50\%$, $\frac{1}{4} = 25\%$, $\frac{1}{5} = 20\%$, $\frac{1}{20} = 5\%$, etc. This becomes particularly easy if the children are familiar with decimal fractions. For instance, they know straight away that since $\cdot75 = \frac{75}{100}$, it is also 75%. Similarly, $\cdot05 = 5\%$, $\cdot15 = 15\%$, etc.

We may then go on to show a method of changing any vulgar fraction to a percentage. The method may be explained, for example, like this:—

$\frac{7}{8}$ = seven-eighths of a whole.
A whole can be thought of as $\frac{100}{100}$ or 100 per cent.
So, $\frac{7}{8}$ of 100 per cent = $\frac{7}{8} \times 100$ per cent = $\frac{700}{8}$ per cent
     = $87\frac{1}{2}$ per cent = $87\frac{1}{2}\%$.

The process can eventually be shortened to $\frac{7}{8} \times 100\%$
$= \frac{175}{2}\% = 87\frac{1}{2}\%$.

A calculation does not always work out exactly. Therefore the children should sometimes be given practice in 'rounding off' their answers to whole numbers or to a given number of places of decimals. For example, $\frac{3}{7} = 42\frac{6}{7}\%$ or $42\cdot8571\%$. This may be 'rounded off' either to $42\cdot9\%$ or 43%.

(e) *Finding percentages of given quantities* (in numbers, money, weights and measures)—Examples arise from the kind of discussion described in (c), page 410. For instance:—

(i) 'A store-keeper finds that about 5% of the eggs he collects from farms are bad. How many are likely to be bad in a box containing 440 eggs?'
Here the children can see exactly what the 5% means: in every hundred eggs (per cent) five are bad. Therefore, $\frac{5}{100}$ of the total are bad. The calculation is then made like this: $\frac{5}{100} \times 440 = 22$; so the answer is: 'Twenty-two eggs are likely to be bad.' The storekeeper can allow for this when fixing the price of his eggs.

(ii) 'In a village where there are 140 children, 55% are girls. How many boys are there?'
Here again, if the children know the meaning of percentage, they realize that 45 out of every 100 are boys. Put in another way, as a fraction, $\frac{45}{100}$ of the total number are boys. This is worked out as before: $\frac{45}{100} \times 140 = 63$.

(iii) 'John has thirty shillings allowance each month from his father. He arranges to spend sixty per cent of it and save the rest. How much does he spend?'
In this example the children change the 60 per cent to a fraction and find $\frac{60}{100}$ of 30s. $= \frac{6}{10} \times 30s. = 18$ shillings.

Similarly, examples can be given in finding percentage quantities of various weights, length, time, etc.

CHAPTER XXIV

LINES AND SHAPES

A—*The child's early experiences*

In their daily lives, almost from birth, children are meeting and dealing with situations which gradually build up ideas about lines, shapes, surfaces, solids, and containers. In their houses and during their play they hear and sometimes use the words which are connected with these ideas. Full, empty, closed, open, inside, outside, up, down, upside down, flat, pointed, round, smooth, rough, crooked, straight,* are just a few of the many words in common use. Children must have full understanding of such words as these if they are to have a sound basis for later learning.

Quite early children also see and begin to recognize, in actual life or in pictures, almost all the shapes with which they are likely to deal in school work. They see and use square, oblong, and round articles in the home: the table, the chair, the picture, cooking utensils, the room itself. They notice big fields and little gardens of particular shapes. They see straight fences and upright poles. They watch workmen building, using a plumb-line, measuring and cutting off equal lengths, and mixing various quantities of sand and cement. They see all kinds of wheels and circular objects on vehicles and in the home. They themselves handle tins and containers, some of which are cylindrical, others rectangular. They pick up bricks and stones of varied shapes, sizes and weight.

In their play children build up their experience and ideas without knowing it. They handle and bounce balls; model clay; join in games in which they have to stand in lines, squares or circles; ride on a see-saw; throw a stone, watching its path in the air and the splash and pattern of circles it makes when it falls into the

* The importance of being careful in the use of words which indicate mathematical ideas has been frequently stressed in this book. The word 'straight' is a particularly good example. We may think of all the meanings attached to this word (or look it up in the dictionary) and notice how all of them are really derived from the mathematical idea of a piece of string stretched tightly between two points.

water. In their indoor play, too, they are continuing this experience of lines and shapes as they sit down to draw, to cut out, and to play table games.

B—*The work in the primary school*

When we begin to teach the child we must make full use of his early knowledge and experience. We must also realize that ideas and knowledge about lines and shapes grew out of the life and work of ordinary men and women doing their everyday tasks like building, cooking, and hunting. This realization helps us to find the best way of introducing the ideas to children: through the everyday things they know rather than through abstract ideas.

The abstract ideas and general truths necessary for a later study of geometry eventually grow out of an understanding of the many experiences which the child links together in his mind. For example, the idea of a square, as a figure of four equal sides in which the four angles are all right angles, is gradually built up in the child's mind, when he folds, cuts, compares, measures, and draws during his earlier years. At the same time he gradually learns the necessary words and phrases because he needs them to express his ideas about the things he is doing.

So we do not try to teach *theory* in a formal way in the primary school. Through many practical experiences the children begin to understand, and are encouraged to find out about, the abstract ideas of lines, shapes, etc.

The next section gives suggestions for suitable activities. They are all important, but need not be introduced in any particular order. An activity often arises from some other topic, or out of lessons in other subjects such as sewing, hand-work, etc. We must be sure to make use of all such opportunities. For example:—

(*i*) When gardening, the children want to plant seeds in a straight row. A piece of stretched string may be used.
(*ii*) A game to be played requires the drawing of a circle. How can we do it?
(*iii*) In the physical education lesson each team is asked to form a straight line. What is the best way of doing this?

(*iv*) Children are told to watch hens and other animals coming for food. They run from all directions in straight lines. The children realize that they themselves do the same thing when they want to get to a particular point quickly.

(*v*) A rectangular plot is to be marked out. How do we make a right angle?

We must also remember that much of children's learning at all levels comes from their own attempts to solve the problems connected with *making things*. Children enjoy using all kinds of material (wood, paper, cardboard, scissors, paste, clay, sand, mud, etc.). At the same time they are learning, in the best possible way, all kinds of mathematical ideas. For example, the child who, after several attempts, makes a good paper model of a circular tent has learned a great deal about the circle and the cone. His very failures give him useful information about the relationships of various shapes. Such work need not, of course, be confined to the arithmetic lesson. History, geography and language lessons become much more 'alive' when models are made and used.

C—*Suggestions for children's work*

(*1*) *Lines*

(*a*) *Straight lines*—These may be shown:—

(*i*) On paper, using a straight-edge or ruler.
(*ii*) On the blackboard, by the chalked thread method (Fig. 142).
(*iii*) Out of doors by stretching a length of string or rope.
(*iv*) By folding paper to make a straight edge.

(*b*) *Curved lines*—Attention is drawn to these by:—

(*i*) The drawing of simple designs.
(*ii*) Noticing curves on pictures and maps.
(*iii*) Noticing curves on roads.
(*iv*) Measuring a curved line by means of a piece of cotton or string.

This should be linked with the work on straight lines, leading to the idea that the shortest distance between two points on a flat surface is the straight line joining them.

(*c*) *Drawing and measuring*—Various simple shapes, regular and irregular but with straight sides, are cut from cardboard and given to the children. They draw round the shapes and measure the lengths of the lines they have made.

(*d*) *Parallel lines*—These are introduced after the activities in (*c*) and may be drawn by using the parallel sides of a rectangle or the parallel edges of a ruler. Later the children may be shown

FIGURE 142.—The chalked thread method of making a straight line on the blackboard. (A piece of thread is well rubbed with chalk. It is stretched tightly, and held firmly at A and B. By means of a small loop of string at its middle, the thread is pulled a little back from the board. When released it chalks a straight line between A and B)

how to draw parallel lines by means of set squares. We encourage them to notice parallel lines in buildings, roads, rails, telegraph wires, etc. The discussion of parallel lines may lead to an interesting and simple introduction to the idea of perspective, if children begin to notice that long parallel lines (for example, the sides of a long straight road or railway line) appear to meet in the distance.

(2) *Shapes*

(*a*) *Folding paper*—This activity is a good introduction to learning about shapes because the children can find out a great deal for themselves and then discuss their 'discoveries'. For example, the teacher says: 'You each have a *square*. Fold it carefully into two parts so that one edge is exactly on top of its opposite edge. Cut along the fold. Now what have you made? Are they squares? They are *oblongs* (*rectangles*). Now fold one of the rectangles across the long side. What have you got now? Two *squares*, but they are smaller than the first square.'

Folding and cutting also enable children to find out how squares and rectangles may be broken up into triangles by folding along diagonals, etc. When the folds are cut, the triangles may be arranged in many different shapes. Paper folding is made more interesting if we show the children how to make simple paper models (such as darts, boats, 'planes, etc.).

Ideas of symmetry begin to arise from these activities. The children notice that similar shapes can be seen on each side of a folding line. Paper designs may be made by cutting or tearing out after folding: when the paper is opened out the torn-out shape is seen to be repeated on each side of the folded line.

Ink-blot shapes are also a very popular method of giving children an idea of symmetry (Fig. 143).

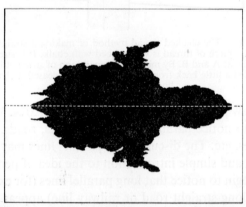

FIGURE 143.—An ink-blot shape (symmetry). (A blob of ink is allowed to dry slightly. The paper is then folded and pressed. Shapes may also be made by folding twice)

(*b*) *Playing with shapes*—The children arrange patterns with various shapes, made from cardboard, wood, or coloured paper (Fig. 144(*a*)). They are also encouraged to use their imaginations in constructing simple pictures of objects (Fig. 145(*b*)). If this is found to be too difficult, we may draw a number of such 'pictures', into which the children fit their shapes. In these activities the children are making themselves familiar with various

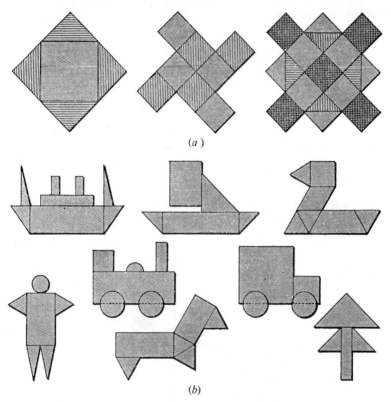

(a)

(b)

FIGURE 144.—Regular shapes, used for: (a) making patterns,
(b) constructing 'pictures'

shapes, and learning their names. They begin to see, for example, that the shape of any particular triangle remains the same, whatever its position.

(c) *Making and drawing circles*—The children may have played with circles in building up patterns and shapes. They should also be given activities to direct their attention more closely to the circle. For instance:—

(i) Drawing round the base or top of various objects (tin, vase, coin, cup) and then cutting out the circular shapes. These shapes may be folded in halves and quarters. The children then meet the words diameter and radius for the first time. (There should be no formal definitions at this stage.) Points at the ends of folded lines can be joined to make other figures (Fig. 145).

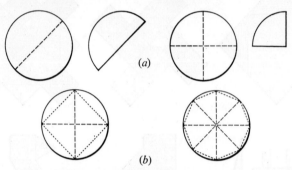

FIGURE 145.—Folding circles: (*a*) into halves and quarters; (*b*) to join ends of fold-lines and make various regular shapes

(*ii*) Drawing circles by use of a pin as centre and looped string to which a pencil is attached. Out of doors a similar method is used for drawing a large circle. A piece of rope or string tied to

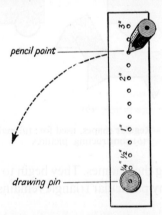

FIGURE 146.—A cardboard strip for drawing circles. (Holes are made, every quarter of an inch along the card, to take the point of a pencil. A circle of required radius is quickly drawn as the card rotates round the drawing-pin)

a stake driven into the ground is stretched to the required length. Keeping the string tight a child walks round marking the ground with sand or whitewash as he goes.

Similarly, a teacher sometimes uses a cloth duster when drawing a circle on the blackboard. One end is held firmly as a centre: the other end, with the chalk, is moved round it.

(*iii*) Drawing circles with a marked-out strip of cardboard (Fig. 146). This is a valuable piece of apparatus, since circles of any particular radius can be drawn quickly and accurately.

(*iv*) Marking a given distance in various directions from a central point. These points are then linked to form a circle.

This method emphasizes that all lines drawn from the centre of a circle to the outer rim are equal.

(*v*) The use of compasses is eventually taught to the children. Young children seldom find it easy. They should be allowed to experiment with the compasses by making patterns of curves. This gives them further experience with shapes, as well as helping them to manage the compasses.

(*d*) *Common solids*—From early school years children should be encouraged to play and build with various solid objects, such as blocks (bricks), cubes, cylinders (round tins), cones and spheres (balls). As they get older they learn the names of these solids and notice the particular properties of each.

They should also be encouraged to notice the shapes of solids: tins, bottles, boxes, packing cases, tree-trunks, pipes, boilers of railway engines, screws, materials used in building, etc.

(*3*) *Direction and angles*

Some knowledge of direction on the earth's surface is useful for many everyday purposes as well as in mathematics. Most children learn something about direction from their own observation of nature and from general conversation. We should build on this knowledge, in geography and arithmetic, to give the children more accurate ideas of angles and the points of the compass.

In early school years the work may consist of nothing more than a discussion of the sun's position at rising, mid-day, and setting. Later, the children may observe and measure the position and length of shadows at different times of the day. They may also be encouraged to watch for the Pole star, or a constellation such as the Southern Cross, at certain times of the year. Older children may see and discuss a mariner's compass. They may perhaps experiment with a magnetized needle.

The four points of the compass may be marked out in the playground or in the class room.

The intermediate points may be added later (Fig. 147). A wind-vane (weathercock) is very useful, but even without one the children may keep a daily record of the approximate direction of the wind, if they have a clear idea of the four points. Games requiring a knowledge of direction may be organized: for example, a 'treasure hunt'. Groups of children are given a card of written directions, such as: 'Start at the door facing

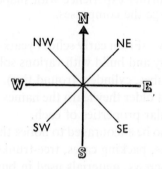

FIGURE 147.—The points of the compass. (The 'four points' are marked out first. Intermediate points may be added later)

North. Walk forwards 100 yards. Now turn North-west and walk for 10 yards. Then turn South and walk for 12 yards. Write down what you see in front of you.'

Angles may be introduced through the activities with lines, shapes and direction. Children notice that some shapes are more 'pointed' than others, and that some have 'square' corners. They see, when drawing, that, unless they are parallel, two straight lines meet (at a point) somewhere. They know of paths or roads which meet at a corner, and notice the fork made by two branches of a tree.

When thinking about direction and the points of the compass, they have probably practised 'turning' to the left and right, to the North, South, East and West. They also know what is meant by 'turn half-way round', 'face the opposite way', 'turn all the way round'.

Their experiences can now be given a more exact geometrical setting.

(a) *Right-angles*—The children learn that when they turn to face the right or left they have turned through a right-angle. If two lines are drawn, showing the directions before and after turning, it is seen that these meet to enclose a 'square' angle. This is known as a right-angle.* The children then make a list of things on which right-angles can be seen (books, tables, desks, blackboard, wall, houses, some cross-roads, etc.).

They are shown a simple way to make a right-angle without

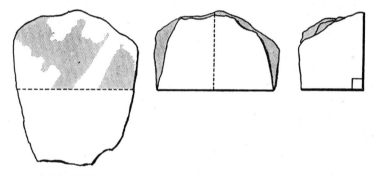

FIGURE 148.—A right-angle (made by folding a piece of paper)

using a set square. A piece of paper is folded down the middle, then folded again along the first folded edge (Fig. 148). The corner shown is a right-angle. The children may use this to 'test' various angles (the corners of the room, the table, the door, etc.). They are also shown how to make a special kind of triangle, with a right-angle in it, by folding and cutting along the diagonal of a square. (The children are asked to find out all they can about this triangle.)

(b) *Other angles*—The children test the angles of various flat shapes to find whether they are greater or less than a right-angle.

The 'movement' of the sun through the day may be noted.

* It is suggested that the measurement of angles in degrees should be left until later.

The children see that by noon it has appeared to 'turn' through a right angle. The angle increases as the day goes on.

The changes of angle between the hands of a clock may be studied. For instance, the children notice that at 12 o'clock there is no angle, while at 6 o'clock there are two right-angles between the hands. The teacher may show, by keeping one hand of a cardboard clock-face still, that the other hand may turn through four right-angles.

(4) Measurement

(a) *Length and distance*—Having learned, through many activities, about various shapes, children should have little difficulty in finding the distance round any *regular* shape (its perimeter). For example, when finding the distance round the edges of a square, they measure one side and then multiply by four; for the perimeter of a rectangle, they make two measurements only.

If the shape includes a curve, the perimeter is found by measuring the length of thread needed to go round it.

Children may find the length of the circumference of a circle by use of a formula given by the teacher, but a practical approach is far better. They make a circle on paper by drawing round a tin or pot (the base of a cylinder). Then they put a piece of string round the article to find the distance, that is, the circumference of the circle. Next they draw a diameter of the circle and measure it.* When they compare the length of the circumference, they find it to be just over three times as long as the diameter (about $3\frac{1}{7}$ times).

Children are surprised to find that this is *always* the case, whatever the size of the circle and whatever means are used for drawing and measuring it. If they try it out several times and in different ways, they soon grasp the idea. They are then ready to be introduced to the formula, should this become necessary at a later stage.

(b) *Area*—The idea of measurement of area may often be introduced through the need to compare the size of surfaces for some

---

* In this very simple case the centre of the circle is not marked. The children draw a line, as best they can, across the 'greatest width'. This is accurate enough at the first stage.

everyday purpose. For example, which of two garden beds is the bigger and will need more seed? Which of two walls will take more paint? Which of two farm plots will require more compost? This should lead to a discussion of the amount of surface, the area, and the need to measure it.

Within the class room the approach to the measurement of area may be through a revision of measuring length. We draw two lines on the blackboard, not parallel and of slightly different lengths. We ask which is the longer, and the children come and measure them, using inches as units.

Next, we show two rectangular pieces of cardboard: a red one 8 × 3 inches, and a blue one 6 × 4 inches. Which is the bigger? —How can we find out? A child measures the lengths of both cards with a ruler, and says the red one is bigger. Another child is asked to try but this time the cards are turned round so that he measures the widths. He says that the blue one is the bigger. This leads to the decision that the ruler, with its inch units of length, is no good for the purpose. The children discuss what other units may be possible. Eventually we introduce the square unit, in this case the square inch. We show how the two cards can be covered with square inches. The children find that both cards, though of different length and width, have the same area (twenty-four square inches).

Each child should be given a number of square inches of paper with which to measure various shapes (not only rectangles). We may then show a piece of card to represent a square foot, and discuss with the children how this is suitable as a unit for measuring larger surfaces (the area of a large table, the door, the blackboard, etc.). Similarly, the children should get to know the size of a square yard, for measuring still larger areas. The square yard may be painted in a suitable place on a wall, or in the playground. Children may experiment to find out how many square feet there are in a square yard.

So far there has been no mention of calculating the area of a rectangle. Some of the children often find out how to do it for themselves, as a result of counting squares in various rectangles. When they have counted several rows of squares, they find that each row has the same number. So they need not count every square. All they have to do is count the number of rows and the number of squares in a row. They then multiply to get the total number of squares in the rectangle. Eventually, we show how this may be set down shortly as:—

Area = Length × Breadth.

The children must understand that measurement of length and width must always be made in the same units.

(c) *Volume*—At the primary school stage we do not expect children to do more than learn the names of the common solid shapes and get a good idea of what is meant by volume. Their varied activities lead up to the connexion between volume and capacity. How much does a particular shape of container hold? How much water in a tank? How much timber in a tree-trunk? How much sand and gravel in a lorry? How much petrol in the tank of a car? How much air-space in a class room?

We point out that, while it is possible to measure the capacity

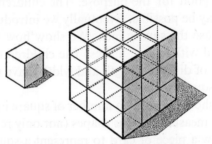

FIGURE 149.—Building up a rectangular solid from cubic units

of a vessel by the amount of liquid it holds, we cannot do this with a solid material. We go on to a consideration of a unit for measuring volume. We remind the children of the need for a unit such as an inch to measure length, and a square inch to measure surface area. They are now shown an inch cube. A number of these cubes are used to build up a rectangular solid (Fig. 149). They are laid carefully in rows (as in demonstrating the unit of area), and the children are encouraged to see for themselves the method of finding the volume of the solid which has been built up.

(d) *Examining and making common solid shapes*—Children should have the opportunity to break down and to build up various solid shapes *for themselves*. This increases their understanding of volume, and, at the same time, shows them the method of calculating the surface area of various solids. For example, each child may break down an empty match-box or cardboard carton,* etc., and see what it looks like. They see that the surface of a box consists of several rectangles, and that of a hollow open cylinder of one rectangle (Fig. 150). Similarly,

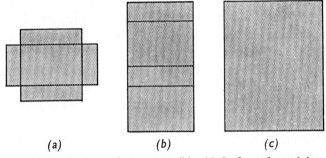

     (a)   (b)   (c)

FIGURE 150.—Surfaces of common solids: (a) Surface of match-box tray; (b) surface of match-box cover; (c) surface of hollow cylinder

older children may build up various shapes from cardboard and clay in their handwork lessons, or when constructing models for other subjects. It must be remembered that, in constructing a box, arrangements have to be made for pasting the parts together (see Fig. 156 (b), page 462, for example).

(5) *Scale*

A child's first ideas of scale probably begin when he realizes that objects appear to get larger as he comes nearer to them, and smaller as he moves away. When he tries to make pictures of objects, he finds that big things can be drawn on a small piece of paper. At first, however, he cannot draw things in proper proportions. For example, he may draw a man, representing his father, almost as big as a tree. Size often depends upon the importance of the object in the child's mind. It is wrong, at this

* It may be necessary to wet cardboard boxes a little before they can be opened out.

P

stage, to insist on correct scale, and so interfere with a child's artistic expression.

(a) *Reading a scale*—Later, however, the teacher may give guidance by discussing the map of the district. 'How far is it on the map from town A to town B?' (The distance may be measured by a ruler, or, if the line between the two towns is curved, by means of a piece of string or cotton.) 'It is twelve inches.' 'Now, how far is it really?'—'Twelve miles.' 'So twelve miles are represented by twelve inches on the map. Therefore, one mile is represented by one inch.' The scale is found to be printed on the map. The children are then set to find distances between various places on the map by using the scale. They may also find the lengths of rivers and railways.

We may be able to show simple plans of houses, schools, etc., and the use of different scales for various purposes. (For example, most building plans are made to a scale of one-eighth of an inch to one foot.)

(b) *Drawing to scale*—It should be pointed out to the children that pictures, photographs and even their own drawings and paintings are usually smaller representations of bigger things. But the scale of the objects in these pictures is rarely accurate. It is impossible, for instance, to tell the exact height of a tree in the background of a picture as compared with a man in the foreground. We explain that drawing to scale is useful if we are going to make furniture, build a house, plan a garden, etc. This makes it necessary for us to know the exact measurements of the object before we can begin to draw a detailed plan.

It is wise to begin scale-drawing exercises very simply, with objects in the shape of rectangles or squares. For example:—

(i) A book may be drawn to a scale of half-size.

(ii) The top of a desk may be drawn to quarter-size.

(iii) The class-room floor may be measured (to the nearest foot). The children then consider these measurements in comparison with the size of their paper. For instance, if the room is twenty-four feet by twenty feet they may decide that one inch to four feet is a suitable scale for a plan, and so draw a rectangle six inches by five inches.

(*iv*) A plan of the school play-ground or playing field probably needs a scale of one inch to a number of yards. Such a plan may not be a simple rectangle. The older children may draw the plan by using their knowledge of direction and angles.

(*v*) Some children may make a plan of their journey to school. At first this is a rough drawing, showing various places and measurements. Later, when a correct scale has been decided, the plan may be drawn more accurately.

(6) Graphs

Closely linked with, and following on, drawing to scale comes the idea of using graphs for showing information in an easy way.

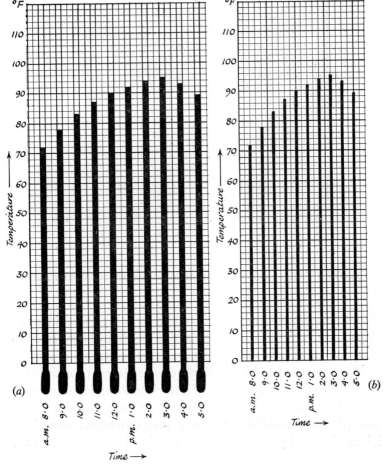

FIGURE 151.—Graphs of temperature readings
(continued on page 428)

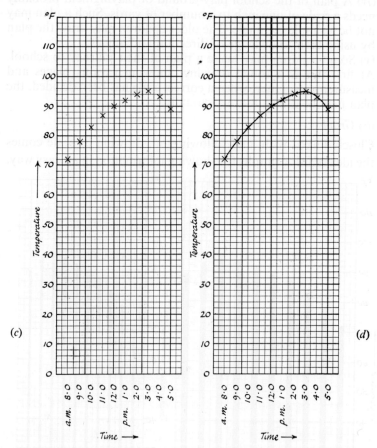

FIGURE 151.—Graphs of temperature readings (in two of four stages)

(Nowadays, graphs are very often used for this purpose in news-papers, etc.) Of course, children at this stage may be expected to read and make only very simple graphs. The making of these is easily understood and enjoyed by young children, provided that the information represented is of interest to them. Here are some examples of the kind of work which children may do. Sometimes the work is individual, done in their own books, sometimes it is carried out by the class, the graph being displayed on the wall.

(*a*) *The recording of the room temperature* at regular intervals during the day (every hour perhaps) gives children a good understanding of line graphs and serves as a useful introduction to the various forms in which information may be represented.

(*i*) The children first record the temperatures on simple scale drawings of thermometers as in Fig. 151(*a*).

(*ii*) On the next occasion, to save time and effort, the temperatures are represented by straight lines as in Fig. 151(*b*).

(*iii*) On a later occasion only the positions of the tops of the straight lines are marked, as in Fig. 151(*c*).

(*iv*) The joining of the tops of the lines by a smooth curve as in Fig. 151(*d*) comes as a natural extension of the early stages. If records of the temperature are taken, *but not plotted*, at the half-hours, the children can compare them with the corresponding readings on the graph and begin to see how the curve can be used.

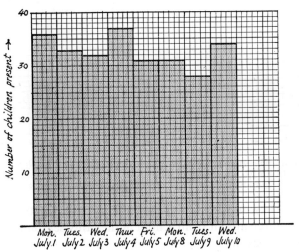

FIGURE 152.—A column graph (of daily attendance)

(*b*) *The daily attendance* of the class is best set down as a 'block' or 'column' graph (Fig. 152). It is important to remember that, with information of this nature, there is no purpose in joining the tops of the columns with a smooth curve (as in the example above on temperature recordings). Intermediate points on the curve have no meaning.

(c) *The rainfall of the district* may also be represented by a column graph as in Fig. 153. Older children may be able to compare the rainfall graph with that of class attendance over a period

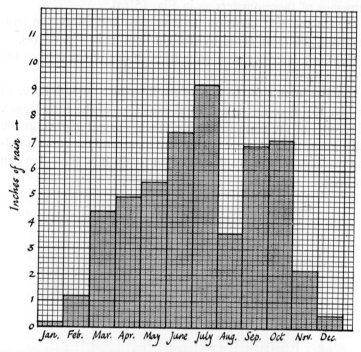

FIGURE 153.—Another column graph (monthly rainfall). (Not merely the amount of rain but the whole shape of such a graph depends on locality. This figure represents a typical year for one particular place)

of time. They may try to find out whether one affects the other —are children absent from school in the rainy season more than in the dry season?

(d) *Graphs of a circular type* show some kinds of information conveniently. They enable comparisons to be made quickly. (It is not suggested that young children should *make* circular graphs, but they can be led to understand them.) For example, Fig. 154 shows how the populations of two towns may be represented by this type of graph. It can be seen at once that town A has nearly twice as many children and only half as many old people as town B. The question arises 'Why is this so?' Many examples of this type of graph may be found in newspapers and magazines. They may form the basis of useful discussions with the children.

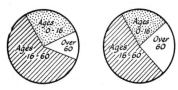

FIGURE 154.—'Circular' graphs (population)

(*e*) In schools where animals and pets are kept, the regular recording of the weights of the animals provides information which may easily be represented in a graphical form. The curves so obtained may give the children their first ideas of 'rate of growth'.

The recording of the growth of a plant is mentioned on page 140.

(*f*) Suggestions for other topics are:—

1. Marks gained in various subjects.
2. House points gained.
3. Daily egg yields from hens.
4. Daily milk yields from cows.
5. Times of high and low tide.
6. Temperature changes on going up a mountain.
7. Depth of the river at various points across its width.
8. Number of children in families.
9. Number of books borrowed from the school library.
10. The extension of a spring (or piece of elastic) when supporting various weights.

The work described in this chapter gives a brief outline of what may be done in the primary school to give children a good understanding of the mathematical ideas necessary for their later study of the geometry of lines, shapes and solids. The emphasis is upon children gaining an insight through doing things and finding out things for themselves.

CHAPTER XXV

FUN WITH FIGURES

Arithmetic can be fun. There is no reason why children should not enjoy their arithmetic lesson as much as any other. And the more they enjoy the work the more successful they are likely to be.

In the past some teachers did not mind if their children found arithmetic an unpleasant task. Whether they liked it or not was unimportant: the children were forced to do it. It was thought that in some way this was good for them and helped to improve their characters! These teachers did not ask *why* the children disliked the subject; they did not consider that the children might have preferred to have *liked* and enjoyed the subject. They did not consider how much better their efforts would have been rewarded if the children's attitude had been more favourable to the work.

Nowadays teachers realize more and more the importance of a child's attitude towards the work he is doing. It is true, of course, that the attitude towards the work is greatly influenced by the relationship which exists between the child and the teachers. But other influences are also important.

Most young children like arithmetic when they begin school. They enjoy their little 'sums' because of the mental satisfaction they get when they see their calculations working out neatly. Their attitude towards the subject is affected by the number of 'sums' they have correct, by the praise they receive from their teacher, and by the recognition of their success.

Such factors have a big influence throughout the whole of the primary school, and most teachers try to take account of them by arranging the work so that each child, whatever his ability, has a chance of experiencing reasonable success at every stage.

As they grow older the children begin to see that arithmetic is a subject worth studying. They see that it has a use in everyday life; they find that it is necessary for a proper study of science;

they find that it has a place in the history of the development of man; they learn that they may have to pass an examination in arithmetic before they can go to the secondary school.

For many children, the relationship with the teacher, the success (or failure) experienced, and the realization that arithmetic is a worthwhile and necessary 'subject', are the chief influences which decide their attitude towards the subject. When these influences are favourable they like arithmetic and are likely to do well. (Throughout this book the importance of *understanding* through *enjoyable* activity has been constantly emphasized.)

But some teachers help children to find more in arithmetic than the pleasure which comes from success. Arithmetic has an appeal of its own. It can quicken and stir the imagination.

The way in which we try to encourage the children's imaginations depends mainly upon our own attitude towards the subject. If we find enjoyment in arithmetic, we seize every opportunity which may help children to find similar enjoyment. (Throughout the course we have chances of introducing something of unusual interest. For example, we may look a little more closely at certain relationships between numbers, tell some simple story from the history of mathematics, examine geometrical patterns, share 'puzzles' and problems, and so on.)

There can be no scheme or syllabus for this kind of work. It depends upon the ability of the teacher to make use of any opportunity. Its success can only be measured by the lively way in which children look forward to their arithmetic lessons.

Here are some examples to suggest various possibilities. Teachers know and can find many more for themselves.

(1) Fun with numbers

(a) Missing numbers—Find the missing numbers in the following examples:—

(*i*) 245 +	(*ii*) 48? −	(*iii*) 5?? ×	(*iv*) 235
1??	??6	7	3)??5
?06	284	36?3	

(*b*) *Sets of numbers*—Find how the following sets of numbers are made up and add two more numbers to each set:—

> (*i*) 1, 3, 5, 7, 9, ?, ?.
> (*ii*) 1, 4, 9, 16, ?, ?.
> (*iii*) 25, 20, 15, ?, ?.
> (*iv*) 1, 12, 23, 34, ?, ?.
> (*v*) 1, 2, 4, 7, 11, ?, ?.
> (*vi*) 2, 3, 4, 6, 8, 12, 16, ?, ?.
> (*vii*) 81, 54, 36, ?, ?.
> (*viii*) 2, 5, 8, 11, ?, ?.
> (*ix*) 2, 4, ?, ?, 32, 64.

(*c*) *Magic squares*—These are two examples of 'magic squares':

(*i*)

4	9	2
3	5	7
8	1	6

(*ii*)

16	3	2	13
5	10	11	8
9	6	7	12
4	15	14	1

In each case the sum of the numbers in each column and each row is the same, and is also equal to the sum of the numbers along each diagonal. Able children can work out the arrangement of the numbers in (*i*) when the idea is explained to them. (There are several possible arrangements.) Less able children enjoy completing partly filled squares.

(*i*)

7	2	9
?	?	?
?	10	5

(*ii*)

5	10	3
?	6	?
?	?	7

(*iii*)

4	?	?	16
15	6	10	3
?	7	?	?
1	12	?	13

(*d*) *Numbers arranged to give other numbers*—Here are two examples: (*i*) 'Make, with the four figures 1, 2, 3 and 4, the largest possible fraction, placing two of them side by side in the top of the fraction and two in the bottom.' (Answer $\frac{31}{42}$.)
(*ii*) 'Arrange four threes (that is 3, 3, 3, 3) so that, with the aid

of the ordinary signs used in arithmetic, they make ten.' (Answer $3 \times 3 + \frac{3}{3}$.) 'Now arrange them to make, in turn, 0, 1, 26, $\frac{1}{9}$.'

(*e*) *Big numbers and little numbers*—Many children are greatly attracted by big and little numbers, even when these have not much meaning for them apart from their 'big'-ness and 'little'-ness. They enjoy looking in their reference books for the information asked for in questions such as:

(*i*) What is the weight of the earth in tons?
(*ii*) How far away from the Earth is the sun?
(*iii*) What is the thickness of a human hair? (They may try to measure one.)
(*iv*) What is the weight of a grain of sand? (Again, they can try measuring this.)

(*f*) *Number oddities*—Examples have already been mentioned (page 246). Here are some more.

(*i*) $\frac{1}{7} = \cdot142857$ (to six places of decimals). (This is of little practical use but it is interesting in that :—

$$14 = 2 \times 7$$
$$28 = 2 \times 14$$
$$57 = 2 \times 28 + 1 \text{ ('for luck', we may say!)}$$
$$\tfrac{2}{7} = \cdot285714; \tfrac{3}{7} = \cdot428571; \text{ and so on.}$$

(*ii*)
$$2178 \times 4 = 8712$$
$$1089 \times 9 = 9801$$

(*iii*)
$$1 \times 8 + 1 = 9$$
$$12 \times 8 + 2 = 98$$
$$123 \times 8 + 3 = 987$$
$$1234 \times 8 + 4 = 9876, \text{ and so on.}$$
$$\text{Now try } 1 \times 9 + 2 = ?$$
$$12 \times 9 + 3 = ? \text{ etc.}$$

(*iv*)
$$1 \times 1 = ?$$
$$11 \times 11 = ?$$
$$111 \times 111 = ? \text{ etc.}$$

(*v*)
$$1 = 1 \quad (1 \times 1)$$
$$1 + 3 = 4 \quad (2 \times 2)$$
$$1 + 3 + 5 = 9 \quad (3 \times 3)$$
$$1 + 3 + 5 + 7 = 16 \quad (4 \times 4) \text{ etc.}$$

(*2*) *Fun with 'short methods'*

Some calculations are usually made by the use of 'short methods'.

Quick ways of multiplying and dividing by ten, and of dealing with certain money calculations, have already been mentioned in this book.

However, care is necessary in introducing short methods to children. There is always a risk that a child may find the short method more difficult than the standard one. His work then takes longer and becomes less accurate. Further, it is better to introduce short methods when suitable occasions occur, rather than to set out to teach them. Children may be given practice with them, but should be allowed to decide for themselves whether to use a short method in any particular case.

In most schools children are shown short methods of making calculations* such as the following:—

(i) Multiplication and division by 10, 100, 1000, etc.
(ii) Multiplication and division by 25, 125, etc.
(iii) Multiplications such as: 199 × 27, 201 × 27, £2. 19s. 9d. × 17, etc.
(iv) Multiplication of pence and halfpence by 12, 24, etc.
(v) Multiplication of shillings by 20, 40, etc.

Many children delight in these short methods, especially when they understand them.

A few children go further and find fun in looking out for ways of shortening calculations. This often leads to very valuable discussion.

Such children often find interest and stimulation in short methods which are not usually met in primary school work, Here are two examples:—

(i) 'Find the sum of all the numbers from one to nine.' The children find the answer by straightforward addition (45). They are then shown that:

$$
\begin{array}{r}
1 + 2 + 3 + 4 + 5 + 6 + 7 + 8 + 9 \\
9 + 8 + 7 + 6 + 5 + 4 + 3 + 2 + 1 \\
\hline
10 + 10 + 10 + 10 + 10 + 10 + 10 + 10 + 10
\end{array}
$$

and that the required sum is therefore $\dfrac{9 \times 10}{2}$ (= 45). When

---

* See, for example, page 193, and the footnote on page 195.

they understand this they may enjoy finding larger sums, such as:

$$1 + 2 + 3 + 4 + \ldots + 98 + 99;$$
$$1 + 2 + 3 + 4 + \ldots + 999;$$
$$1 + 3 + 5 + 7 + \ldots + 19.$$

(*ii*) Children who know the short way of writing 2×2, $2 \times 2 \times 2$, etc., may make up a table like this:

$$2 = 2^1$$
$$4 = 2^2$$
$$8 = 2^3$$
$$16 = 2^4$$
$$32 = 2^5$$
$$64 = 2^6$$
$$128 = 2^7$$
$$256 = 2^8$$
$$512 = 2^9$$

They then work out examples like 4×16, 8×16, 4×64, etc. by the usual multiplication process. Comparing their answers with the table, they may be led to see a short method of finding such products. A few children may even be able to find out an explanation of the short method.

(*3*) *Fun with lines and shapes*

(*a*) *Counting shapes*—Here are some examples:—

(*i*) How many rectangles are there in this figure?

(*ii*) How many squares are there in this figure?

(*iii*) How many separate squares can be made by joining sets of four points in this figure?

(*iv*) How many triangles are there in this figure?

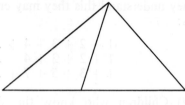

(*v*) How many triangles are there in this figure?

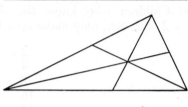

(*vi*) How many triangles are there in this figure?

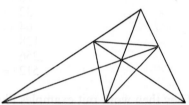

(*4*) *Fun with 'problems'*

Children are helped to build up a happier attitude towards problem-solving if, from time to time, class and teacher work out interesting little problems together. This is better than setting written 'problems' taken from a text-book. The solving of these little problems then takes on the nature of a game. Even though children do not solve a problem, they enjoy talking about it and trying it out on other children. That they have failed to get the right answer for themselves becomes less serious.

Here are some examples of such problems:—

(*i*) Two villages are twenty-four miles apart. A man leaves one village and walks towards the other at four miles per hour. At the same time another man leaves the second village and cycles towards the first at eight miles per hour. Just as the first man leaves his village a fly settles on his nose and then flies at twenty m.p.h. towards the second village, until he meets the second man. It settles on his nose for a moment and then flies back to the first man. The fly continues in this manner until the two men meet. How far does the fly fly?

(*ii*) A man has ten white socks and eight black socks. He keeps them all in the same drawer in his room. If he goes to his room in the dark, how many socks must he take from the drawer in order to be sure of having a matching pair?

(*iii*) I have some money in each of my two pockets. From my left-hand pocket I take as much as is already in my right-hand pocket and put it in the right-hand pocket. I do this a second time, and then a third time. My left-hand pocket is now empty, and in my right-hand pocket I have three shillings and eight-pence. How much did I have in each pocket at first?

(*iv*) A man travels ten miles South, then ten miles East and then ten miles North. He finds himself back where he started. Where is his starting point? (There is more than one possible answer.)

(*v*) A new machine is said to do twenty per cent more work in twenty per cent less time. How much better is it, in simpler terms, than the old machine?

(*vi*) I have two jugs. One holds five pints and the other six pints. If I go to the river, how can I get exactly two pints of water into one of the jugs?

(*vii*) What is the least number which, when divided by each of the numbers 7, 6, 5, 4, 3 and 2, leaves remainders of 6, 5, 4, 3, 2 and 1 respectively?

(*viii*) A 'bus, which would not hold more than forty children, was hired to take a class on a journey. The children agreed to pay equal shares of any money they spent on the way. They spent fifteen shillings and three halfpence and paid equal shares. How many children were there in the class?

As a rule children should not be given 'catch questions'. But, at the right time and as a change from the usual examples, they enjoy a little puzzle. (In such a case, of course, we explain that they have to look out for a catch or trick.) Puzzle-type questions, like the following, particularly if they are humorous, often lead to varied, amusing, useful and interesting discussions, not only of number but of words and language.

(*i*) A duck in front of a duck. A duck behind a duck. A duck in the middle. How many ducks in all?

(*ii*) Six wet towels, hung on a line in the sunshine, dry in thirty minutes. How long does it take one towel to dry?

(*iii*) Which is the heavier: a pound of iron or a pound of feathers?

(*iv*) What is a half of two and two? (Three different answers are sometimes given to this question, although only one is correct arithmetically. What are they and how are they obtained?)

(*v*) A man weighs ten stones when he is twenty years old. How much will he weigh when he is sixty?

(*vi*) How many minutes are there from two to two to two two?

It must be repeated that the greater our own interest and sense of fun the more likely are our children to enjoy their arithmetic.

(*Fractions*)

In the section preceding Chapter XIV it is pointed out that there are a variety of words and phrases which indicate that division must take place. For instance:—
    'Share 56 oranges between 8 people.'
    'How many times can I take 8 from 56?' etc.
Unless children recognize these words and phrases and understand what they mean they are likely to have difficulty in dealing with many of the problems in which division is needed.

Now let us look at another group of related phrases which children meet in everyday life and when learning arithmetic.

We, as teachers, know that the symbol '$\frac{3}{4}$' can be expressed in a variety of phrases such as: three-quarters (or three-fourths); three divided by four; three out of four; in the ratio of three to four. But we also know that each of these phrases represents a slightly different idea. These ideas can perhaps best be seen if set down as diagrams (Fig. 155, next page). The last item of the diagram may also be expressed as $4)\,\overline{3}$. This link between 0 and $4)\,\overline{3}$ is needed in changing fractions to decimals.

Children meet all these ideas (except perhaps 'ratio') and the phrases which indicate their use, in their arithmetic at the primary school. For instance, in trying to solve the following written problems, children need to see that the various phrases used all lead to the use of the symbol $\frac{3}{4}$.

(*i*) There are 120 children in a village. Three-quarters of them go to school. How many children go to school?

(*ii*) There are 120 children in a village. Three out of

every four go to school. How many children go to school?

(*iii*) There are 120 children in a village. Three times as many go to school as do not. How many children go to school?

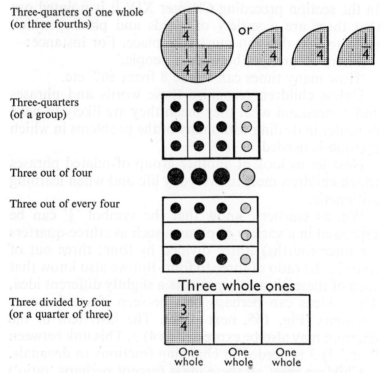

Three-quarters of one whole
(or three fourths)

Three-quarters
(of a group)

Three out of four

Three out of every four

Three whole ones

Three divided by four
(or a quarter of three)

One whole   One whole   One whole

FIGURE 155.—The meanings of '¾'

(*iv*) There are 120 children in a village. Thirty of these children do not go to school. What fraction of the children go to school?

(*v*) Three bars of chocolate are shared between four children. How much do they each receive?

It is interesting to note that the solving of these, and similar examples, does not require the use of any of the rules (about 'L.C.M.s', 'cancelling', 'turning upside down and multiplying', etc.) commonly given for the working of fractions. Many children can apply such rules to examples which are apparently more difficult. Yet they cannot do these simple problems. This is because they do not understand the meaning of the phrases used.

CHAPTER XXVI

MORE ABOUT FRACTIONS

The work and activities described in Chapter XXII are mainly concerned with helping children to understand what fractions are. It shows how fractions may be thought of in 'families', and how it is possible to change one kind of fraction for another (equivalence). The children are also expected, at that stage, to learn how to find the simple fractional parts of money and various measures; and how to deal with easy calculations in addition, subtraction, and multiplication.

In going on to further work with fractions, in the primary school, it is well to think again about the scope of the work. In Chapter XXII it is strongly suggested that the primary school is *not* the place for dealing with difficult and involved fractions; that we should deal mainly with the fractions commonly met in everyday life and business. If this work is understood and well practised, then those primary school children who go on to study mathematics at the secondary level will have a good foundation on which to build.

A—*Further work in addition of fractions*

There are no new ideas to be learnt in 'addition', but children may practise more difficult examples. For instance, they may add together *more than two fractions*, such as, (*i*) $\frac{1}{2} + \frac{2}{3} + \frac{3}{4}$; (*ii*) $\frac{3}{4} + \frac{2}{5} + \frac{7}{10}$. This is also the stage when the teacher may introduce the words numerator and denominator, and the phrase 'lowest common denominator'. The children are already familiar with the ideas. These ideas may now be connected with names, so that description and reference become easier.*

---

* The *denominator* is the figure at the bottom of the fraction which gives it its name (Latin: *nomen*). It tells us into how many parts the whole has been divided. It therefore gives us an idea of the size of each part. The *numerator* is the figure at the top of the fraction. It tells us the number of these parts with which we are dealing. Thus, if we know the *size of the part* and the *number of parts*, we know the size of the complete fraction.

When adding or subtracting fractions of different kinds, for example, $\frac{1}{4}$ and $\frac{1}{6}$,

B—*Further work in subtraction of fractions*

The next stage in subtraction occurs when the mixed number from which we are subtracting contains a fraction smaller than that in the number we are taking away: for example $3\frac{1}{4} - 1\frac{3}{4}$.*

This *stage* in subtraction has been considered with whole numbers in Chapter XII, and in dealing with the calculation of measures. It is an idea with which the children are already familiar and it should be shown to them as such. The method of teaching should be the same as for the previous type of subtraction example.

But first it is wise to give the children some revision of this kind, referring to apparatus if necessary: $1 - \frac{1}{4}$, $1 - \frac{2}{3}$, $1 - \frac{5}{8}$, $1 - \frac{7}{10}$, $1 - \frac{5}{12}$. In each case they need to think of the whole one in terms of the fraction they are taking away. That is, they think of: $\frac{4}{4} - \frac{1}{4} = \frac{3}{4}$, $\frac{3}{3} - \frac{2}{3} = \frac{1}{3}$, $\frac{8}{8} - \frac{5}{8} = \frac{3}{8}$, etc.

The ability to do this is necessary when they come to examples such as that already given, namely $3\frac{1}{4} - 1\frac{3}{4}$. It is suggested that, when first dealing with an example of this kind, it should be set out in vertical form like an ordinary subtraction example. Children who have dealt with halfpennies and farthings in British coinage can do this easily. But even in other countries the principle is familiar to the children, if they have followed the subtraction methods outlined in Chapter XII.

$$3\frac{1}{4} -$$
$$1\frac{3}{4}$$
$$—$$

The standard phrasing and the thought processes using the method of subtraction known as *decomposition* † go like this:—

---

it is necessary to change both to the same kind of fraction. There are many denominators common to both, but it is best to look for the *lowest common denominator* because fractions with small denominators are easier to deal with.

(If children are familiar with factors, we may show that the idea depends upon whether there are common factors. But it is not *necessary* to deal with this at the primary stage.)

* We can, of course, change both numbers to improper fractions, and then proceed to subtract in the usual way. But this causes trouble and leads to mistakes when we have to deal with large numbers (for example, $127\frac{1}{4} - 36\frac{3}{4}$).

† If the method of *equal additions* is used, four quarters are added to the fraction in the top number, and one whole is added to the unit in the bottom number as shown here.

$$3\frac{\frac{5}{4}}{4}—$$
$$1\frac{3}{4}$$
$$—$$

'I cannot take three-quarters from one quarter.
So I use one of the three units (leaving two units) and change
it into quarters, making five quarters in all.
Now I begin again.

Three quarters from five quarters leaves two quarters.
Put the two quarters in the fractions-column of the
answer.
Now deal with the units.
One from two leaves one, etc.
The answer is $1\frac{2}{4}$, that is $1\frac{1}{2}$.'

$$2\ \tfrac{5}{4}$$
$$3\ \tfrac{1}{4} -$$
$$1\ \tfrac{3}{4}$$
$$1\ \tfrac{2}{4}$$

When the children have practised this they go on
to easy examples such as the one shown here, in which
the $\frac{1}{2}$ has to be changed for $\frac{2}{4}$.

$$3\ \tfrac{1}{4} -$$
$$1\ \tfrac{1}{2}$$

Similar examples should then be worked out in horizontal
form like this:—

(i) $2\frac{1}{4} - \frac{3}{4} = 2 + \frac{1}{4} - \frac{3}{4} = 1 + \frac{4}{4} + \frac{1}{4} - \frac{3}{4} = 1 + \frac{5}{4} - \frac{3}{4} = 1\frac{2}{4} = 1\frac{1}{2}$

(ii) $3\frac{1}{2} - \frac{3}{4} = 3 + \frac{1}{2} - \frac{3}{4} = 2 + \frac{4}{4} + \frac{4}{4} - \frac{3}{4} = 2 + \frac{6}{4} - \frac{3}{4} = 2\frac{3}{4}$

(iii) $4\frac{1}{3} - 2\frac{2}{3} = 2 + \frac{1}{3} - \frac{2}{3} = 1 + \frac{3}{3} + \frac{1}{3} - \frac{2}{3} = 1\frac{4}{3} - \frac{2}{3} = 1\frac{2}{3}$.

The teacher shows that the ideas are just the same as those
used in the vertical arrangement.

In example (iii), however, the units are subtracted *before* the
fractions.

In the next step there is again no new idea, but the children
have to find common denominators before decomposition and
subtraction can take place, as in this example:—

$$5\frac{1}{4} - 2\frac{1}{3} = 3 + \frac{1}{4} - \frac{1}{3} = 3 + \frac{3}{12} - \frac{4}{12} = 2 + \frac{12}{12} + \frac{3}{12} - \frac{4}{12}$$
$$= 2 + \frac{15}{12} - \frac{4}{12} = 2\frac{11}{12}.$$

C—*Further work in multiplication of fractions*

(1) *Multiplying a fraction by a fraction*

We help children by returning, when the occasion demands, to
practical examples of arithmetical ideas. Most children are
helped to understand the method and meaning of multiplying a
fraction by a fraction if we again give them paper for folding,
cutting, drawing and shading.

(a) *The use of the word 'of'*—The children each have two equal rectangles of paper. They fold and cut one of these pieces into halves. The teacher then writes on the blackboard '$\frac{1}{2}$ of $\frac{1}{2}$', and says: 'I want you to find, by folding and cutting, a half of a half.' The children do this, finding, by comparison with the whole, that a half of a half is a quarter of the whole. This is put down on the blackboard: $\frac{1}{2}$ of $\frac{1}{2} = \frac{1}{4}$.

Similarly by the use of folding and cutting, or by drawing and shading on squared-paper (see page 382), the children find, for example, that:—

$$\frac{1}{2} \text{ of } \frac{1}{3} = \frac{1}{6} \qquad \frac{1}{2} \text{ of } \frac{1}{4} = \frac{1}{8} \qquad \frac{1}{3} \text{ of } \frac{2}{5} = \frac{2}{15}$$

$$\frac{1}{2} \text{ of } \frac{2}{3} = \frac{2}{6} \text{ or } \frac{1}{3} \qquad \frac{1}{2} \text{ of } \frac{3}{4} = \frac{3}{8} \qquad \frac{2}{3} \text{ of } \frac{2}{5} = \frac{4}{15}$$

(*b*) *The word 'of' replaced by the multiplication sign*—We should next remind the children of one of the interpretations of the multiplication sign. For example:

2×3 may mean two lots *of* three;

7×2 may mean seven lots *of* two;

6×3 pence may mean six groups *of* three pennies.

Similarly, we can say that:

$7 \times \frac{1}{4}$ means seven *of* the fraction $\frac{1}{4}$;

and $\frac{1}{2} \times \frac{1}{4}$ means a half *of* a quarter;

and $\frac{2}{3} \times \frac{1}{4}$ means two thirds *of* a quarter.

Thus we show that, in general, they can replace the word 'of' by the multiplication sign.

(*c*) *Working out the answer*—The examples already worked out, by using rectangles and squared-paper, are now set down again, using the multiplication sign as shown here. We now point out to the children that the results suggest a way of getting the answers quickly. That is, by multiplying the two numerators together we get the numerator

(*i*) $\frac{1}{2}$ of $\frac{1}{3} = \frac{1}{2} \times \frac{1}{3} = \frac{1}{6}$

(*ii*) $\frac{1}{2}$ of $\frac{1}{4} = \frac{1}{2} \times \frac{1}{4} = \frac{1}{8}$

(*iii*) $\frac{1}{2}$ of $\frac{2}{3} = \frac{1}{2} \times \frac{2}{3} = \frac{2}{6} (= \frac{1}{3})$

(*iv*) $\frac{1}{2}$ of $\frac{3}{4} = \frac{1}{2} \times \frac{3}{4} = \frac{3}{8}$

(*v*) $\frac{1}{3}$ of $\frac{2}{5} = \frac{1}{3} \times \frac{2}{5} = \frac{2}{15}$

(*vi*) $\frac{2}{3}$ of $\frac{2}{5} = \frac{2}{3} \times \frac{2}{5} = \frac{4}{15}$

of the answer; and by multiplying the two denominators together we get the denominator of the answer. For example:—

$$(i) \ \tfrac{1}{2} \times \tfrac{1}{2} = \frac{1 \times 1}{2 \times 2} = \tfrac{1}{4}$$

$$(ii) \ \tfrac{1}{2} \times \tfrac{2}{3} = \frac{1 \times 2}{2 \times 3} = \tfrac{2}{6} \ (= \tfrac{1}{3})$$

$$(iii) \ \tfrac{2}{3} \times \tfrac{2}{5} = \frac{2 \times 2}{3 \times 5} = \tfrac{4}{15}$$

$$(iv) \ \tfrac{3}{4} \times \tfrac{5}{6} = \frac{3 \times 5}{4 \times 6} = \tfrac{15}{24} \ (= \tfrac{5}{8}).$$

(d) Simplifying the answer—The children are already familiar with the idea of expressing fractions in a different form. They also know that, without change of value, a fraction may have its numerator and denominator multiplied (or divided) by the same number. For instance, in dealing with the 'answers' above, the children can see that $\tfrac{2}{6}$ may be changed to $\tfrac{1}{3}$ by dividing the top and bottom by 2. Similarly, they can see that $\tfrac{15}{24}$ becomes $\tfrac{5}{8}$, if top and bottom are divided by 3.

(e) *Simplifying before working out*—Before going further, we must make an important principle clear to the children. (The understanding of the principle is also necessary for much of the work done later at the secondary school level.)

The principle may best be explained by means of definite examples.

(i) Let us consider '6 × 5' divided by 2. The children can obtain the answer '15', by multiplying five by six and dividing the thirty so obtained by two. We can point out, however, that '6 × 5' may mean six groups of five. If these six groups are divided by two (that is, if we take a half of them) we have three groups of five, that is, 15.

(ii) An example such as '7 × 6' divided by 2 may be worked in a slightly different way. Here we have to find a half of seven groups of six. Now, a half of one group of six is three, so that if we treat each group of six in the same way we have seven groups of *three*, that is, twenty-one.

(iii) A third example such as 6 × 4 divided by 2 can be

worked in either of the two ways already described, so that the answer is obtained from either 3 × 4 or 6 × 2.

From these and other similar examples the children see why *only one* of the two numbers (which are to be multiplied together) has to be divided, and why they may choose the most convenient one.*

When this method is understood, it is possible to go on to show the children that, in the multiplication of fractions we can avoid long calculation by simplifying the example *before* doing all the multiplication.

Let us look at example (*iv*) given under (*c*), that is:—

$$\tfrac{3}{4} \times \tfrac{5}{6} = \frac{3 \times 5}{4 \times 6} = \tfrac{15}{24} = \tfrac{5}{8}.$$

Bearing in mind the examples, such as 6 × 5 divided by 2, which they have just been doing, and knowing that they can divide the top and the bottom of a fraction by the same number, the children do not find it difficult to see that $\dfrac{3 \times 5}{4 \times 6}$ can be simplified before further multiplication takes place. They can divide both the '3 × 5' and the '4 × 6' by three; in the first case they divide the '3' of the '3 × 5' by three, in the second case they divide the '6' of the '4 × 6' by three. So that the expression $\dfrac{3 \times 5}{4 \times 6}$ becomes $\dfrac{1 \times 5}{4 \times 2}$, which, on multiplication, gives $\tfrac{5}{8}$.

The example is first set down in full as:

$$\tfrac{3}{4} \times \tfrac{5}{6} = \frac{3 \times 5}{4 \times 6} = \frac{1 \times 5}{4 \times 2} = \tfrac{5}{8}.$$

Later, the children are shown that the written work is reduced by setting down the example as:

$$\tfrac{3}{4} \times \tfrac{5}{6} = \frac{\overset{1}{3} \times 5}{4 \times \underset{2}{6}} = \tfrac{5}{8}.$$

* Children might be *trained* to do all this, working to rules and using the word 'cancel', without much understanding of what they are doing. But this way invariably leads to confusion and mistakes in later work, especially when they go on to learn algebra in the secondary school.

A later step shows how division of the top and bottom of the fraction may be done more than once. For example:

$$\frac{2}{3} \times \frac{3}{4} = \frac{\overset{1}{\cancel{2}} \times \overset{1}{\cancel{3}}}{\underset{1}{\cancel{3}} \times \underset{2}{\cancel{4}}} = \frac{1 \times 1}{1 \times 2} = \frac{1}{2}.$$

We first divide both top and bottom by '2'. Then we divide both top and bottom by '3'.

(2) Multiplying mixed numbers

When multiplying mixed numbers it is usually necessary to change them to improper fractions. We can then see whether simplification is possible before the multiplication proceeds. For example:

$$2\frac{1}{4} \times 1\frac{1}{3} = \frac{\overset{3}{\cancel{9}}}{\underset{1}{\cancel{4}}} \times \frac{\overset{1}{\cancel{4}}}{\underset{1}{\cancel{3}}} = \frac{3 \times 1}{1 \times 1} = 3.$$

D—Division of fractions

Teachers are often content to give their children a rule for the division of fractions, without explaining the reasons for it. Explaining the rule to children is admittedly difficult, but it is not impossible. Above all, it is important that we, as teachers, should understand the basic reasons for the use of the rule. The method of arrival at the rule may be quite clearly shown by carefully graded stages.

(a) *Dividing fractions by a whole number*—We show, for example, that to divide a number by two we may find a half of it:—

$$6 \div 2 = \tfrac{1}{2} \text{ of } 6 = 3$$

and
$$10 \div 2 = \tfrac{1}{2} \text{ of } 10 = 5.$$

Similarly,
$$8 \div 4 = \tfrac{1}{4} \text{ of } 8 = 2$$

and
$$12 \div 4 = \tfrac{1}{4} \text{ of } 12 = 3.$$

In the same way, $\frac{1}{2} \div 2 = \frac{1}{2} \text{ of } \frac{1}{2} = \frac{1}{2} \times \frac{1}{2} = \frac{1}{4}$.

(The children already know that $\frac{1}{2} \times \frac{1}{2} = \frac{1}{4}$ from their work in multiplication.)

Similarly $\qquad \frac{2}{3} \div 2 = \frac{1}{2}$ of $\frac{2}{3} = \frac{1}{2} \times \frac{2}{3} = \frac{1}{3}$

and $\qquad \frac{1}{2} \div 4 = \frac{1}{4}$ of $\frac{1}{2} = \frac{1}{4} \times \frac{1}{2} = \frac{1}{8}$.

We are thus dealing with the *sharing* idea of division.* For example, $\frac{1}{2} \div 2$ means that we are breaking up the half into two equal parts, each part being equal to one quarter of the whole.

(b) *Dividing whole numbers by easy fractions* (for example, $\frac{1}{2}$, $\frac{1}{3}$, $\frac{1}{4}$)—In explaining this next step we use the *grouping** idea of division.

An example such as $1 \div \frac{1}{4}$ may be put into these words: 'How many quarters in one whole?' The answer is *four*. Similarly $2 \div \frac{1}{4}$ (How many quarters in two?)—The answer is *eight*. And $10 \div \frac{1}{4}$ (How many quarters in ten?)—The answer is *forty*. Similarly, $2 \div \frac{1}{3}$ (How many thirds in two?)—The answer is *six*. And $5 \div \frac{1}{3}$ (How many thirds in five?)—The answer is *fifteen*.

When the children have dealt with many examples like this they can be led to see that the answer may be quickly obtained by *multiplying* the first number by the denominator of the fraction, for example, $5 \div \frac{1}{3} = 5 \times 3 = 15$.

(c) *Dividing a fraction by a fraction* (for example, $\frac{1}{2}$, $\frac{1}{3}$, $\frac{1}{4}$)—The same idea of division by *grouping* is now extended to examples like this: $\frac{1}{2} \div \frac{1}{4}$ ('How many quarters in a half?')—We know the answer is two. But, using the previous idea, we multiply the half by four (the denominator of the fraction by which we are dividing), so that $\frac{1}{2} \div \frac{1}{4} = \frac{1}{2} \times 4 = 2$.

Similarly, $\qquad \frac{1}{2} \div \frac{1}{3} = \frac{1}{2} \times 3 = 1\frac{1}{2}$

and $\qquad \frac{1}{4} \div \frac{1}{3} = \frac{1}{4} \times 3 = \frac{3}{4}$.

(d) *Dividing by other fractions* (for example, $\frac{2}{3}$, $\frac{3}{4}$, $\frac{5}{8}$)—In order to complete the steps for understanding the rule for division of fractions, it is first necessary to show that *the bigger the quantity we are dividing by, the smaller will be the answer*.

For instance, $24 \div 3 = 8$. When we double the dividing number we have: $24 \div 6 = 4$, and the answer is halved. If we increase the dividing number four times, we have: $24 \div 12 = 2$, and the answer is only a quarter of the first answer. Similarly, $36 \div 3 = 12$, and $36 \div 9 = 4$. (Here we have increased the

* See pages 91–4 and 212–14 where ideas of division are discussed in detail.

number, by which we are dividing, by three times; so the answer is only one third of the first answer.)

In the same way:—

since $\quad 2 \div \frac{1}{4} = 2 \times 4 = 8$

then $\quad 2 \div \frac{2}{4} = \dfrac{2 \times 4}{2} = 4$

and $\quad 2 \div \frac{3}{4} = \dfrac{2 \times 4}{3} = \frac{8}{3} \ (= 2\frac{2}{3}).$

Similarly, since $\quad \frac{1}{2} \div \frac{1}{4} = \dfrac{1 \times 4}{2} = 2$

then $\quad \frac{1}{2} \div \frac{3}{4} = \frac{1}{2} \times \frac{4}{3} = \frac{2}{3}.$

The children are then led to see that a general rule applies: to divide by a fraction we turn that fraction upside-down and replace the division sign by a multiplication sign. The working then proceeds as in multiplication examples.

E—*Summary of points to remember in teaching fractions*

1. Understanding should come before 'rules' are given. The rules may then be applied intelligently, thus reducing the risk of errors.
2. In the early stages, particularly, the children should learn about fractions from their own practical activities.
3. We should make sure that children understand each idea in turn before they are introduced to the next.
4. We should deal mainly with the easy fractions which are in everyday use.
5. The work should be carefully graded. The suggested steps in teaching are given in Analysis 10 (pages 454–7).

ANALYSIS 10

ANALYSIS 10

Suggested stages and steps in the teaching of fractions
(see Chapters XXII and XXVI)

Continued for Multiplic…

1. STAGE	2. ACTIVITIES	3. ADDITION	4. SUBTRACTION
Many activities, such as those suggested in column 2, are necessary to give experience and ensure understanding. These should come before written work in the arithmetical processes with fractions. The stages in the written work are clearly shown in the appropriate columns.	(1) The *dividing of objects and groups* of objects into a number of equal parts. Writing down the fractional names of the parts, e.g. (i) Dividing a stick into four equal parts. (ii) Sharing 24 marbles between three boys. (2) The *folding and cutting of lengths* of material into a number of equal parts. Writing down the fractional names on the parts, e.g. (i) Folding and cutting a length of ribbon into three equal parts. (ii) Folding and cutting equal strips of paper into various numbers of equal parts, e.g. 2, 4, 6, 8 parts. Writing the names on the parts. (iii) Making simple fraction boards. (3) The *measuring and drawing of lines* in inches and fractions of an inch. (4) The *dividing of various shapes* into fractional parts, e.g.	A. *Fractions of the same kind.* (i) Examples such as: $\frac{1}{4} + \frac{1}{4} + \frac{1}{4} = \frac{3}{4}$ $\frac{1}{8} + \frac{1}{8} = \frac{5}{8}$ $\frac{1}{8} + \frac{1}{8} + \frac{1}{8} + \frac{1}{8} + \frac{1}{8} = \frac{5}{8}$ (ii) Examples such as: $\frac{1}{8} + \frac{2}{8} = \frac{3}{8}$ $\frac{2}{5} + \frac{2}{5} = \frac{4}{5}$ $\frac{1}{4} + \frac{3}{4} = 1$ $\frac{3}{4} + \frac{3}{4} = 1\frac{2}{4} = 1\frac{1}{2}$ (or $= \frac{2}{4} = 1\frac{1}{2}$) (iii) Examples such as: $1\frac{1}{4} + \frac{1}{4} = 1\frac{2}{4} = 1\frac{1}{2}$ $3\frac{1}{8} + 2\frac{3}{8} = 5\frac{4}{8} = 5\frac{1}{2}$ B. *Fractions of different kinds* (i.e. where changing is necessary). (1) One fraction only is changed. (i) $\frac{1}{2} + \frac{1}{4} = \frac{2}{4} + \frac{1}{4} = \frac{3}{4}$ (ii) $\frac{1}{2} + \frac{3}{8} = \frac{4}{8} + \frac{3}{8} = \frac{7}{8}$ (iii) $1\frac{1}{2} + \frac{3}{8} = 1\frac{4}{8} + \frac{3}{8} = 1\frac{7}{8}$ (iv) $1\frac{1}{2} + 3\frac{3}{8} = 4 + \frac{4}{8} + \frac{3}{8} = 4\frac{7}{8}$	A. *Fractions of the same kind.* (No changing of whole numbers.) (i) Examples such as: $\frac{3}{4} - \frac{1}{4} = \frac{2}{4} = \frac{1}{2}$ $\frac{5}{8} - \frac{1}{8} = \frac{4}{8} = \frac{1}{2}$ (ii) Examples such as: $1\frac{3}{4} - \frac{1}{4} = 1\frac{2}{4} = 1\frac{1}{2}$ $3\frac{5}{8} - 1\frac{3}{8} = 2\frac{2}{8} = 2\frac{1}{4}$ B. *Fractions of different kinds.* (Common fraction found by inspection.) (1) No changing of whole numbers. (i) $\frac{1}{2} - \frac{1}{3} = \frac{3}{6} - \frac{2}{6} = \frac{1}{6}$ $\frac{1}{4} - \frac{1}{5} = \frac{5}{20} - \frac{4}{20} = \frac{1}{20}$ (ii) $\frac{2}{3} - \frac{3}{8} = \frac{16}{24} - \frac{9}{24} = \frac{7}{24}$ $\frac{5}{6} - \frac{3}{4} = \frac{10}{12} - \frac{9}{12} = \frac{1}{12}$ (iii) $3\frac{1}{2} - \frac{1}{8} = 3 + \frac{4}{8} - \frac{1}{8} = 3\frac{3}{8}$ $5\frac{3}{4} - 2\frac{1}{2} = 3 + \frac{9}{12} - \frac{4}{12} = 3\frac{5}{12}$ (2) Changing of whole numbers. (i) $1 - \frac{1}{4} = \frac{4}{4} - \frac{1}{4} = \frac{3}{4}$ $1\frac{1}{4} - \frac{3}{4} = \frac{5}{4} - \frac{3}{4} = \frac{2}{4} = \frac{1}{2}$ (ii) $2 - \frac{2}{3} = 1 + \frac{3}{3} - \frac{2}{3} = 1\frac{1}{3}$

sion and Problem-type examples on pages 456–7.

...squares, rectangles and triangles.

(5) The *use of squared-paper* to find fractional parts of figures, such as rectangles, by counting squares.

(6) The *use of drawing activities* to give further understanding of fractions.
e.g. 'Draw eight birds on a tree. Colour two of them. What fraction of the birds have you coloured?'

(7) The *use of everyday happenings* in which fractional ideas occur.

(8) The *use of fraction boxes.*

(9) The *playing of suitable games.*
e.g. 'The changing game'.

mon fraction found by inspection.)

(i)
$$\frac{1}{2} + \frac{1}{3} = \frac{3}{6} + \frac{2}{6} = \frac{5}{6}$$
$$\frac{1}{3} + \frac{1}{4} = \frac{4}{12} + \frac{3}{12} = \frac{7}{12}$$

(ii)
$$\frac{2}{3} + \frac{1}{4} = \frac{8}{12} + \frac{3}{12} = \frac{11}{12}$$
$$\frac{3}{8} + \frac{2}{5} = \frac{15}{40} + \frac{16}{40} = \frac{31}{40}$$

(iii)
$$\frac{3}{4} + \frac{1}{3} = \frac{9}{12} + \frac{4}{12} = \frac{13}{12} = 1\frac{1}{12}$$
$$\frac{3}{4} + \frac{2}{3} = \frac{9}{12} + \frac{8}{12} = \frac{17}{12} = 1\frac{5}{12}$$

(iv)
$$1\frac{1}{3} + \frac{1}{4} = 1\frac{4}{12} + \frac{3}{12} = 1\frac{7}{12}$$
$$1\frac{2}{3} + 2\frac{1}{8} = 3 + \frac{16}{24} + \frac{3}{24} = 3\frac{19}{24}$$
$$3\frac{3}{4} + 2\frac{2}{3} = 5 + \frac{9}{12} + \frac{8}{12}$$
$$= 5 + \frac{17}{12} = 5 + 1\frac{5}{12}$$
$$= 6\frac{5}{12}$$

(v)
$$\frac{1}{2} + \frac{1}{3} + \frac{1}{4} = \frac{6}{12} + \frac{4}{12} + \frac{1}{12}$$
$$= \frac{11}{12}$$
$$\frac{1}{2} + \frac{2}{3} + \frac{3}{4} = \frac{6}{12} + \frac{8}{12} + \frac{9}{12}$$
$$= \frac{23}{12} = 1\frac{11}{12}$$

$$= \frac{6}{4} - \frac{3}{4} = \frac{3}{4}$$

$$2\frac{1}{2} - \frac{3}{4} = 2\frac{2}{4} - \frac{3}{4}$$
$$= 1 + \frac{6}{4} - \frac{3}{4}$$
$$= 1\frac{3}{4}$$

$$3\frac{1}{3} - \frac{3}{4} = 3\frac{4}{12} - \frac{9}{12}$$
$$= 2 + \frac{16}{12} - \frac{9}{12}$$
$$= 2\frac{7}{12}$$

(iv) $$3\frac{1}{3} - 1\frac{2}{3} = 2 + \frac{1}{3} - \frac{2}{3}$$
$$= 1 + \frac{4}{3} - \frac{2}{3}$$
$$= 1\frac{2}{3}$$

$$5\frac{1}{4} - 2\frac{2}{3} = 3 + \frac{3}{12} - \frac{8}{12}$$
$$= 2 + \frac{15}{12} - \frac{8}{12}$$
$$= 2\frac{7}{12}$$

$$7\frac{3}{8} - 4\frac{4}{5} = 3 + \frac{15}{40} - \frac{32}{40}$$
$$= 2 + \frac{55}{40} - \frac{32}{40}$$
$$= 2\frac{23}{40}$$

ANALYSIS 10 (*continued from preceding pages.*)

1. STAGE	5. MULTIPLICATION	6. DIVISION	7. 'PROBLEM'-TYPE EXAMPLES For instance:—
Many activities, such as those suggested in column 2 (page 454), are necessary to give experience and ensure understanding. These should come before written work in the arithmetical processes with fractions. The stages in the written work are clearly shown in the appropriate columns (*continued from pages 454–5*).	A. *Multiplying a fraction by a whole number.* (*i*) $3 \times \frac{1}{4} = \frac{1}{4} + \frac{1}{4} + \frac{1}{4} = \frac{3}{4}$ $2 \times \frac{3}{8} = \frac{3}{8} + \frac{3}{8} = \frac{6}{8} = \frac{3}{4}$ (*ii*) $\begin{cases} 4 \times \frac{1}{3} = \frac{1}{3} + \frac{1}{3} + \frac{1}{3} + \frac{1}{3} = \frac{4}{3} = 1\frac{1}{3} \\ 4 \times \frac{2}{3} = \frac{2}{3} + \frac{2}{3} + \frac{2}{3} + \frac{2}{3} = \frac{8}{3} = 2\frac{2}{3} \end{cases}$ [(*i*) and (*ii*) lead to the idea of getting the answer by multiplying the top of the fraction by the whole number.] (*iii*) $3 \times 1\frac{1}{4} = 3 \times 1 + 3 \times \frac{1}{4} = 3 + \frac{3}{4} = 3\frac{3}{4}$ and $3 \times 1\frac{1}{4} = 3 \times \frac{5}{4} = \frac{15}{4} = 3\frac{3}{4}$ $3 \times 1\frac{1}{2} = 3 \times 1 + 3 \times \frac{1}{2} = 3 + 1\frac{1}{2} = 4\frac{1}{2}$ and $3 \times 1\frac{1}{2} = 3 \times \frac{3}{2} = \frac{9}{2} = 4\frac{1}{2}$ B. *Multiplying a fraction by a fraction.* (*1*) First ideas, using 'of'. Practical exercises to show that: $\frac{1}{2}$ of $\frac{1}{2} = \frac{1}{4}$ $\frac{1}{2}$ of $\frac{1}{4} = \frac{1}{8}$ $\frac{1}{2}$ of $\frac{2}{3} = \frac{2}{6} = \frac{1}{3}$ $\frac{1}{2}$ of $\frac{3}{4} = \frac{3}{8}$ $\frac{1}{3}$ of $\frac{3}{5} = \frac{3}{15} = \frac{1}{5}$ (*2*) The idea of replacing 'of' by '×' (see pp. 447–8). (*3*) The repetition of the examples in Step (*1*) in the form: $\frac{1}{2}$ of $\frac{1}{2} = \frac{1}{2} \times \frac{1}{2} = \frac{1}{4}$ $\frac{1}{2}$ of $\frac{2}{3} = \frac{1}{2} \times \frac{2}{3} = \frac{2}{6}$	A. *Dividing a fraction by a whole number.* e.g. $\frac{1}{3} \div 2 = \frac{1}{6}$ of $\frac{1}{3} = \frac{1}{6}$ $\frac{2}{3} \div 2 = \frac{1}{2}$ of $\frac{2}{3} = \frac{1}{3}$ $3\frac{3}{4} \div 2 = 2\frac{1}{4}$ of $1\frac{3}{4} = \frac{3}{4} \times \frac{5}{6} = \frac{5}{6}$ B. *Dividing by fractions* such as $\frac{1}{2}, \frac{1}{3}, \frac{1}{4}$, etc. (i.e. with a '1' at the top). (*1*) Dividing a whole number by a simple fraction. $1 \div \frac{1}{4}$ (How many quarters in 1) $= 4$ $2 \div \frac{1}{4}$ (,, ,, ,,2) $= 8$ $10 \div \frac{1}{4}$ (,, ,, ,,10) $= 40$ $4 \div \frac{1}{3}$ (,, thirds in 4) $= 12$ [Leading to the idea that the answer can be obtained by multiplying the first number by the number at the bottom of the fraction.] (*2*) Dividing a fraction by a simple fraction. $\frac{1}{2} \div \frac{1}{4}$ (How many quarters in one-half?) $= 2$ $\frac{3}{4} \div \frac{1}{4}$ (How many quarters in three-quarters?) $= 3$ $\frac{1}{2} \div \frac{1}{3}$ (How many thirds in one-half?) $= 1\frac{1}{2}$ [Leading to the same method of obtaining the answer as in Step (*1*).] C. *Dividing by fractions of any kind.* (*1*) The working of examples such as. $24 \div 3 = 8 \qquad 36 \div 3 = 12$ $24 \div 6 = 4 \qquad 36 \div 9 = 4$	(*a*) 'The school garden is divided into sixteen equal plots. What fraction of the garden is each plot?' (*b*) 'The children go to school for six hours each day. What fraction of the day (24 hours) are they at school?' (*c*) 'The hen sat on twelve eggs, but had only nine chicks. What fraction of the total was this?' (*d*) 'John read half the book on Thursday and a quarter on Friday. How much had he read altogether? What fraction has he still to read?' (*e*) 'The children set some bulbs. Half the flowers were red and a third were yellow. The others were white. What fraction of the flowers were coloured?' (*f*) 'Mary had three parcels in her basket. One weighed $1\frac{1}{2}$ lb., the second $\frac{3}{4}$ lb. and the third $2\frac{1}{4}$ lb. The basket weighed 2 lb. What was the total weight of the basket and parcels?' (*g*) 'Two out of every five children cycle to school. The rest walk. What fraction of the children walk?' (*h*) 'The farmer sold half his crop and put one-sixth in his store.

ing the answer. That is, for example,

$$\frac{2}{3} \times \frac{2}{5} = \frac{2 \times 2}{3 \times 5} = \frac{4}{15}.$$

(4) The idea of simplifying the expression before multiplication takes place.

(i) The working of examples such as:

2 × 3 divided by 3 = 2
2 × 3 divided by 2 = 3
5 × 7 divided by 7 = 5
5 × 6 divided by 2 = 5 × 3 = 15
4 × 9 divided by 3 = 4 × 3 = 12
8 × 3 divided by 4 = 2 × 3 = 6

(ii) The working of examples such as:

$$\frac{3}{4} \times \frac{5}{6} = \frac{3 \times 5}{4 \times 6} = \frac{5}{4 \times 2} = \frac{5}{8}$$

$$\frac{3}{4} \times \frac{2}{9} = \frac{3 \times 2}{4 \times 9} = \frac{2}{4 \times 3} = \frac{1}{2 \times 3} = \frac{1}{6}$$

(iii) The repetition of the examples in Step (4) (ii) with the working set down in a shorter form.

e.g. $\frac{3}{4} \times \frac{5}{6} = \frac{3}{4} \times \frac{5}{6} = \frac{5}{8}$

$\frac{3}{4} \times \frac{2}{9} = \frac{3}{4} \times \frac{2}{9} = \frac{1}{6}$

The working of many and various similar examples.

(5) Multiplying mixed numbers.

(i) $1\frac{1}{2} \times \frac{3}{4} = \frac{3}{2} \times \frac{3}{4} = \frac{9}{8} = 1\frac{1}{8}$

(ii) $1\frac{1}{2} \times 1\frac{3}{4} = \frac{3}{2} \times \frac{7}{4} = \frac{21}{8} = 2\frac{5}{8}$

(iii) $2\frac{1}{4} \times 1\frac{1}{3} = \frac{9}{4} \times \frac{4}{3} = 3$

(2) The working of series of examples such as:

(i) $2 \div \frac{1}{4} = 8$
$2 \div \frac{2}{4} = \frac{8}{2} = 4$
$2 \div \frac{3}{4} = \frac{8}{3} = 2\frac{2}{3}$

(ii) $3 \div \frac{1}{8} = 24$
$3 \div \frac{2}{8} = \frac{24}{2} = 12$
$3 \div \frac{3}{8} = \frac{24}{3} = 8$ etc.

[Leading to the idea that in dividing by a fraction, the answer can be obtained by inverting the fraction and replacing the '÷' sign by the '×' sign.]

(3) The use of the method suggested in Step (2) to work examples such as:

(i) $\frac{1}{2} \div \frac{3}{4}$; $\frac{3}{4} \div \frac{3}{4}$; $\frac{2}{3} \div \frac{3}{4}$

(ii) $1\frac{1}{2} \div \frac{2}{3}$; $\frac{2}{3} \div \frac{2}{3}$; $4\frac{1}{3} \div \frac{2}{3}$

(iii) $2\frac{1}{4} \div 1\frac{1}{2}$; $3\frac{3}{4} \div 2\frac{2}{3}$

(j) 'John lives 1¼ miles from school. Tom lives ⅛ mile from school. How much further does John have to go than Tom?'

(k) 'The box contains 24 tins, each weighing ¾ lb. What is the total weight of the tins?'

(l) 'Mary sorted the coloured pencils. One-quarter were red and half the others were blue. What fraction of the total were blue?'

(m) 'What is two-fifths of 3¼ inches?'

(n) 'How many quarter pound packets of tea may be made up from a box containing fifty-six pounds?'

(p) 'How many pieces of ribbon each 2¼ inches long, can be cut from a length of 31½ inches?'

The working of examples, such as:

(i) Write ¾ in words.
(ii) Write seven-tenths in figures.
(iii) Add three-quarters and one-sixth.
(iv) Find the difference between three-fifths and two-thirds.

(The metric system)

From time to time in the history of most countries it has become necessary to standardize the units of measure in common use. For example, because various trades were adding different amounts to the original hundred-pound weight (the hundredweight) it became necessary to standardize its value at 112 lb.

The people of France found similar difficulties in the eighteenth century, but, instead of standardizing the units in common use, they decided to introduce a completely new set of units. In 1792 they adopted a system of units based on *one* standard unit, the metre. This was originally defined as $\frac{1}{10,000,000}$ of a quarter of the great circle on the earth which passes through Paris and the North and South poles. From this unit of length they worked out units of area, volume, capacity and weight. The smaller and larger units for length were so arranged that each unit was ten times the next smaller unit, likewise for the other measures. In this way it was claimed that, because of the decimal nature of such an arrangement, calculations would be made easier. The people of France were instructed by law to use these units in place of those used formerly. This system of units is called the metric system.

Some people claim that it would be helpful if the metric system were used by all countries, but so far only some have adopted it. Others use it, side by side with their own systems of units, for scientific measurements.

Chapter XXVII is written for teachers in countries which do not use the metric system for all everyday purposes. If you live in a country where the metric system is the common one, you may have to teach just a little about some other system. By comparison, this chapter may suggest the extent of such work.

THE METRIC SYSTEM

A knowledge of the common units of the metric system is necessary in studying science. It is also helpful when reading about world affairs. For instance, measurements in international sports are given in metric units. In the Olympic Games, for example, there are races over distances of one hundred, four hundred, eight hundred, fifteen hundred metres, etc.

It is not suggested that children in primary schools should learn about *all* the units of the metric system and their relationships. Nevertheless, they may well be introduced to the more common units, and get some idea of their size. It is not necessary, at this stage, that children should learn the *exact* relationship between their own common units and those of the metric system. It is sufficient, for example, if they know that a metre is a little longer than a yard (about thirty-nine inches). It is unnecessary and unwise to make them learn that 1 metre = 39·37 inches. Similarly, it is quite enough if they learn, through their experiences, that a kilogram (kilogramme) is just over two pounds.

The various units should be introduced in the same way as those discussed earlier in this book. The children get to know the metric units through actual measurement and estimation, through establishing the relationships between the various units, and through making simple calculations (see Chapters X and XVII–XXI).

(1) Length

Children are often interested in the origin and history of the metric system, and this sometimes makes a good introduction. The original definition of the *metre* has little meaning for children in terms of an actual length, but they may like to have it as an interesting piece of information. The metre becomes real to them, however, only when they handle a metre-length of cane, wood, etc. They may then estimate its length roughly in terms of the units of length which they normally use. For example, they see that a metre is about three feet or one yard. Using their own foot-rulers they can measure the metre more exactly. They find, for example, that it is just over thirty-nine inches, that is, about a yard and three inches. This is the only information about the equivalence of the yard and the metre that most children need. It enables them to change metre lengths to their own units. For example, a hundred metres race can then be thought of as 'just over a hundred yards'. (To be a little more exact, a hundred yards plus a hundred 'three-inches'. That is, about one hundred and nine yards.)

The kilometre is introduced by reference to longer distances. Maps and descriptions of journeys, in which distances are given in this unit, are useful at this stage. Again the children may work out how their own unit of distance corresponds with the kilometre. For example, taking a metre as $1\frac{1}{12}$ yards (that is, thirty-nine inches), a kilometre is approximately 1,084 yards, which again is about five-eighths of a mile ($\frac{1}{8}$ mile = 220 yds., $\frac{5}{8}$ mile = 1,100 yds.).

This knowledge helps to give meaning, for example, to discussion of a race over ten thousand metres (ten kilometres). The distance may be thought of as $10 \times \frac{5}{8}$ miles, that is, about six and a quarter miles.

Children who are likely to go on to a further study of science should be introduced to the smaller units of length. Metre sticks divided into a hundred equal parts should be provided and be used by the children to measure lengths in metres and centimetres (to the nearest centimetre). The reason for the name *centimetre* should be discussed, and the proper abbreviations should be used when writing down the measurements.

For measuring short lengths the children find that the centimetre is too big a unit. So the *millimetre** is introduced to give greater accuracy. Metre 'sticks', divided into centimetres and millimetres, are shown to the children. They see that each centimetre is divided into ten equal parts, the whole stick being

* From the French word '*mille*'—a thousand.

divided into one thousand equal parts. Thus, each of these parts is a thousandth of a metre, that is, a millimetre. The children now measure lengths in centimetres and millimetres, using rulers. The results are written down in centimetres and millimetres (for example, '7 cm., 6 mm.') or in decimal form (for example, '7·6 cm.').

It is a useful exercise for the children to work out how the centimetre corresponds to the unit which they themselves normally use for measuring short lengths. For example, by drawing a line four inches long, and measuring it in centimetres, they find that one inch is just over two and a half centimetres.

By the end of this work on length the children should know:—

1 metre (m.)	=	100 centimetres (cm.)
1 metre (m.)	=	1,000 millimetres (mm.)
1 centimetre (cm.)	=	10 millimetres (mm.)
1,000 metres (m.)	=	1 Kilometre (Km.)
1 metre	≏	39 inches*
1 kilometre	≏	$\frac{5}{8}$ mile
1 inch	≏	$2\frac{1}{2}$ centimetres.

(2) Area

If children understand the idea of area they should be able to deal confidently with the calculation of any areas they may have to find when using metric units. They may have to find areas in *square centimetres* in their science lessons but the need to use other units is unlikely to arise.

(3) Volume and capacity

In science *cubic centimetres* and *litres* are the usual measures of volume and capacity. Misunderstandings and absurd answers may be avoided if children, from the beginning, have the right idea of the size of these units.

They know how to find volume in their own everyday units. When it becomes necessary to find volumes in cubic centimetres, the children should be shown or, better still, they should make a number of cubic centimetres. They may do this by

* The symbol '≏' means 'equals approximately'

cutting off one-centimetre lengths from a piece of wood of one centimetre square section (Fig. 156(a)); or, they may cut the

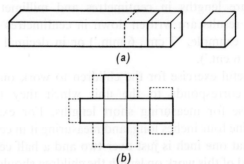

(a)

(b)

FIGURE 156.—The cubic centimetre: (a) One centimetre cube (that is, one c.c.) cut from rod of section one centimetre square. (b) A shape for making a cube (one c.c.) from paper. The flaps, shown by dotted lines, may be turned over the edges and pasted to hold the cube together

appropriate shape from paper and paste it together in the form of a cube (Fig. 156 (b)). These cubes help children to understand what is meant by a cubic centimetre, and they may be compared with other units of volume such as the cubic inch.

FIGURE 157.
—A measuring cylinder

Some of the paper cubes should be made with only five sides so that they may be used as little vessels to be filled with water or sand. Using these as measures it is possible to measure out small quantities of liquid, or to measure the capacities of small containers. The slowness of this measuring, using a cubic centimetre, helps the children to see the need for a container which is marked to show the number of cubic centimetres it holds at various levels (Fig. 157). They see, too, why a narrow container is better than a wide one to give accurate measurements of capacity.

If possible a graduated measure of this kind should be provided for the children's use.

Through finding the capacities of various tins, cups, jars, etc., they begin to get some idea of the 'size', for example, of '50 c.c.' of water. When they actually see it, the

'50 c.c.' becomes more than an abstract number. To measure a pint, and other common measures, of water in cubic centimetres is an exercise which provides helpful comparisons.

The need for a larger unit than the cubic centimetre arises when large quantities of liquids are to be measured. 'A thousand cubic centimetres' may sound a large amount to the children, but when they are shown a litre in the form of a cube, of side 10 cm., they realize that it is not a very big unit. They may compare a litre measure with one made to hold another unit amount, such as a pint. For example, on looking at litre and pint measures they see that the litre is the larger. By filling the pint measure with water or sand, and emptying it into the litre measure until it is full, they find that a litre is about one and three-quarters of a pint. (This result may be compared with that obtained when measuring a pint of water in cubic centimetres.)

The children may find the capacity of various kinds of containers by using a litre measure and a vessel graduated in cubic centimetres. They may also measure out required quantities of liquids.

The results of such activities should be written not only in litres and cubic centimetres, but also in the units which the children normally use. (These need only be rough approximations.)

Through these simple activities the children gain a clear idea of the size of the units, and learn that:—

1 litre = 1,000 cubic centimetres (c.c.)*
1 litre $\fallingdotseq$ 1¾ pints.

(4) Weight

The open paper cube (one cubic centimetre), made when dealing with capacity, may be used to introduce the metric unit of weight. The *weight* of the *cold* water required to fill one of these cubes (if it were *exactly* one cubic centimetre) is called one gram (gramme). (It is wise to emphasize that the water must be

* This was originally true by definition. The definition of the litre has been changed, however, so that this is no longer *strictly* true (1 litre = 1,000 millilitres = 1,000·028 c.c.). The difference is so small that it may be ignored for everyday purposes.

cold, since the definition of the gram weight is: 'the weight of one cubic centimetre of water at a temperature of 4° C'. A more detailed explanation of why this particular temperature is chosen should be left until the children learn, in their science lessons, about the variation of density with changes of temperature.)

We go on to point out that weighing by means of water is neither convenient nor easy! So, instead of a cubic centimetre of water, we usually use a piece of metal of *the same weight* (*not size*). Some one-gram weights should be available for the children to handle, and to use in the weighing of various small articles. Five, ten, twenty, fifty and one-hundred gram weights should also be available, in order to avoid the use of a large number of gram weights.

The children see that even the hundred-gram weight is not very 'heavy'. They find, for example, that it takes more than four hundred-gram weights to balance a pound weight. The need for a larger unit leads us to the kilogram (kilogramme) weight, a thousand grams. At least one such kilogram weight should be available for the children to handle. Otherwise, as with all the other units, it is almost impossible for them to gain any real idea of the kilogram.

Larger objects may now be weighed in kilograms and grams. The kilogram itself may be weighed in the units in common use, and a rough equivalent may be worked out. For example, a kilogram is just a little more than two pounds and three ounces, or about two and one-fifth of a pound. A rough guide of this kind helps children to make quick comparisons of weights given in metric units with those stated in the units they commonly use.

Weights may be written down as kilograms and grams, or as kilograms with decimal parts. By writing down the weights in these two ways, from the early stages, children begin to see that the metric units form a 'system' based on decimals.

(5) *Adoption of the metric system*

It is claimed that, in any country, replacement of other units by the metric system makes calculations in commerce, industry and science much easier. Similarly, it is said that the learning of arithmetic, including money and measures, becomes much easier for children in schools.

In such a change, however, there are difficulties. In many countries the everyday units have a long history. Many of them are 'natural' units, and have their origins and continued use in the ordinary lives and work of the people. Moreover, people find it difficult to give up the old familiar units and accept new ones which they do not understand. It seems inevitable that, where new units are officially introduced by law, the old units continue to be used for many years in the everyday affairs of the people.

Schools must surely play a large part in making such a change effective. But it is not enough merely to make the children learn a new table of 'facts'. It is more important than ever that they should be given regular practical experience with the new units. They must *see*, *handle* and *use* actual metre rulers, and get to know local distances in kilometres. They must handle and use gram and kilogram weights. Above all, they must use metric 'money' in the class-room 'shop'. Activities of this kind are essential for understanding and to bring familiarity with the new units, because for a long time, outside the school, grown-ups will go on working and thinking in terms of the old units

CHAPTER XXVIII

PROVIDING EQUIPMENT AND MAKING APPARATUS

A—*The need*

We help children's understanding by providing them with the experiences which give meaning to the particular work they are doing. Sometimes it is enough to remind them of the things and happenings in their homes and surroundings. Often, however, the experience must be more immediate and direct. For this reason it is vital that teaching apparatus and equipment should be available in the class room at the moment they are needed.

It must be emphasized, however, that the use of apparatus does not in itself lead to success. The materials and devices described in this book are only *aids to* learning and *aids to* teaching. Their importance and value depend on the teacher, on the way he uses them, and on friendly relationship between himself and the individual child.

The best apparatus is usually that which is easy to make and to use. Complicated devices, difficult to handle and understand, are not much use to a young child (they may even confuse him), no matter how interesting they may be for grown-ups to make.

It is advisable to consider each piece of apparatus in view of the requirements of a particular class or an individual child. Many of the pieces described in this book may have to be adapted to particular needs. For example, apparatus for showing the relationship between units of money, and other measures, are useless unless they are adapted for the units used locally. Sometimes, of course, the teacher may invent something more suitable for his own class, because he knows the children and the environment in which they live.

B—*Difficulties*

When first we begin to teach it often seems a difficult task to get all the apparatus and material we want in order to do the work properly. It seems impossible if the class is large and the amount of time and money available is small. This is understandable, but we should not be discouraged. If we begin at once to make a *few* necessary items and make sure they are properly stored, we soon find that our stock 'grows'. After two or three years it becomes quite big. Again, we should get the older children in the school to help, particularly in making the easier apparatus: for example, in cutting and marking out sets of flash-cards or practice-cards.

We should be sure, when making sets of apparatus, to make a few more than are necessary for the children in the present class. This saves any inconvenience when bits of apparatus are lost or broken, or when the size of the class increases.

Apparatus should be attractive to children (colourful, if possible) so that they like to handle it and are keen to use it. As far as possible it should also be self-explanatory and self-corrective, so that children may use it advantageously, without the direct supervision of the teacher.

C—*Materials*

(1) Materials for general use

Very few schools can afford to *buy* all the material they need, but teachers who are alive to the possibilities may make excellent use of much 'scrap' material. A resourceful teacher collects material, and encourages his children to do so, from all kinds of sources. For example:—

(*i*) We may approach government departments for the gift or loan of maps, other geographical information, mechanical scrap, paper waste, small timber off-cuts, and so on. We should also ask for useful hints and advice.

(*ii*) We may get to know the teachers at the nearest secondary school. They can sometimes lend apparatus to illustrate various points to the children.

(*iii*) We can get our families and friends, and the families of our children, to collect empty cardboard packets, tins, newspapers, etc.

(*iv*) We may be able to get containers, off-cuts, scrap of all kinds, from friendly traders, builders, etc.

By getting the goodwill of our community, we may thus collect a great deal of material for use in the arithmetic lesson and for making suitable apparatus.

Here are a few tips regarding particular items:—

(*a*) Scrap cardboard may be painted over, or have white paper pasted on it.

(*b*) When large sheets of thick paper are not available for wall charts, etc., several sheets of ordinary newspaper may be pasted together and then painted over to give a clean surface.

(*c*) The covers of old exercise books are sometimes useful, since they are usually stiffer than ordinary writing paper.

(*d*) Paste may be made by mixing water and any starchy powder. The paste should be smooth and free from lumps. In some areas it is possible to use the gum from certain trees to act as an adhesive. Gum is usually better than paste, particularly in a humid region. In most tropical areas where there is a hot wet season, paper and cardboard apparatus need frequent replacement unless they are varnished to keep out moisture and prevent insect attacks.

(*e*) Suitable wood may sometimes be obtained from packing cases and crates, since it is usually thin and may be cut easily. Straight branches from trees or bushes may also be useful.

(*f*) The list in Appendix A, page 487, suggests materials which may usefully be kept in store for use as occasion arises.

(2) *Materials for special use*

Some cardboard, and various kinds of paper, usually have to be bought. It is important to gather as much information as possible about this material before ordering it, if waste and unnecessary expense are to be avoided, because manufacturers in various parts of the world have many names for the different kinds of card and paper. The thickness of card, for example, is sometimes indicated by the weight of a number of standard cards put together. Sometimes the thickness is indicated by the word 'sheet'. 'Eight sheet' card, for example, is about one-thirtieth of an inch thick.

Moreover, the sizes in which card and paper may be bought vary from place to place and according to the kind of material. It is important to know the sizes, because the size of a large piece of card determines the size and number of the pieces of apparatus which may be made from it. Thus, unless we are careful, we may quite easily waste a lot of material.

As an example, some information about card and paper manufactured in Great Britain is given in Appendix B, page 489. This shows that it is advisable to ask for information from dealers, and if possible to get samples for inspection before making an order.

D—*Storage*

This is quite a problem, particularly in areas where the climate tends to cause rapid decay of materials. It is wise to keep material which is not in frequent use (for example, pieces of apparatus used from time to time for demonstration) in a closed cupboard. If no cupboard space is available, it should be protected as far as possible (for example, by wrapping in newspaper). Other material, such as flash-cards, which the children use from day to day for their own incidental learning, should be kept in strong envelopes or boxes *clearly labelled* to show the contents. The children should be given full details, so that they know not only where to go in order to get the apparatus they need but also where to put it when they have finished.

Bits of apparatus are sometimes mislaid or dropped on the floor. It is useful to have a 'lost-property box' on the teacher's desk. Any 'lost' piece is put in the box and later put back (by a monitor) into the proper envelope or box.

E—*Some further details of apparatus*

(*a*) *Number-slides*—These may be made in the following lengths for different purposes: ten, twelve, twenty and twenty-four inches. Construction is easy and the same in each case.

(*i*) *Fig. 16*, page 34. For the '10' number-slide a piece of fairly thick cardboard, 10 by $3\frac{1}{8}$ inches, is cut out. Two strips, 10 by 1 inches, are cut out and pasted along the outside edges of the first piece (Fig. 158(*a*)), thus leaving a groove, $1\frac{1}{8}$ inches wide, down the middle. One side is marked off and numbered as shown. We then cut eleven strips, each one inch wide, in the following lengths: 10, 9, 8, 7, 6; two of 5; 4, 3, 2, 1 inches. (The quickest way to do this is to take a piece of cardboard 10 by 6

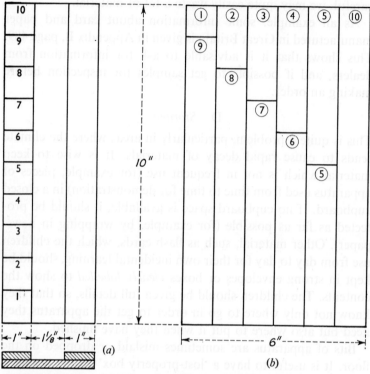

FIGURE 158.—The '10' number-slide: (a) The slide. (b) A quick method of making the unmarked strips

inches and mark it out as in Fig. 158(b).) The strips are neither marked nor numbered.

(ii) *Fig. 24*, page 44. In this case the strips for the '10' number-slide are numbered to show their lengths.

(iii) *Fig. 56*, page 106. The '24' slide is provided with a 'runner' to cover up numbers not wanted. (Thus, a child may work out a division example such as '17 ÷ 3' by measuring off a 'three' strip as far as the number '17', and find that it goes five times with two over.) The runner is made of thick paper. This is folded along the dotted lines (Fig. 159) and wrapped around the number-slide. The shaded portion is then gummed down.

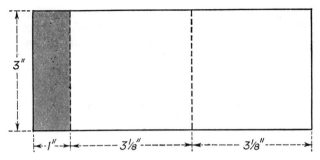

FIGURE 159.—Making a 'runner' for a number-slide. (The paper strip is wrapped round the slide and the shaded part gummed down)

(*b*) *Number-tops* (Fig. 26, page 45)—A circle of radius two inches is drawn on light-coloured cardboard. Round the circumference six points, two inches apart, are marked off, that is, using the same radius. These points are joined to form a regular hexagon. The shape is cut out and marked as in Fig. 160. A short pointed stick is pushed exactly through the centre of the hexagon.

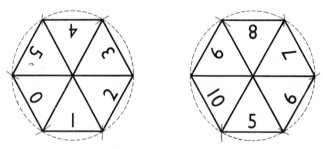

FIGURE 160.—Making a number-top

Glue is applied at the centre to keep the stick upright and rigid. Several number-tops should be made, and the sections numbered so that, in playing a game, children may cover *all* the primary facts.

(*c*) *The fishing game* (Fig. 27, page 46)—This may be used at various stages. For instance (see Fig. 161):—

(*i*) The 'fish' caught are used as objects for counting.
(*ii*) The 'fish' are marked with number-patterns to be recognized.

(*iii*) The 'fish' are marked with figures to be recognized.

(*iv*) The 'fish' have incomplete number 'facts' on them. (When the fish are 'hooked' they have to be 'landed' by putting

FIGURE 161.—Various 'fish' for the 'fishing game'

them on the appropriate number. For example, a fish marked '4 × 3 =' must be 'landed' on a spot, on the floor, or table, marked '12'.)

(*v*) The 'fish' are marked with weights in pounds and ounces.

A steel paper-clip is attached to each fish (cut out of paper) which is placed in a box or on the floor. The children, in groups of two or three, each have a line to which a small horseshoe magnet is attached. They try to catch a fish by attraction of a clip to the magnet. Each time they catch fish they write in their books. If we have no magnets and cannot borrow them from science teachers at a nearby secondary school, the game may still be played. Hooks (or bent wire) are put on the lines. One of the children sits under the table and hooks fish on to the lines of children waiting above.

(*d*) *Flash-cards* (Fig. 34, page 60; Fig. 38, page 73; etc.)—

Suitable sizes, as already recommended, are 3 by 2 inches (for children's use in individual and group activities) and 8 by 4 inches (for teacher's use in demonstrations and class games). One corner (the same one in each case) is cut off each card. They are then easy to stack so that all the question sides, or all the answer sides, are uppermost. This saves much time in arrangement, and often avoids the spoiling of a game.

It is suggested that, when a set of flash-cards is being prepared, *all* the question sides be written first, and then *all* the answer sides. There is then much less risk of confusion.

(*e*) *The 'division train'* (Fig. 49, page 96)—The method of construction is similar to that of the number-slides. In fact a separate apparatus is not essential, as the '24'-slide may be used for the purpose.

(*f*) *A pair of scales*—Four pieces of wood A, B, C and D, are cut to the sizes shown in Fig. 162(*a*). A hole is made one inch from

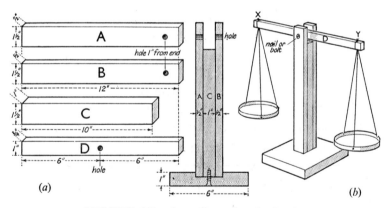

(*a*)   (*b*)

FIGURE 162.—An easily-made pair of scales

one end of A, to carry a nail or bolt. A similar hole is made in B. Also a hole is made at the middle point of piece D. A, C and B are glued, nailed or screwed together to form the pillar, as shown, and this is fastened firmly into a heavy wooden base (at least six inches square). The beam, D, is then pivoted on a nail or bolt. Tin-lids, about four inches in diameter, are used as scale-pans. Each is held by three strings through holes in the edge. Loops of string are used to hang the pans on the beam, small grooves being cut at X and Y to keep them in position. The beam is then balanced by shaving off a little of the wood at the heavier end. Fig. 162(*b*) shows the complete apparatus.

(*g*) *Clock-faces* (Fig. 80, page 139)—This piece of apparatus should be big enough for the whole class to see at the same time. The rectangle of strong white cardboard is about two feet by sixteen inches. The large clock face, showing the minute positions painted in black, has a diameter of about one foot. The smaller clock face, showing only the hours, is a detachable circle and has a diameter of about nine inches. A small nut and bolt hold the fingers in position. A wing-nut is most suitable as it enables the small face to be detached more quickly.

(*h*) *The place-value slide* (Figs. 91 and 140, pages 195 and 404)— This is also used in connexion with decimals, and for demonstrating quick methods of multiplication and division by ten and a hundred.

It is very similar in construction to the number-slides. It consists of four pieces of thick cardboard:—

$$21'' \times 6'' \quad \text{Base}$$
$$21'' \times 2'' \quad \text{Strip A}$$
$$21'' \times 3'' \quad \text{Strip B}$$
$$21'' \times 1'' \quad \text{Strip C}$$

Strips A and C are stuck on to the base, leaving a groove along which strip B may slide. The apparatus is marked as in Fig. 163.

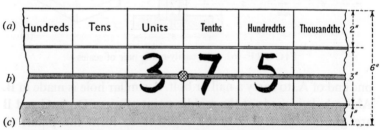

FIGURE 163.—The place-value slide. (The head of a nail or screw represents the decimal point)

A slit is cut in strip B along its length to a point about an inch from each end. A nail or screw is driven through the slit and into the base, so that its head acts as a decimal point between the units and the tenths.

When the slide is used for ordinary numbers, as described in Chapter XIII, a piece of paper is folded round the slide to cover up the decimal places and point.

These examples are sufficient to show that, with care, apparatus may be made simply and cheaply.

CHAPTER XXIX

ORGANIZATION, TESTING AND MARKING

In some places schools are required to follow a scheme of work laid down by a central authority. In other areas, head teachers and their staffs are responsible for deciding and planning the nature and extent of the arithmetic work.

A—*Planning for the whole school*

It is suggested that a head teacher who is planning his own arithmetic schemes should keep in mind the following points:—

(*a*) It is best, first of all, to decide upon the desirable *minimum* standard to be attained by the majority of his pupils by the time they leave the primary school. In other words, he asks himself:—

(*i*) 'What arithmetic do they *need* to know in order to live full, happy lives, and in view of their future work, careers, or study?'

(*ii*) 'What arithmetic can I properly expect most of my boys and girls to learn during the years they are with me?'

The answers to these two questions should be written down in detail.

(*b*) Some of the children whose abilities are above average may go on to further studies in mathematics and science. These probably need more arithmetic than the minimum. This 'extra' work should extend and enrich their mathematical thinking, and *not merely give them more practice at mechanical examples which they are already capable of doing.* Moreover, it should be given at each stage of their progress through the primary school, not only in the final year.

(*c*) Some children, on the other hand, may be unable to achieve the desirable minimum. Their ability is such that less can be expected of them and their progress is necessarily slower.

(*d*) Each teacher should try to find out about the range of ability in his class, so that he can take steps to organize work to suit the different children. In some larger schools it is possible to 'stream' the classes, so as to keep the able, the average, and the less able members of any particular age-group in separate classes. Each class works at a different level and at a different pace. When such 'streaming' takes suitable account of ability in arithmetic there is no problem: all the children in a class are able to work at much the same level and rate. But, if arithmetic plays a comparatively small part in the 'streaming', some children may be in a class unsuited to their ability or attainment in the subject. Some head teachers have attempted to provide for this in the upper parts of the school by organizing arithmetic 'sets'. The arithmetic period is arranged at the same time for all classes, and children go to their particular arithmetic 'set', which may be higher or lower than their own class. Thus a twelve-year-old child may go to an arithmetic 'set' in which most of the children are ten years old. Similarly, a ten-year-old may be doing mathematics at a higher level with older children. In the same way, each class of a single-stream school may be arranged in 'sets'.

(e) In deciding on the extent of the work to be expected from each year-group, the head teacher should bear in mind not only the number of his teachers but the quality of each as a teacher of arithmetic. Thus he may rightly decide to increase the extent of the arithmetic to be covered in one class, while limiting certain topics in those with teachers who are less interested or mathematically less able. He has to ensure, of course, that as far as possible there is no undesirable gap in the arithmetic syllabus for the school as a whole. If a child does less arithmetic in one year, he must make it up in the next.

(f) In deciding what arithmetic is to be covered and the methods by which it is to be taught, it is essential to study the surroundings of the children's homes and the school. The children in a school in a town or in an industrial area have different needs from those in a rural area. The arithmetic they need is different, and many of the ways in which they learn it may also be different.

(g) It is wise to consult all teachers in the school when a syllabus is being planned, so that each may know his own class's part in the general scheme. Discussion meetings should also be arranged regularly throughout the year so that methods may be standardized. Teachers who have special qualifications or particular interests in arithmetic can be invited to put forward their ideas for general discussion.

(*h*) It is unwise to base the planning upon the use of one particular text-book throughout the school. The syllabus then depends upon the contents of the text-book. This is unsatisfactory because it takes little account of the special circumstances and needs of the school. Though the text-book may be well written and eventually necessary for the scheme, it has probably been written by somebody with no knowledge of the surroundings of the school or of the children. A better plan is to decide upon the work to be covered, and then to look for text-books to help the scheme to be carried out successfully. Sometimes it may be necessary to use various text-books, each of which is useful at particular stages in the scheme.

(*j*) When planning that part of the scheme which is applicable to the very young children, it is probably best to think of a programme of activities rather than of a fixed amount of arithmetic to be learned. The most important thing at this stage is that the children's attitude to number work should be healthy. This means that they should enjoy their activities with numbers and want to find out more about them. The right attitude will have a far-reaching influence on their later development in arithmetic. This does not suggest, of course, that the early work need not be planned. Indeed, it is necessary to prepare very carefully, in order to give these young children all kinds of number experience, as described earlier in this book.

B—*Class-room organization by the teacher*

When the teacher receives the scheme designed for his own class, he has the freedom and responsibility of carrying out the work in his own way. But, again, there are many considerations which he should keep in mind.

(*a*) The work fits into a plan for the whole school. Methods should be agreed upon, so that children are not confused because one teacher uses a different method from another.

(b) As far as possible, it must be arranged that children work at a level and at a rate suited to their ability. In this way they are likely to achieve success and make continuous progress.

This means that the teacher may have to organize perhaps three or four groups of children, each group doing different work. Teaching time is then given to each of the groups according to their particular needs.

A teacher sometimes finds it possible to arrange parts of the scheme so that children can work individually at their own level and pace. This is particularly valuable when they are practising mechanical processes, since they can mark and correct their own work, allowing the teacher to give more attention to those children who are having difficulty.

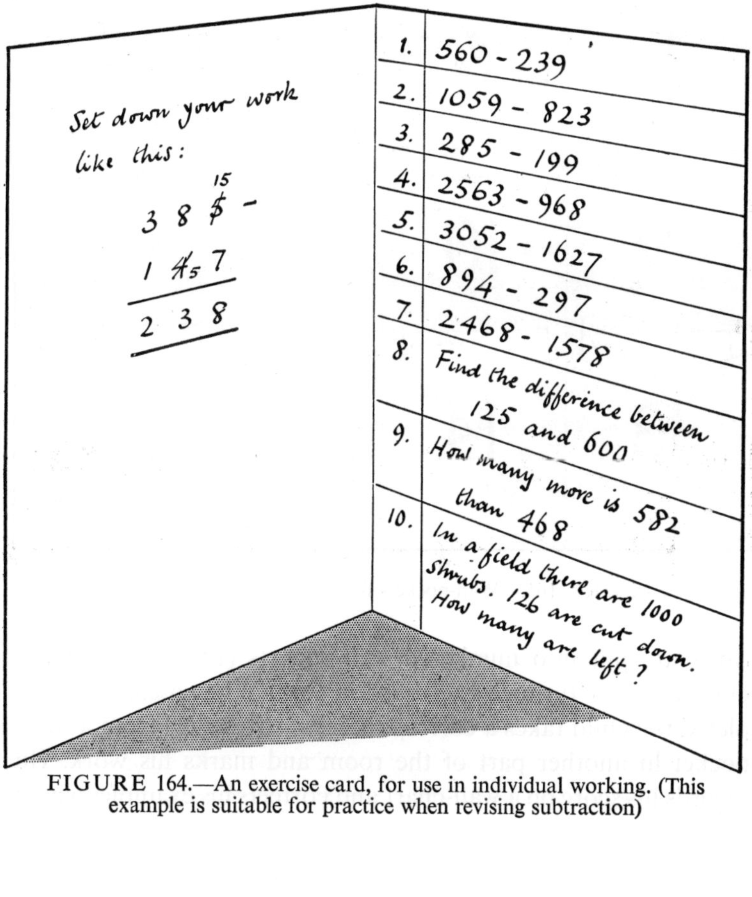

FIGURE 164.—An exercise card, for use in individual working. (This example is suitable for practice when revising subtraction)

In an individual scheme of this kind the work should be graded carefully into stages and steps (such as those outlined in the various Analyses in this book). Cards of exercises are prepared for each stage and step. One side of a card shows how the examples should be set down and worked (see Fig. 164). The

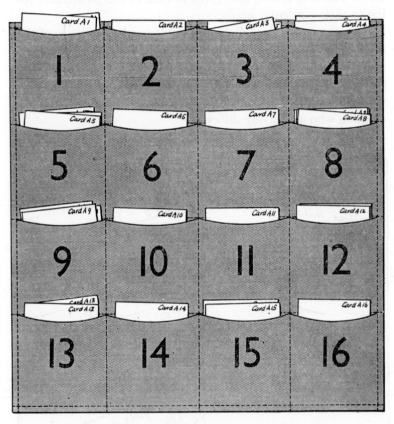

FIGURE 165.—Wall-pockets for storing exercise cards, etc.

cards are put into numbered wall-pockets (Fig. 165) and the children work through each card in turn. When a card is completed the child takes a corresponding answer-card from a wall-pocket in another part of the room and marks his work. He records his score on a wall-chart and corrects his examples where necessary. When in difficulties he informs the teacher, who attends to him as soon as possible.

When properly organized the individual scheme works well, but there are some *disadvantages*:—

(*i*) It cannot cover adequately all the arithmetic needed in the primary school. It should be reserved mainly for practice.
(*ii*) It tends to make the arithmetic too formal. The value of group and class working may be lost. Much group discussion of arithmetical ideas is necessary if children are to understand them properly.
(*iii*) There is a danger that the teacher may lose the stimulation that comes from teaching the children as a group.

On the other hand, a well-organized individual scheme enables the teacher to see, at a glance, the progress of any individual child. It also helps every child to see the work ahead and to notice his own progress.

(*c*) When planning, it is necessary to break up the year's work into smaller amounts, to be covered each term. Many teachers also plan the work for each week. This may often be necessary, but it is a mistake to keep rigidly to a weekly plan which may mean trying to teach too much too quickly. Some teachers become inefficient (and their children fail to learn) because they are anxious to complete the syllabus in time. Thus they often go on to new work before previous steps are properly known. Arithmetic is a subject in which each new step depends upon a thorough understanding of the earlier steps. Moreover, it should be remembered that a good plan for a school allows for the situation where a class does not complete the work arranged for it. Thus the plan should ensure that each new class spends a little time revising the work arranged for previous years before bringing in fresh ideas.

C—*Testing*

We should test the children at regular intervals, in order to check accuracy and speed, find out difficulties and discover where further teaching is necessary.

(1) Tests of mental arithmetic

(a) Questions answered orally—The main purpose of the two or three minutes of quick oral questioning at the beginning of a lesson is to stimulate the children and prepare them for the thinking they have to do in the rest of the lesson. We have to make sure that *all* the children take part.

(b) Questions answered on paper—Not more than ten to twenty should be given (orally) and these should be carefully planned. Each question should have a definite purpose, and *the teacher should use the knowledge he gains from the results of the test.* The purpose of a test may be:—

(*i*) To check the children's knowledge of the 'facts'.

(*ii*) To find out whether details of the current work are understood.

(*iii*) To revise and keep fresh in the children's minds certain aspects of work done in previous weeks.

(*iv*) To test ability to apply knowledge to everyday situations in the form of simple problems stated in words.

(*v*) To give the children the satisfaction and stimulation of trying to solve problems and 'puzzles' (see Chapter XXV).

(*vi*) To give the children opportunities to use short methods of calculation (see pages 193–6 and 435–7).

(*vii*) To test the spelling of words used in arithmetic lessons.

These mental tests have little value unless we analyse the results and act upon them. As usual, the children who do well are encouraged, and those who do not are given extra attention. But much more important, and so often neglected, is the analysis which tells us which items are not well known and therefore merit further teaching. For instance, the analysis of a ten-question test for forty children may look like that in Fig. 166.

This analysis takes only two minutes to work out, if the children indicate their correct answers by a show of hands. The teacher knows immediately that questions three, five and nine probably contain material which is not properly understood and known by the majority of children. Further work is needed here. The results of questions five and seven suggest that the questions were badly phrased, or that some of the children had an

insufficient background to be able to answer properly. It is worth
while to inspect the individual papers from time to time in order
to obtain further information.

Question number	Number of answers correct	Number of answers wrong	Number not attempted
1	37	3	—
2	35	5	—
3	4	30	6
4	38	2	—
5	10	20	10
6	37	3	—
7	20	12	8
8	36	4	—
9	0	21	19
10	33	7	—

FIGURE 166.—Analysis of marks in a mental arithmetic test

(2) *Written arithmetic tests*

These have similar purposes to the mental tests, but they take
longer and are given less frequently. The type of test depends
upon its purpose. The results may be used:—

(*i*) To grade children into groups of similar ability at the beginning of the year. Here the test should contain examples of all the
arithmetic the children are expected to have covered.

(*ii*) To find out what steps in a particular process have been
missed or are not known. This is called a diagnostic test because
the results should give a diagnosis of the difficulties of individual
children. These tests must be very carefully compiled and very
carefully marked. It is suggested that teachers should use
examples similar to those given in graded order in the Analyses
for each of the processes (Chapters XI to XIV). An examination
of the mistakes should indicate the stage at which children are
going wrong and show the nature of the errors.

D—*Marking and corrections*

It is suggested above that children may mark their own examples
in an individual scheme, thus leaving more time for the teacher
to teach. A great deal of the work may be marked in the same
way, particularly where it is concerned with the practice of
mechanical processes.

Ideally, of course, each piece of work should be considered by teacher and pupil together, so that mistakes can be discussed, put right, and avoided in the future. But this is not always possible, and often the teacher can do no more than give the answers in class and ensure that the children do the necessary corrections. What is important, however, is that every child should be aware that his work is supervised continuously, and checked from time to time, by a teacher who is interested in his progress. If a child marks his own work he should be encouraged to find out not only *where* he is wrong but *why* he is wrong.

Some teachers use a system in which children change books and mark each other's work. This is unsatisfactory because it implies that the children cannot be trusted. Moreover, it encourages the children to be interested only in the marks they have obtained rather than in the work and how it has been done.

In some schools children are required to correct (that is, do again) *every* piece of incorrect work. This may not be advisable, as it may lead to boredom and frustration. We should always consider carefully whether corrections are necessary. Everything depends upon the character of the child, the kind of error and the nature of the work.

E—*Keeping records*

A simple record of his class is a great help to a teacher. It should show a few details of the progress of each individual child. Such a record need not be official, but may be kept privately in an ordinary exercise book. A page for each child may show such details as these:—

Name and date of birth.
Address.
Birthday. (This is often an important annual event for a child, and the teacher may well take note of it.)
Father's occupation.
Names and ages of other members of the family.
Particular interests at home and at school.
Physical defects (if any).

Results of initial testing and information gained at particular times from diagnostic tests such as:—
which facts are not known;
whether there are difficulties with 'carrying';
whether reading difficulties arise in the solving of problems; etc.

Further relevant details may be added as the year progresses.

By the end of the year the teacher has a record not only of the child's progress in arithmetic but also of his general development.

SOMETHING MORE TO THINK ABOUT?

It is suggested more than once in this book that, as teachers, we should be able to justify the inclusion of everything we teach in the primary school. We may be able to 'cut out the dead wood', that is, to leave out some part of the arithmetic which is usually taught in schools but has little everyday importance or value. For example, rather than spend time on lengthy calculations of a kind rarely needed in everyday life, we may help children by the introduction of simple ideas of geometry and graphs.

In our particular school we may find it desirable to omit other parts of the usual course and, perhaps, to introduce a very elementary treatment of topics often ignored until the secondary stage of schooling. We should always be prepared to re-examine our work and to give careful thought to all the possibilities. We must find out what is best for our children in our own schools, and we can do this only by trying out fresh ideas for ourselves.

The good teacher always feels that there is room for improvement, not only in his teaching methods but also in what he teaches. Since we live in a changing world there is always something new and fresh for us to think about.

USEFUL MATERIALS

1. *Materials to be collected locally*

Materials such as the following may readily be obtained by every teacher. They are useful in many activities and games, and in making apparatus.

Tins (empty and cleaned), of various shapes and sizes: e.g. milk, cigarette, biscuit, polish, kerosene
Glass jars (empty and cleaned), of various shapes and sizes: e.g. jam, paste, ointment
Earthenware pots: e.g. local utensils
Bottles (empty and cleaned), of various kinds: e.g. mineral-water, beer, medicine
Boxes (empty and cleaned), of various sizes and types: e.g. match-boxes, cardboard cartons, wooden cases
Packages (empty and cleaned), of all kinds suitable for 'playing shop': e.g. packets, cartons, tins, jars, bottles, boxes

Paper, of all kinds: e.g. brown, coloured, packing, writing, drawing, newspaper
Cardboard, of all kinds: e.g. from boxes, cartons, writing-pads, note-books, registers
Wood: e.g. from boxes, crates, straight branches of trees, carpenters' scrap, builders' off-cuts
String, rope, etc.
Cotton thread, tape, ribbon, etc.
Wire: e.g. from boxes, crates, etc.
Rubber bands: e.g. cut from old inner tubes of bicycle and motor-car tyres
Paste, gum, etc.
Razor-blades (fixed in wooden handles—for cutting out cardboard, etc.)
Pins, safety-pins, etc.
Nails, screws, nuts and bolts, etc.
Wheels, of various kinds and sizes: e.g. from worn-out clocks, gramophones, bicycles, cars. (These and other useful mechanical scrap are often available from bicycle mechanics, garages, public works departments, etc.)

Pebbles (small), shells, fruit stones (dry), etc.—for counting, etc.
Beads, nuts (dry), etc.—for threading
Sand (clean), beans (small, dry), seeds (dry), etc.—to be 'poured' and

measured. (Material of this kind should be kept in strong, clearly-labelled boxes of convenient size.)

Clay—for modelling. (To be kept in tins with close-fitting lids.)

Labels, from discarded packages: e.g. prices, names, descriptions, pictures

Transport tickets (used): e.g. bus, train, steamer, etc.

Calendars, almanacs, time-tables (bus, train, etc.)

Newspaper and magazine cuttings: e.g. pictures; graphs; advertisements (as colourful and attractive as possible)—for 'shopping' activities; diet sheets and meal recipes—for references to quantities; results of athletic meetings, league tables, cricket averages; etc.

2. *Materials to be made*

Much of the apparatus mentioned in this book may be made by a resourceful teacher, often with the help of the children, from material such as that mentioned in section 1. For instance:—

Sticks (small, short)—for counting, grouping, etc.: e.g. from twigs or carpenters' off-cuts

Skittles, cubes and other wooden blocks: e.g. from branches or carpenters' off-cuts

Measuring sticks, 12 and 36 inches, and/or $\frac{1}{2}$ and 1 metre

Weights: e.g. sand in bags or sealed boxes or tins

Measuring vessels: e.g. from tins, bottles or jars

Pair of scales; see-saw

Number-trays, number-boards, number-slides, etc.

Shadow stick; rain-gauge

3. *Materials that may have to be bought*

Rulers, 1 foot and 1 yard, and/or $\frac{1}{2}$ and 1 metre

Tape-measure (preferably steel, to be kept well-greased and preserved carefully)

Weights, standard set: ounce–pound and/or gram–Kilogram

Measuring vessels, standard: pint, quart, gallon, litre

Thermometers: wall, clinical, etc.

Spring balances

Tools: e.g. hammer, screwdriver, saw, chisel, pliers, pincers, snips, file, scissors, knives

Pencils (coloured), paints, varnish, inks (including 'water-proof'), paint-brushes

It should be remembered that items in section 3 are often needed for lessons other than arithmetic: for example, in science, handwork, geography, etc.

APPENDIX B

SOME DETAILS OF PAPER
AND CARDBOARD
(See pages 468-9)

Name	Size	Thickness
Cartridge Paper (Usual school drawing paper)	Usual size is 30″ × 22″ (This is known as *Imperial Size*.) But it may also be bought in these sizes, which are fractions of Imperial Size: Folio— 22″ × 15″ Quarto—11″ × 15″ Octavo—11″ × 7½″.	Varies in thickness but usual school paper is about 40 lb. per ream (480 sheets).
Manilla Paper (Useful for making folders and envelopes)	30″ × 20″ This size is known as *Double Crown*.	About 80 lb. per ream (480 sheets).
White Card (Useful for flash-cards, etc.)	25″ × 20″ This size is known as *Royal*.	Thickness specified by a number; e.g. six (sheet), eight (sheet).
Greyboard Strawboard Leatherboard	Usual size is 40″ × 30″	Thickness specified by weight; e.g. 16 oz., 20 oz., 22 oz.
Hardboard	Sold usually in multiples of four feet; e.g. 8′ × 4′, 8′ × 12′, etc.	Very thick. Must be sawn. May be nailed.

R

APPENDIX C

SOME BOOKS FOR THE MATHEMATICS LIBRARY

There are hundreds of books on all the various aspects of mathematics. The teacher has to make his own appropriate selection. The following list is intended *as a guide* towards the choice of books which may help the teacher of primary school Arithmetic.

(G)—published in Great Britain
(U)—published in the United States of America

1. PRINCIPLES AND TEACHING METHOD

ADAMS. *A Background of Primary School Mathematics.* Oxford University Press (G)

BARNETT, FAITHFULL & THEAKSTON. *Juniors Learning Mathematics.* E.S.A. (G)

BASS & DOWTY. *Counting and Arithmetic in the Infants School.* Harrap (G)

BRUECKNER & GROSSNICKLE. *How to Make Arithmetic Meaningful.* Winston (U)

BUCKINGHAM. *Elementary Arithmetic; Its Meaning and Practice.* Ginn (U)

CUISENAIRE & GATTEGNO. *Numbers in Colour.* Heinemann (G)

DANIEL. *Activity in the Primary School.* Blackwell (G)

DEWEY. *The School and Society.* Chicago University Press (U)

DRUMMOND. *Learning Arithmetic by the Montessori Method.* Harrap (G)

PIAGET. *The Child's Conception of Number.* Routledge, Kegan Paul (G)

STERN. *Children Discover Arithmetic.* Harper (U)

WHEAT. *The Psychology and Teaching of Arithmetic.* Heath (U)

WILSON. *Teaching the New Arithmetic.* McGraw-Hill (U)

2. HISTORICAL

BALL. *Short Account of the History of Mathematics.* Macmillan (U)

BELL. *Development of Mathematics.* McGraw-Hill (U)

CAJORI. *History of Mathematics.* Macmillan (U)

CAJORI. *A History of Mathematical Notations.* Open Court (U)

HOBSON. *John Napier and The Invention of Logarithms.* Cambridge University Press (G)

KLINE. *Mathematics in Western Culture.* Allen & Unwin (G)

SANFORD. *Short History of Mathematics.* Houghton-Mifflin (U)
SMELTZER. *Man and Number.* A. & C. Black (G)
SMITH. *Source Book in Mathematics.* McGraw-Hill (U)
SMITH. *Number Stories of Long Ago.* Ginn (G)
SMITH & KARPINSKI. *The Hindu-Arabic Numerals.* Ginn (U)
YELDHAM. *Story of Reckoning in the Middle Ages.* Harrap (G)
YELDHAM. *Teaching of Arithmetic Through 400 Years.* Harrap (G)

3. MEASURING

BOWMAN. *Romance in Arithmetic.* University of London Press (G)
GROOM. *The Money Book.* Rockcliff (G)
HALLOCK & WADE. *The Evolution of Weights and Measures and the Metric System.* Macmillan (U)
HOAD. *How Time is Measured.* Oxford University Press (G)
HOGBEN. *Man Must Measure.* Publicity Products (G)
NICHOLSON. *Men and Measures.* John Murray (G)
QUIGGAR. *Survey of Primitive Money.* Methuen (G)
SMITH. *Story of Measurement.* Blackwell (G)
WATKINS. *Time Counts.* Neville Spearman (G)

4. GENERAL

BAKST. *Mathematics; its Magic and Mystery.* Van Nostrand (U)
BALL. *Mathematical Recreations and Essays.* Macmillan (G)
BELL. *Development of Mathematics.* McGraw-Hill (U)
BELL. *Mathematics, Queen and Servant of Science.* Bell (G)
BELL. *Men of Mathematics.* (2 Vols.) Penguin (G)
BROOKES & DICK. *Introduction to Statistical Method.* Heinemann (G)
BURNS. *First Steps in Astronomy.* Ginn (G)
CLARKE. *Fun with Figures.* Heinemann (G)
DANTZIG. *Number, the Language of Science.* Allen & Unwin (G)
DAVIS & KELLY. *Short Course on Surveying.* McGraw-Hill (U)
DEGRAZIA. *Maths is Fun.* Allen & Unwin (G)
DUDENEY. *Amusements in Mathematics.* Nelson (G)
GARRETT. *Statistics in Psychology and Education.* Longmans (G)
HART. *Makers of Science.* Oxford University Press (G)
HEATH. *Works of Archimedes.* Dover (U)
HOGBEN. *Mathematics for the Million.* Allen & Unwin (G)
HOOPER. *Makers of Mathematics.* Faber & Faber (G)
HUFF. *How to Lie with Statistics.* Gollancz (G)
LARSON. *Enrichment Program for Arithmetic.* Row Peterson (U)
RICHARDSON. *Surveying for Schools and Scouts.* Pitman (G)
TURNBULL. *Great Mathematicians.* Methuen (G)

5. CHILDREN'S BOOKS

(It is often impossible to find a book or series of books completely suited to the needs of children in a particular school or region. Frequently such books do not exist. However, the teacher may select for adaptation to local conditions many useful points from books like those listed here.)

BURNISTON. *Real Arithmetic*. Collins (G)

CAREY FRANCIS. *Highway Arithmetics*. Longmans (G)

CLARK & GRIFFITHS. *Rightway Arithmetic*. University of London Press (G)

CLARK, JUNE & CLARK. *Growth in Arithmetic*. World Book Co. (U)

DURELL. *Junior School Arithmetic*. Bell (G)

GUNDERSON & HOLLISTER. *Learning to use Arithmetic*. Heath (U)

HAMILTON. *London Arithmetic*. University of London Press (G)

SCHONELL & CRACKNELL. *Right from the Start Arithmetic*. Oliver & Boyd (G)

TAYLOR. *New Nation Arithmetics*. Nelson (G)

WHITWELL & GODDARD. *New Primary Arithmetic*. Schofield & Sims (G)

WILLIAMS. *Kingsway Junior Arithmetic*. Evans (G)

(Anon.) *Practical Malayan Arithmetic*. Longmans (G)

Note—Although arithmetic books written for particular areas are not very common, their numbers are increasing nowadays. Teachers should always be on the alert for the publication of books designed for use in their own regions.

INDEX

Activities, informal, 19–37
—, oral class, 46–7, 60, 73, 88–9, 107, 249–51
Activities, children's, in addition, 41–50, 53–62
—, — — area, 422–3
—, — — capacity, 134–6, 349–50
—, — — counting, 21–2, 26–30
—, — — division, 93–7
—, — — fractions, 378–86, 388–90
—, — — grouping, 77–9
—, — — length, 124–31, 302–6
—, — — metric system, 460–4
—, — — money, 264–8, 271–2
—, — — multiplication, 77–80, 244–55
—, — — subtraction, 64–6, 73
—, — — tables, 244, 247–53
—, — — time, 137–42, 361–6
—, — — weight, 131–4, 325–9
—, — — volume, 424–5
Addition, 38–62, 143–66
—, activities in, 41–50, 54–62
—, analysis of steps in, 158–66
— board, 153–4
—, with capacity, 352
—, complementary 265
— of decimals, 399
—, errors common in, 153–6
—, facts of, 43, 47–8, 49–60
—, flash-cards for, 58–60
—, of fractions, 388–90, 444
—, idea of, 39
—, language of, 38–9
— of length, 307–9
— — money, 116–17, 271–4
—, practice-cards for, 39, 40, 43, 53–60
—, 'problems' in, 60–2
— rhymes, 46–7
— sign, 39–40
— — time, 368
— — weights, 330–1
Analysis of teaching steps in:
addition, 158–66
capacity, 354–8
division, 222–39
fractions, 454–7
R*

length, 315–21
money, 284–91
multiplication, 203–11
subtraction, 180–5
time, 372–6
weight, 336–45
Angles, 419–22
Apparatus, 466–75
—, materials for, 467–9
—, storage of, 469
—, use of, 47
Area, 422–4, 461
Arithmetic, and science, 7
—, how much?, 8
Arranging, 23
Astronomy, 366
Athletics, 304, 459

Balance, scales, 132, 473–4
—, spring, 327
Bank, class, 118, 265
Barter, 262
Bead bars, 29, 49, 153
Beads, 24, 33, 43, 78
Bills, 271–2
'Bingo', 248
'Birds' nests', 78, 80
'Blind man's' game, 78
Board, addition, 153–4
—, fraction, 267–8, 384–5, 405
—, number, 35
Bushel, 346–7, 351
Buying, and selling, 111–20

Calendar dates, 253
Calendars, 360–1, 366–7
Cancelling, 386
Capacity, 123–4, 134–6, 346–58, 461–3
—, activities in, 349–50
—, addition of, 52
—, analysis of steps in, 354–8
—, changing units of, 351
—, division of, 353
—, estimation of, 134
—, facts of, 346–7, 352
—, first ideas of, 123–4
—, flash-cards for, 351

Capacity in metric system, 461–3
—, multiplication of, 353
—, subtraction of, 352
—, tables of, 346–7, 351
— and volume, 461–3
—, work-cards for, 350
Cardboard, 489
Cards, see 'Exercise', 'Flash-', 'Number', 'Number-pattern', 'Picture', 'Practice-', 'Work-'
'Carrying' in addition, 143–6, 151–7
— — multiplication, 190–1
— — money, 272–4
Centimetre, 460–1
—, cubic, 461–2
Chain, as unit, 303
'Chain tag', 25
'Changing' of fractions, 384–8
— — length, 307
— — money, 117–18
— — weight, 329–30
Changing-game, 49–50, 58, 153, 386
Charts of capacity, 351
— — money, 268–9
— — length, 306–7
— — tables, 85, 244–5, 256–60
— — time, 366
— — weight, 329
Circle, 417–19
—, circumference of, 422
—, fractions of, 381
—, 'sewed', 385
Clock-face, 249–50, 422, 474
Clocks, 137–40, 362–6, 422
—, twenty-four hour, 363
Coins, 95, 115–19
—, history of, 110
—, recognition of, 115–16
Coin-rubbings, 115
Collecting, 23, 33
Common denominator, 387
Common errors, see 'Errors'
Common fractions, see 'Fractions'
Comparing, 63–4
Compass points, 420
Compasses, 419
Complementary addition, 265
Correcting, 483–4
Counting, 21–30, 147–8
—, activities in, 21–30
— in groups, 28–30, 79–80
— in tens, etc., 148
—, oral, 26–30
Cube, 424, 461–2

Cubic centimetre, 461–2
Cubic inch, 424
Cubit, 299
Cylinder, 425

Dance rhythms, 25
Dates, calendar, 253
Day, as unit, 140, 359
Decimal point, 396
Decimals, 392–406
—, addition of, 399
—, division of, 400
—, extending H.T.U., 402–5
—, multiplication of, 400
—, subtraction of, 399–400
Decomposition, method of, 171–4, 275–7, 310, 333, 352, 445–6
Degree, of angle, 393, 421
Denominator, 387
Diaries, 140–1
Digit, 299
Direction, 419–20
Division, 91–109, 212–39
—, activities in, 93–9
—, analysis of steps in, 232–9
—, aspects of, 212–14
—, by ten, etc., 224
—, difficulties in, 91–2
—, errors in, 229–30
—, facts of, 99–107, 216–24
—, flash-cards for, 107–8
—, idea of, 91–3
—, language of, 93
—, long or short?, 213–16
—, practice-cards for, 102–6
—, 'problems' in, 108–9
—, remainders in, 96–7
— rhymes, 97
— sign, 98
— 'train', 95, 473
—, 'trying-out', in, 224–8
Division with capacity, 353
— — decimals, 400
— — fractions, 450–2
— — length, 312–14
— — money, 119, 280–3
— — time, 369–70
— — weight, 334

Eighths, see 'Fractions'
Elephant, model, 252–3
Equal additions, method of, 174–7, 276–7, 310, 333, 352, 445
Equals sign, 40

Equivalence, of coins, 117–19 264–8
— — fractions, 384–6
Errors common in addition, 153–6
— — — division, 229–30
— — — multiplication, 200–1
— — — subtraction, 177–9
Estimation (guessing), 298
— of area, 423
— — capacity, 134
— — length, 126, 297–8
— — time, 364
— — weight, 131
— — volume, 424
Everyday examples, 26, 47, 73, 89,
  97, 107–8, 242, 255, 297–8, 413–
  414
Exercise (revision) card, 479–80
Experience, children's, 1, 19–22, 41,
  60–5, 76–80, 92–7, 110–14, 122–4,
  241–2, 377–84, 412–17

Factors, multiplication by, 199
Facts, arithmetical, 49–50, 240–4
— of addition, 42, 48, 49–60
— — capacity, 346–7, 352
— — division, 99–107, 216–24
— — length, 306–7
— — money, 268–9
— — multiplication, 82–9, 188–93,
        240–60
— — subtraction, 67–73
— — time, 366–7
— — weight, 329
Figures, cut-out, 34
'Find your partner', 250
Fishing-game, 46, 471–2
Fixing the facts, 42–6
'Flags and castles', 33, 78, 80, 95
Flash cards, 247, 472–3
— for addition, 58–60
— — capacity, 351
— — division, 107, 252
— — money, 266–7
— — multiplication, 86–8, 247–8,
        252
— — subtraction, 73
— — weight, 330
Folding, 415–16, 418
— and cutting, 379–80
Foot, standard, 125–6
Foot-stick, 125–6
Fourths, see 'Fractions'
'Fox and goose', 25
Fraction-boards, 267–8, 384, 405

Fraction-boxes, 386
Fractions, common, 377–91, 441–
  457
—, addition of, 388–90, 444
—, analysis of steps in, 454–7
— as percentages, 410–11
—, changing to decimal, 405–6
—, changing to percentages, 410–11
—, children's experience of, 377–8
—, division of, 450–2
—, equivalence of, 384–6
—, idea of, 378–9
—, improper, 388
—, mixed numbers and, 388
—, multiplication of, 391, 446–50
— of lines and shapes, 381–3
— of measures, 380–1, 387–8
—, 'problems' in, 456–7
—, subtraction of, 390–1, 445–6
Fractions, decimal, see 'Decimals'
Fun with figures, 432–40
Furlong, 303

Gallon, 348
Games:
  'Bingo', 248
  'Blind man's', 78
  'Chain tag', 25
  'Changing', 49–50, 58, 153, 386
  'Find your partner', 250
  'Fishing', 46, 471–2
  'Flags and castles', 33, 78, 80, 95
  'Fox and goose', 25
  'Guessing', see 'Estimation'
  'Having visitors', 64–5
  'I spy', 24
  'Man-eater', 64
  'Ninepins', see 'Skittles'
  'Noah's ark', 78
  Olympic, 459
  'Oranges and lemons', 25, 65
  'Patience', 247
  'Playing house', 23
  'Quoits', 28
  'Relay race', 250–1
  'Roulette', 248–9
  'Shop', 111–21
  'Skittles', 27, 33, 43, 49, 64, 66
  'Sky-writing', 36, 249
  'Snakes and ladders', 251–2
  'Snap', 248
  'Spinning arrow', 248–9
Geography, 366
Geometry, 421

Government departments, 467
Grading, 2, 11, and see 'Analyses'
Gram (gramme), 463–4
Graphs, 140–1, 427–31
Gravity, pull of, 322
Grouping in division, 91–7, 212–14,
  282–3, 313, 334–5, 353
— — multiplication, 77–80
Groups, counting in, 28–30
Growth, plant, 141
Guessing, see 'Estimation'
Gum, 468

Halves, see 'Fractions'
Hand-clapping, 47
Handling of materials, 21
'Having visitors', 64–5
Hearing, 20
— and speaking, 243–4
History, 366
— of measures:
  decimal system, 393
  length, 295–6, 299–301
  metric system, 458
  money, 261–3
  time, 359–60
  weight, 322–4
Hundreds column, 151, 153
Hundredths, 400–402
Hundredweight, 323, 327

'I spy', 24
Improper fractions, 388
Inch, standard, 126–9
—, cubic, 424
—, fractions of, 302–3, 380–1
—, origin of, 296
—, square, 423
Ink-blot shapes, 416
Inset tray, 24, 32

Kilogram, 464
Kilometre, 460

Language of addition, 38–9
— — division, 93
— — multiplication, 80–2
— — subtraction, 66
— — lines and shapes, 413
Length, 122, 124–31, 299–321, 459–
  461
— in metric system, 459–61
—, activities in, 124–31
—, addition of, 307–9

Length, analysis of steps in, 315–21
—, changing units of, 307
—, division of, 312–14
—, estimation of, 126
—, facts of, 301, 306
—, flash-cards for, 330
—, fractions in, 388
—, history of, 295–6, 299–301
—, multiplication of, 311–12
—, subtraction of, 309–11
—, tables of, 306–7
—, work-cards for, 308–10
Lines, curved, 414
—, parallel, 415
—, straight, 414
Litre, 463

'Magic' squares, 434
'Man-eater', 64
Maps, 426
Marbles, 28
Markets, 111–12, 272
Marking, 483–4
Matching, 32–3
Matching-board, 35
Materials, 25–6, 467–9, 487–9
Measures and measuring, 122–42,
  292–8, 396–7, 422–5
— —, history of, 295–6, 299–301,
  322–4
— — in fractions, 387–8
— —, 'natural', 299–301
— —, standard, 299–301
— — of area, 387, 422–4
— — of capacity, 134–6, 349–50
— — of length, 124–31, 299–301,
  380, 422
— — of money, 110–21, 264–9
— — of time, 136–42
— — of weight, 131–4
— — of volume, 424–5
Measuring apparatus, 126–31, 132–
  142, 473–4
— cards, 127, 397
— wheel, 304
Memorizing, 53–60, 69–73, 84–9,
  99–108, 242–54
Mental arithmetic tests, 482–3
Metre, as unit, 458–60
Metric system, 458–65
Mile, as unit, 299, 303–4
Millimetre, 460–1
Minus sign, 66
Mixed numbers in fractions, 388

Models, 78–9, 111–15
Money, 95, 110–21, 261–91
—, activities in, 110–21, 264–8, 271–2
—, addition of, 116–17, 271–4
—, analysis of steps in, 284–91
—, changing units of, 117–18, 264–9
—, decimals of pound, 398–9
—, division of, 119, 280–3
—, facts of, 268
—, —, first ideas of, 110
—, flash-cards for, 266–7
—, fractions in, 267–8
—, history of, 261–3
—, multiplication of, 119, 277–80
—, practice-cards for, 119–21, 265–6
—, subtraction of, 118, 275–7
—, tables of, 268
—, work-cards for, 119–21
Month, as unit, 140, 360
Moon, 359–60, 366, 422
Multiplication, 76–90, 186–211, 240–60
— and word 'times', 81
—, activities in, 77–80, 244–55
—, analysis of steps in, 203–11
— by factors, 199
— by ten, etc., 193–6
—, errors common in, 200–1
—, facts of, 82–9, 186–7
—, flash-cards for, 86–8
—, idea of, 76–7, 188–90
—, language of, 80–2
—, long, 196–9
—, practice-cards for, 84–6
— 'problems' in, 89
— rhymes, 80
—, short methods of, 190–3
— tables, 82–9, 240–60
Multiplication with capacity, 353
— — common fractions, 391, 446–450
— — decimals, 400
— — length, 311–12
— — money, 119, 277–80
— — time, 369
— — weight, 333–4

'News', 24
'Ninepins'—see 'Skittles'
'Noah's Ark', 78
Noughts, 33–4, 36, 44, 50, 53, 66, 81, 84, 194

Noughts in multiplication, 201
— in division, 221–4, 230
Number, 13–37
— board, 35
— cards, 33–4, 39, 40, 66, 149
— names, 13–16, 30–2
— 'oddities', 246, 435
— patterns, 245–6
— rhymes, 25
— series, 434
— slide, 34–5, 44, 49, 80, 95, 106, 153, 469–70
— songs, 25
— squares, 246
— 'story' apparatus, 44–5, 58, 65
— strips, 30, 44–5
— symbols, 13–16, 30–7
— systems, 144–6, 148
— tales, 79
— tops, 45, 49, 471
— tray, see 'Tray'
Numerator, 387

'Olympic games', 459
'Oranges and lemons', 25, 65
Organization, 476–85
Ounce weight, 133, 323

Pacing-stick, 305
Palm, as unit, 299
Paper, buying of, 489
—, folding and cutting, 379–80 415–16, 418
—, squared, 36–7, 148, 150, 190 194, 382–3, 397–8, 402–3
Parallel lines, 415
'Patience', 247
Pattern number cards, 28–9
Patterns, number, 245–6
Peg-board, 23
Pence table, 268–9
Pendulum, simple, 365
Percentage, 406–11
Perimeter, 422
Perspective, 415
Physical education, 25, 97
Pint, 135
—, fractions of, 388
Place-value, 49, 143–6, 150–1
—, idea of, 147–8
Place-value slide, 195–6, 224, 404–5, 474–5
Plan, for school, 256–60, 476–8
Planning, see 'Analyses'

Plans, 305, 426–7
Playing, 21–2
'Playing house', 23
Plus sign, 39
Point, decimal, 396
Points of the compass, 420
Posting-box, 23
Pound (currency), 261–3, 266–9
— —, fractions of, 384, 405
— (weight), 132–3, 323
— —, fractions of, 323, 325
Practice-cards for addition, 54–9
— — addition and subtraction, 72
— — division, 102–6
— — length, 127
— — money, 119–21, 265–6
— — multiplication, 84–6
— — — and division, 102–3
— — subtraction, 70–73
Practice revision sheet, 254–5
Prices, 114–15, 272
Primary facts of addition, 49–54
— — — division, 99–107
— — — multiplication, 82–7
— — — subtraction, 67–73
Prime numbers, 253
Problem-type examples in addition,
    60–2, 159–65
— — — capacity, 357
— — — division, 108–9, 233–9
— — — fractions, 456–7
— — — fun, 438–40
— — — length, 319–21
— — — money, 288–90
— — — multiplication, 89, 205–11
— — — percentages, 410–11
— — — subtraction, 74–5, 181–4
— — — time, 375
— — — weight, 340–2
Puzzles, 439–40

Quart, 135
Quarter as fraction, 377–9
— — weight unit, 326–7
'Quoits', 28

Radius, 418
Railways, 415
Rainfall graphs, 430
Readiness for learning, 18–19
Ready reckoners, 281
Recording, children's, 40–1, 66, 80–
    82, 98–9, 116–21, 129, 305, 349–
    350, 369–70, 399–400, 406, 449–50

Records, teachers', 53–5, 484–5
Rectangle, 416, 423–4, 437
—, fractions of, 382
Reduction, see 'Changing'
'Relay-race', tables, 250–1
Remainder, in division, 96–7, 103–
    105, 218–21
Revision exercise card, 479–80
Revision practice sheet, 254–5
Rhymes, addition, 46–7
—, counting, 21–2, 25, 27, 31
—, division, 97
—, multiplication, 80
—, subtraction, 65
Right angle, 421
'Roulette', 248–9
Ruler, 125, 127–8, 130
Rules, arithmetical, 9–10

Sand, 36
Scale, 425–7
— drawing, 426–7
—, wall, 129
Scales, 132, 473–4
Science, 366
— and arithmetic, 7
Screen, blackboard, 189–90
Second, as time unit, 360–1, 364–5
Seeing, 20, 244–8
See-saw, 326
Senses, learning through the, 19–22,
    242–55
'Sewed' circle for fractions, 385
Shadows, 419
Shapes, 415–31, 437–8
—, fractions of, 381–2
Sharing, in division, 91–7, 212–14,
    282, 312, 334, 353
Shillings table, 268–9
Shopping, 119–21, 271–2
Shops, class-room, 111–21
Short methods, 280, 435–7
Sign, addition, 32
—, division, 98
—, equals, 40
—, multiplication, 82
—, subtraction, 66
'Skittles', 27, 33, 43, 49, 63, 66
'Sky-writing', 36, 249
Slide, number, 34–5, 44, 49, 80, 95,
    106, 153, 469–70
—, place-value, 195–6, 224, 404–5,
    474–5
'Snakes and ladders', 251–2

'Snap', 248
Solids, 419, 425
Sorting, 22, 28
Span, as unit, 299
Spastic children, 21
'Spinning arrow', 248-9
Spring balance, 327
Square, fractions of, 382
Square foot, 423
— inch, 423
— yard, 423
Squared-paper, see 'Paper'
Standard measures, see 'Units'
Stencils, 36
Steps, in teaching, see 'Analyses'
Stone, as weight unit, 323, 326
Storage of materials, 469, 480
Straight line, 414
Striding, 27
Subtraction, 63-75, 167-85
—, activities in, 64-6, 73
—, analysis of steps in, 180-5
—, aspects of, 63-4, 168-70
—, decomposition method of, 171-174
—, 'downwards' method in, 170
—, equal additions method of, 174-7
—, errors common in, 177-9
—, facts of, 67-73
—, flash-cards for, 73
—, idea of, 63
—, language of, 66
—, practice-cards for, 70
—, 'problems' in, 74-5
— rhymes, 65
—, 'upwards' method in, 170
Subtraction with capacity, 352
— — common fractions, 390-1, 445-6
— — decimals, 399-40
— — length, 309-11
— — money, 118, 275-7
— — time, 368-9
— — weight, 331-3
Surfaces, 425
Symbols, number, 13-16, 30-7
Symmetry, 416

Tables, multiplication, 82-5, 193, 240-60
—, charts, 244-5
—, meaning of, 240-1
— oddities, 246-7

Tables of capacity, 346-7, 351
— of length, 306, 461
— of money, 268-9
— of time, 366-7
— of weight, 329
Taking away, 63-4
Temperature graphs, 427-8
Tens column, 148-57
Tens, multiplication by, 193-6
—, quick division by, 224
Tenths, see 'Fractions'
Testing, 481-3
Threading beads, see 'Beads'
Time, 6, 124, 136-42, 359-76
—, allocation of teaching, 260
—, analysis of steps in teaching, 362-6
—, and the arithmetical processes, 368-70
—, children's activities in, 362-6
—, estimation of, 364
—, facts of, 366
—, first ideas of, 124
—, history of units, 359-60
—, table of units, 366
—, telling the, 136-40
—, work-cards for, 368
Times, in multiplication, 80-1
Time-tables, 365, 371
Ton weight, 323
Tops, number, 45, 49, 471
Tracing paper, 36
Tray, inset, 24, 32
—, number, 22-3, 28, 32-3, 77-8, 80, 94, 116, 118
'Treasure hunt', 420
'Trying out' in division, 224-8
Twelfths, see 'Fractions'

Units column, 150-7
Units of measurement:
area, 422-3
capacity, 346-7, 351, 461-3
length, 299-301, 306-7, 459-61
money, 262, 268
natural and standard, 125, 299-301
time, 359-60, 366
weight, 322-4, 329
volume, 424

Varnish, 468
Volume, 424-5, 461-3
—, metric, 461-3

Wall pockets for cards, 480
Week, as unit, 140
Weight, 123, 131–4, 322–45, 463–4
—, activities in, 131–4, 325–9, 463–4
—, addition of, 330–1
—, analysis of steps in, 336–45
—, division of, 334
—, estimation of, 131–2, 326
—, facts of, 329
—, first ideas of, 123
—, flash-cards for, 330
—, history of, 322–4
—, in metric system, 463–4
—, multiplication of, 333–4
—, subtraction of, 331–3

Weight, table of, 329
—, work-cards for, 330–3
Work-cards for:
    capacity, 350
    length, 308–13
    money, 119–21, 266
    time, 368–70
    weight, 330–3

Yard, standard, 129–30, 300
—, square, 423
Yard-stick, 129–30
Year, 360–1

Zero, see 'Nought'